Outlines of Environmental Education

Featuring Articles By

Allen
Ames
Archbald
Ashbaugh
Ayers
Brennan
Brewer
Bryson
Caldwell
Chaney
Clark
Cole
Dambach
Dasmann
Evison
Foster

Fox
Hafner
Hansen
Harrison
Harrar
Logan
McConnell
Menesini
Nash
Roth
Sargent
Scheffey
Shomon
Stapp
Wang
Weidner

And Others

Books by the Editor

Everybody's Ecology

Cabins, Conservation, and Fun

Wisconsin Sideroads to Somewhere

Canada Goose Management (editor, with Ruth Hine)

The University and Its Publics

Effective Feature Writing

Publicity Media and Methods

The Shape of Summer Sessions to Come (editor)

Year—Round Education (with Neil Schmitz)

University Extension (with T. J. Shannon)

The American University in Summer (with Donald Zillman)

Outlines of Environmental Education

Edited by Clay Schoenfeld

Joint Professor of Journalism and Wildlife Ecology, and Chairman of the Center for Environmental Communications and Education Studies, The University of Wisconsin, Madison; Editor of Environmental Education Quarterly.

rom the 1969-70 and 1970-71 Issues of the Journal of

ENVIRONMENTAL EDUCATION

Dembar Educational Research Services; Inc. • Box 1148
Madison, Wisconsin 53701

CONSERVATION is a state of harmony between men and land. Despite a century of propaganda, conservation still proceeds at a snail's pace... The usual answer to this dilemma is "more conservation education." No one will debate this, but is it certain that the *volume* of education needs stepping up? Is something lacking in the *content* as well?...The "key-log" which must be moved to release the evolutionary process for a land ethic is simply this: quit thinking about decent land-use as an economic problem. Examine each question in terms of what is ethically and esthetically right, as well as what is economically expedient. A thing is right when it tends to preserve the integrity, stability, and beauty of the biotic community. It is wrong when it tends otherwise....By and large our present problem is one of attitudes and implements. We are remodeling the Alhambra with a steam shovel, and we are proud of our yardage. We shall hardly relinquish the shovel, which after all has many good points, but we are in need of gentler and more objective criteria for its successful use. —ALDO LEOPOLD

OUTLINES OF ENVIRONMENTAL EDUCATION

Reprinted and Preprinted from
ENVIRONMENTAL EDUCATION
by
Dembar Educational Research Services, Inc.
Printed in the United States of America
Library of Congress Catalog Number 78-149599

Preface

CULTIVATING more concern for the environmental consequences of society's activity is becoming a national goal. Hence, environmental education programs are growing in number and size. The scope and velocity that characterize this growth are little short of stunning, as more and more people sense that man may well be the most endangered species of all. While many environmental education practices continue to be founded more on folklore than on fact, research is underway to identify factors actually related to the development of environmental awareness, imaginative field projects are discovering better ways to convert that awareness into ecological action, and new forms of conservation communications are emerging.

One such conservation communication is *Environmental Education*, a quarterly journal of research and development launched in September 1969. In its first 2 years of publication, this journal has stimulated and recorded a remarkable series of manuscripts at the growing edge of its chosen field—the crucial point where ecology and education impinge: something of the conservation history of America; the dimensions of environmental degradation; the political configurations, economic stresses, social values, and esthetic perceptions that condition any quest for environmental quality; critical factors in translating ecological concepts into action programs on the landscape; public policy processes by which resource management decisions seem to be crystallized; communications techniques designed to build public interest, understanding, and support for enlightened resource use; and educational media and methods that seek to develop an ecological conscience and improve environmental housekeeping.

Out of past, current, and coming issues of *Environmental Education* we have selected outstanding articles, organized them into logical sections, and added suitable editorial remarks—to form *the first national review of education for today's ecological crisis*. Chapters deal with the setting for environmental education, definitions and directions, elementary and secondary school curricula, university dimensions, new nature centers, and community action programs.

The overall goal of this book is to help professionalize the new field of environmental education. The measure of its success will be the degree to which it is of service to the growing numbers of people engaged systematically in relating man to his world. In short, we do our best here to present clear, relevant reporting of rigorous investigations, creative developments, and imaginative insights in conservation communications. Aldo Leopold was once constrained to say that conservation consisted mostly of letterhead pieties and convention oratory. We trust this book isn't that. We are trying to help inject deep-digging research, practical field approaches, and vaulting imagination to a field that may represent the difference between human survival at the cesspool level and the fulfillment of the American promise.

1 January 1971   *C.A.S.*

v

Contents

Introduction

A T LEAST five gross attitudes can be identified in American man-land relationships. The f i r s t is the *economic* impulse, which tends to view natural resources essentially as a God-given stockpile to be manipulated largely for private profit. The second is the *evangelical* attitude, which prefers to sense in nature a mystic shrine that is to be adored but not altered. The third attitude is the *esthetic-athletic*, seeking enjoyment of one kind or another in the outofdoors. The fourth is the *apocalyptic* attitude, which sees a mushrooming population, a rampant technology, and a fragile biosphere on a collision course toward inexorable catastrophe. The fifth posture is the *ecological*, under which we recognize the validity of each of the other approaches and attempt-through some sort of scientific understanding, technical design, and social entente-to achieve a viable balance that will protect without penalizing, develop without destroying. These attitudes d o n o t necessarily exist in a pure and exclusive state either within a culture or within an individual. That the five approaches are at one and the same time competitive and complimentary renders man-land relationships frustrating for the biologist, fascinating for the social scientist, and functional for the politician.

While all five approaches to man-land relationships have existed for many years and exist side-by-side today, each has had an ascendancy at a particular time. Prior to the turn of the century in America, the economic motive was dominant in resource use. With an almost religious fervor, all of society acquiesced in an exploitation of natural resources. As William Freeman Vilas expressed the philosophy of the day, if God had not meant Wisconsin's virgin pineries to be clear-cut to build Chicago, He would not have caused the major rivers of the state to flow southward. The government bestowed various bounties on the more adroit explorers; society r e served its accolades for the barons of rampant industry; the universities devoted some of their growing skills toward a more efficient assault on field, forest, and mine.

While the exploitation of natural resources can scarcely be said to have been halted, since about 1900 t h e sheer economic attitude toward man-land relationships has had to answer increasingly to the evangelists and their vision of nature's "vast, pulsing harmony." The evangelical attitude has found its expression in three principal developments: the scientific study of the dynamics of nature; the *preservation* of such natural phenomena as rare scenery and remnant wildlife populations; and a populist revolt against monopolistic practices of resource waste. Confronted with these thrusts, the economic attitude became tempered by a concern f o r resource management more in the public interest. Using as its touchstone the term *conservation*, this wedding of research and reform has seen attempts at manipulation for wider and wiser use of soil, water, forest, range, and game. S t a t e and federal bureaus have been founded to foster various brands of conservation, and the courts have rendered several classic decisions defending the integrity of the biota. Schools and colleges came to devote a portion of their enterprise to conservation education. Conservation creeds became linked to broad programs of arid land reclamation, water power development, public welfare, economic pump-priming, and national defense. Indeed, by becoming all things to all men, the conservation movement tended to lose some of its viability as a man-land ethic.

In more recent years, the esthetic-athletic attitude toward man-land relationships came to be heard from in swelling tones. The well-nigh cabalistic word for it was *recreation*. Recreation enjoyed an "in" phrase as a catchall term to describe the manifold outdoor activities of millions of Americans, and as a politically attractive device for developing a region's economy. The term should not be dismissed as mere phrasemaking. Its wellsprings are deep in the American psyche. Americans and their outofdoors have been carrying on a l o v e affair for a long time. It is no accident of the songwriter's art that two of our favorite national songs speak of "woods and templed hills," "spacious skies," "amber waves of grain," and "purpled mountain majesty." It is of some significance that one of the most popular movies and record albums of all time starts out with magnificent views and strains of "hills alive with the sound of music." Americans simply possess this deep yearning to get i n t o the outdoors. Be he a Thoreau or a lathe operator, when an American looks for meaning in life, he seeks it not in ancient ruins or in the canyons of a city but in a forest, by a river, or at the edge of a lake. The outdoors is a source of inspiration and, literally, re-creation-a renewing experience, a refreshing relief from alarms and routine, plus a dab of physical exercise.

Scarcely had recreation had its day as a phrase with political sex appeal when it was overtaken at the turn of the decade by a revival of Malthusian fear. The new Jeremiahs, with their apocalyptic warnings of impending disaster, substituted sheer human *survival* as the basic motivation in man-land relations. Over-pollution a n d over-population, they said, render man the most endangered species of all.

These four attitudes toward man-land relationships—the economic, the evangelical, t h e esthetic-athletic, and the apocalyptic—have led to two principal—and competing—doctrines of conservation. T h e first, what Prof. Samuel P. Hays has called the "gospel of efficiency," has perhaps never been better expressed than by Gifford Pinchot in his dictum that land and water use should be governed by a concern for "the greatest benefit for t h e greatest number of people for the longest possible time." This principle runs hard up against a second view of conservation—what might be called the Muir-Leopold thesis, that what we should really seek is "a state of harmony between man and land," in the attainment of which we must recognize that land and water, as well as people, have certain inalienable rights.

The schism inherent in these competing philosophies of conservation is rendered even more intense by the fact that modern conservation issues seldom involve raw exploitation versus preservation, but rather excruciating conflicts between prudent use of resources for one acceptable purpose versus prudent use for another, as a growing population impinges on a shrinking, or at best a static, resource base. Irrigation versus power, access highways versus wild rivers, logging and grazing versus downstream siltation, potato plantations versus trout streams, wheat fields versus duck factories, pulp mills versus clean water, artificial lakes versus ancient canyons, camp grounds versus forest cloisters, smokestacks versus prairie vistas, suburban sprawl versus parklands, air conditioned offices versus power plant pollution, automobiles versus smog, convenience packaging versus mountains of garbage, worm-free apples versus silent springs—the list is unending and overpowering.

For example, even the so-called outdoor recreation movement can hardly be considered homogeneous. On the contrary, it is composed of a wide variety of essentially competitive activities and values. The water skier, the fisherman, the duck hunter, the bird watcher, the lotus fancier, the cottager, the hermit all compete for the same patch of water. The quality of a mountain view for one hiker is in inverse ratio to the number of campers who seek to share that view. Indeed, high-density outdoor recreation has the capacity to destroy the very enjoyment it sets out to capture. The number of fans at a football stadium does not detract from, and may even enhance, the sport. The same cannot be said for grouse hunting on a back 40 or even for picnicking in a park.

Importantly, the contending parties in conservation are not asking simply, "When are we going to 'run out' of my resource?" Long before we are aware of an impending "running out," we are becoming acutely aware of something else that is happening to us—a deterioration in the *quality* of the resource. The basic issue in resource conservation today is hence not quantity but quality. The great concern in the management of resources has become the maximization of quality of output. It is not the quality of the resource itself that we are concerned with so much as its capacity to enhance the quality of life. This is a very sticky problem, as Ayers Brinser said, and becomes involved in many subjective evaluations.

It is the making of sophisticated choices, then, the rendering of subtle value judgments, that is the essence of conservation today. Should we do it, and if we do it, what do we gain, at what cost, and what do we lose, at what cost? These are the questions, and the term "cost" is being used in the context of physical and mental health as well as simply in reference to dollars. In the words of John C. Weaver, conservation has become more ethics than economics.

Enter, thus, the *ecological* attitude toward man-land relationships—the attempt to balance the demands of an industrialized, urbanized society against the demands of the living landscape, both of them being basic to modern health and happiness. This attitude thinks of man *in* nature, rather than of man *and* nature. It is the long, integrated view: Landscape is something to enjoy, not merely to mine or till. Space is something to roam in, not merely to fill. Beauty is something personally to cultivate, not merely to read about. Flora and fauna are something to cherish, not merely to harvest. Water and land and air are resources with an all-to-fragile integrity that defies any doctrine of anthropocentricism. Yet, man is something more than an animal. His spirit merits something more than a niche on the African veldt.

In this decade of ecological concern, what are our major environmental problems? Using my state of Wisconsin as a parameter, key issues include the following:

Pollution will certainly show up at the top of anybody's list. There is the problem of gross municipal and industrial water pollution; the problem of more subtle over-enrichment of water from agricultural and residential sources; the problem of air, land, water, and even human pollution from the use of chemicals as pesticides. The harmful effects of all types of pollution must be determined through continued research and eradicated through improved technology and control.

By any standard, another major land and water use problem is *soil erosion*. Despite over 30 years of federal and University efforts, we have completed only about a third of the erosion control job in Wisconsin. Scarcely one-quarter of the landowners in Wisconsin have conservation plans, and many of the existing plans are only haphazardly followed. Soil erosion is a serious problem on over 6 million acres of Wisconsin farmland. Top soil continues to disappear, robbing us of food and fiber and silting our streams, lakes, and wetlands.

A third major problem is *timber land management*. Some suitable acres of Wisconsin could yet be replanted or newly planted to trees. Many unsuitable acres already have been or are being replanted or newly planted to trees. Many acres of extensive forest land require timber stand development measures, applied with an eye to multiple use. The many widely scattered woodlots which account for some 40 percent of the state's timber acreage need protection from encroachment by unsuitable land uses, as well as good forest management practices.

What may seem like a narrow problem yet one with wide repercussions is the problem of *waning wetlands*. Wetlands are those little pockets of damp countryside characterized by a high water table and heavy emergent vegetation. They are vital to upland game bird, furbearer, and waterfowl populations, are relevant frequently to game fish production, play a role in the recharge of underground aquifers, act as pollution-filters for lakes and streams, and invariably are associated with various forms of outdoor recreation. We have lost wetlands at an alarming rate over the past 4 decades to agriculture and urbanization, in some counties as much as 90 percent. The preservation of a viable array of wetlands is absolutely essential to a healthy Wisconsin landscape.

A fifth problem is what we might call collectively the *crime of the city*. It has two aspects: (1) the noise, congestion, dirt, foul air, foul water, and general lack of amenities in the inner city—uncultured blight; and (2) the encroachment of the outer city and its appurtenances like transportation systems, dumps, septic tanks, and "slurbs" in nearby cropland, open space, woodlots, wetlands, and recreation areas—unintelligent sprawl.

A sixth broad problem is the *degradation of outdoor recreation areas* through improper and conflicting land-use development in relationship to agricultural practices, parks, highways, waterways, resort areas, natural areas, beaches, and so on; to the point where water, fish, game, scenery, and other recreational resources are being destroyed by the very people who seek them out, where persistent unintelligent use of floodplains subjects people to economic loss and even loss of life, where unzoned shorelands are taking on the appearance of outdoor slums, and where fewer and fewer people have access to a natural heritage of decent quality.

All of the problems so far listed concern man's stake in the man-land equation. There is a seventh collective problem in land and water use; namely, the preservation of the biota. Here our concern is with scientific areas, wild rivers, remote forests, rare flora, disappearing birds. Call this problem the problem of *preserving natural beauty*—what Stewart Udall described as "our groping for something we cannot forget—the long waves and the beach grass; white wings on morning air, and, in afternoon, the shadows cast by the doorways of history."

We can say some things about this list: First, it is parochial. Other states have somewhat different stresses. Second, the list represents a gross oversimplification of what is in reality a congeries of problems which could easily become a roster of fourscore or more. Third, it tends to identify symptoms of disease rather than the disease itself. What *really* causes our basic problems in land and water use?

At the bottom, of course, is the simple fact that we have too many people in the wrong places who do not exercise restraint. If we do not practice some form of "people management," all other approaches to conservation will be for naught. Yet there are some other very profound reasons for our current land and water use problems. Robert Ardrey suggests one of them in his book, *The Territorial Imperative*. It is seemingly a biological law that an individual or a troup stake out a piece of real estate—a territory—and call it their own. Those of us who go out into the country to buy land, to do with it what we will, may think we have some very advanced economic or cultural motives for so doing. In reality we are simply reacting to the territorial instinct which our ape ancestors acquired on the African veldt. The institution of private property, with all its attendant threats to resource management in the public interest, may be immutable.

Our Western culture complicates conservation. Unlike an aborigine who has no concept of "ownership" and who views himself as simply one of many manifestations of nature, we have been given "dominion over the fish of the sea, and over the fowl of the air, and over the cattle, and over all the earth, and over every creeping thing that creepeth upon the earth"; and we exercise that dominion as a coach rather than as a team player.

Our economic system complicates conservation. What frugal land and water use requires of us is that we manage our resources at least in part for other people who cannot or will not pay us because they are either not direct customers or they are not yet born. There is nothing, or very little, in our system of interest rates to encourage such management. In fact, under our pervasive doctrine of conspicuous consumption, we are driven in just the opposite direction, to make a fast buck today by catering to the demands of a market.

Our tax practices often mitigate against wise land and water use. We persist in billing the wrong people too much and the right people too little for conservation services rendered by the state. We are often hamstrung in reform by constitutional provisions, irrelevant precedents, and unrepresentative legislative bodies; witness the widespread reluctance to impose user fees for recreational purposes.

Our research posture complicates conservation. While our colleges and universities house a number of disciplines related to land and water use, each department has an *intra*disciplinary approach. What have been lacking are *inter*disciplinary studies concerned with the total relationship of man and his environment.

Our attitude toward teaching complicates wise land and water use. We are so objective we define no right or wrong, assign no obligations, call for no sacrifice, imply no change in philosophy of values. We have been too timed, too anxious for quick success, to tell our students the true magnitude of their obligations. We are prisoners of antiseptic concepts. We march up to the moment of decision and then turn and run.

Our action techniques complicate wise land and water use. Too often we seize on oversimplified solutions, cloak them in catch-words, and peddle them like lightning rods to customers who apply them with religious fervor and then wonder why earthly salvation continues to elude them.

Our instrumentalities of government complicate wise land and water use. State, county, and municipal boundaries were laid out at the whim of surveyors a century ago; they bear little or no relationship to the configurations of the land and water with which units of government must deal. We desperately need new political and social devices which stand a decent chance of translating value judgment into action on the living landscape. Listen to these words: "The true enemy of preservation of our environment is our system of government, particularly local governments and county governments which are entirely dependent upon the property tax and the payroll structure. Conservation can never be accomplished so long as local government must as a means of its financial survival get new development into its boundaries." And those are not the words of a Berkeley fanatic; they are the words of a Republican Congressman.

All of these problems contribute to one central problem: unilateral approaches to land and water management. Time and again we persist in applying to our environment a practice which, while it may be beneficial for one purpose, is deleterious for other purposes. Our governmental agencies, our educational institutions, our socioeconomic patterns, our cultural standards, are all seemingly in league to force us into these unilateral approaches, and hence to introduce or aggravate land and water use conflicts. Somehow we must break out of our assorted straight jackets to take an integrated view of our surroundings and carry out programs which truly reflect the "oneness" of our environment, its problems and its needs.

This is the crucial challenge to American education today. In this book we reconnoiter the critical terrain features of the response that is emerging under the broad rubric of environmental education. ∎

I *The Environmental Decade*

WE ARE experiencing what you might call the third American revolution. The first American revolution 200 years ago was of course a political revolution. The second American revolution 100 years ago was a technological revolution. The third American revolution is a cultural revolution, characterized by a new man-land ethic. The spirit of the seventies is a spirited concern for environmental quality. We are figuratively and literally sick and tired of a mis-development of America that diminishes daily the quality of the human experience: water pollution; air pollution; soil erosion; forest, range, and wetland deterioration; waning wildlife; urban sprawl; preempted open spaces; vanishing wilderness; landscapes scarred by highways, litter, noise, and blight—a not-so-quiet crisis of decreasing beauty and increasing contamination that threatens not only the pursuit of happiness but life itself. And we are beginning to *do* something about environmental quality conservation, redevelopment, and maintenance. How we got into this revolution and where we are going is the story of one of the crucial currents in American history.

As never before, Americans are coming to appreciate this "oneness" of the elements of their environment—that insects, birds, fish, animals, water, soil, wilderness, trees, plants, and man are all part of the same scheme of nature, a sort of intricately woven fabric; snip one thread and the whole thing begins to unravel. Americans are coming to appreciate as well a continuing and intimate relationship with their natural surroundings that surmounts the curtains of civilization. New Yorkers, for example, during the drought of recent years, saw air conditioners silenced, lawns browned, and water glasses banished from restaurant tables, while the Hudson River was daily carrying 11 billion gallons of undrinkable, uncleanable water past the city and dumping it into the ocean.

As seldom before, Americans are expressing a deep concern about the management of their environment. The public prints have made "the rape of the land" a headline story. Our affluence, our general values, and our social objectives are beginning to permit us to make viable choices respecting the utilization of natural resources. We no longer assume that all land and water must inevitably be devoted to the basic sustenance and protection of human life. We are ready for what Prof. Philip Lewis, Jr., calls "a second integrated look" to identify the meaningful natural and cultural resources which, if protected and enhanced, can provide many types of environmental experiences for richer living, working, playing—and survival.

As seldom before, Americans are acting to conserve. Too often, the act may be too little, too late, but each act is at least some evidence of faith, hope, and maybe even love. Legislative bodies at all levels of government, public agencies, and private groups are seeking answers to the difficult questions posed by multiplying man and disappearing land. The alarm has been sounded by senators like Gaylord Nelson, calling on "the energy, idealism, and drive of the oncoming generation" to save us from the "poisonous air and deadly waters of the earth." The alarm has been sounded by ecologists like Paul Ehrlich, asking us to see "the connection between growing population and steady deterioration of the quality of life before our planet is irreversibly ruined." The alarm has been sounded also by hucksters like Arthur Godfrey intoning that "our country's highest priority in the 1970's must be survival." Epitomizing public response to such warnings is the establishment, under a 1969 National Environmental Policy Act, of a 3-man Council on Environmental Quality to "advise, assist, and support the President of the United States on all environmental concerns."

That ecological thinking is growing the public prints bear increasing witness. Ecologist Leonard Hall asks us to think large about "the dilemma which mankind faces today":

1. The danger of planet-wide environmental poisoning from nuclear fallout and nuclear waste disposal; or of a nuclear or biological holocaust that would end the world we have known.

2. The danger of famine, starvation, and pestilence affecting hundreds of millions of human beings in the world's unproductive areas, if we cannot bring about a drastic and revolutionary flattening of the world's population curve. And while it is easy to say the consequences cannot reach our rich and comfortable enclave, this ignores the fact of the chaos that would sweep the planet.

3. Destruction of the environment for humans and countless other living creatures through the poisoning of soil, air, and water by sewage and industrial wastes; by combustion and overuse of fertilizers, pesticides, and herbicides; and by erosion and soil exhaustion caused by today's monoculture and the continued stripping of forest cover.

4. Destruction of the esthetic environment—which is to say, the *quality of life*—through sustained attack on wilderness and wild nature, on wildlife, on the beauty of the rural scene, and on the equally essential and largely neglected orderliness of the urban and suburban areas where 75 percent of our people live today.

The administrator Edward C. Crafts asks us to think large about " hard, unavoidable steps to reverse the trend of environmental retrogression":

> Population control, higher taxes, higher consumer prices, lower corporate profits, lower material standard of living, revision of national priorities, and coercion.

Look magazine asks us to think large about an "agenda for survival":

> Man's quarrel with nature is nothing new. It is rooted in the Book of Genesis, in God's command to "be fruitful and multiply, and fill the earth and subdue it; and have dominion over... every living thing." Armed with this injunction and a mischievous new technology of awful power, we have multiplied recklessly and asserted our dominion by random slaughter. The question now is: What can we do to repair the damage we have done and avert future disaster?
>
> First, we must get rid of the notion that the rest of Creation exists only for man's convenience and profit and that other forms of life are somehow inferior-enemies to be conquered, harnessed, or crushed. The fact is, man is just one member of a natural and interdependent community of every living thing.
>
> Then, we have to check population growth. Without an immediate commitment to an effective program of birth control, the underdeveloped world is doomed to death by famine, and the affluent world to social chaos.
>
> We must take stock of our planet's resources to learn how much and what kind of development our environment can sustain and how best to protect the irreplaceable wilderness we have left. Such an undertaking will have to be coordinated internationally by the UN—and might, in fact, give that body a new lease on life. In America, we should strengthen the President's Environmental Quality Council and create like groups at every level of government.
>
> And we must clean up the mess we have already made. Industry and government together must restore our polluted air and water and our defiled landscape. The cost of a healthy environment must become part of the basic cost of doing business.
>
> We need not be discouraged. When threatened, man is capable of almost anything. Nothing less than our survival is at stake. The problem is getting enough people to realize this ·blunt truth while there is still time to act.

Eighty Congressmen ask us to think large about what we can do as individuals:

> Among citizens, we turn to youth as the great hope for the Environmental Decade. Young people are understandably outraged by the cynicism and materialism of their older generation. We urge them to substitute constructive impulse for negativism, and to build for future generations an environment worthy of free men and women. We hope they will conduct studies, sponsor educational forums, initiate petitions, support court suits, pressure administrative agencies, and draft legislation, as well as do the many private things needed to help protect against environmental destruction.

All American institutions and individuals must adjust their functions and policies in the spirit of the quest for environmental quality. The implications for American education are particularly clear. To paraphrase Aldo Leopold, barring love and war, few enterprises continue to be undertaken with such abandon, or by such diverse individuals, or with so paradoxical a mixture of appetite and altruism, as that group of vocations and avocations known collectively, precisely or not, as conservation. It is, by common consent, a good thing to practice conservation. But wherein lies the goodness, and what can be done to encourage its pursuit? On these questions there continues to be confusion of counsel, and only the most uncritical minds are free from doubt. America certainly has as yet no magic formula for capsuling conservation and administering it to assorted people and places. It increasingly recognizes the importance, however, of confronting researchers and implementers with sets of resource management principles and values, and encouraging professionals and public officials alike to face the broad environmental problems upon which the American public is being asked to render crucial judgments. Perhaps out of this flux will come integrated programs and techniques based on, and consistent with, a synthesis of new knowledge in both the natural and social sciences, and which will find their expression through public policies; private management decisions; actions of businessmen, farmers, and labor; consumer behavior in the market; and voter behavior at the polls. In essence, we are coming to address ourselves to laying a basis for action, to elucidating the choices in land and water use and relating them to general values and social objectives, to instilling in people a desire for constructive change, and to providing practical guidelines characterized by integrated approaches. This is the changing role of America in conservation, as American life and American learning proceed together toward what can yet be broader lands and fairer days.

It may well be that modern man can never achieve complete harmony with land, any more than we shall achieve in our day justice or liberty for all people. In these higher aspirations, as Leopold said, the important thing is to strive. We must cease being intimidated out of hand by the argument that an action is impossible if it does not yield quick profits, or that an action is necessarily to be condoned because it seems to pay; that philosophy is dead in human relations, and its funeral in land relations is long overdue. The third American revolution is the appearance of this ecological conscience.

To support and sustain this third American revolution we will require an educational program as massive as the problem of human survival. In this introductory chapter we examine in some detail the dimensions of today's environmental problems, and we speculate about the nature of the educational programs that will be required to accomplish what Odum calls "ecosystem surgery" in the decade of the environment. ∎

AN ENVIRONMENT FIT FOR PEOPLE

Raymond F. Dasmann

A CONCERN for keeping the world a fit place for people is the basis for the social movement known as conservation. Like our environment, the meaning of conservation has been changing. It has necessarily become broader, its concerns reach more deeply into human experience. The conservationist was once involved mostly with the natural world and the rural scene--with wildlife and fisheries, forests and rangelands, soils and river basins, or with the minerals and fuels available for man's use. He was concerned with these things because their care was usually neglected by a human society bent upon growth and material advancement. The natural world and the raw materials upon which man depended were exploited with no thought for tomorrow: forests went up in smoke, or fell before the indiscriminate axe; soils blew or washed away; wildlife vanished from the land. The attention of the conservationist was rarely directed toward the towns and cities where people were concentrated; the dangers of pollution were at worst local and seemed a small price to pay for progress; the population explosion was unheard of in a world that seemed large, mostly untamed, and with room for many kinds of people and many ways of life.

But today the world is small, shrunken by the rapid expansion of its population, tied in a tight web by networks of transportation over which people and goods move in greater speed and greater volume. Human increase and unchecked exploitation threaten the most remote corners of the earth. Cities have become focal points in a threatened decline in the quality of human life. Pollution spreads everywhere. The conservation movement has therefore shifted its emphasis. The old problems remain, but the new ones become more acute.

THE MEANING OF CONSERVATION

Conservation is now defined as the rational use of the environment to achieve the highest quality of living for mankind. Such a definition, however, requires explanation. What is meant by rational use? What is meant by quality of living?

Rational use of the environment takes the future into account. It is based on an understanding of the continuing long-term needs of humanity. It involves consideration of the natural laws that govern man's occupancy of the planet. It will involve at times non-use of resources, if these happen to be scarce and their preservation of importance. It will at all times be based on a consideration of tomorrow's require-

ments as well as today's necessities.

It is non-rational to use a forested area, for example, for the production of some immediate food crops if this involves destruction of the forest, loss of soil, and a loss of the long-term productivity of the area. It would be rational to use the area in such a way that its productivity of wood, water, wildlife, and other forest products would be sustained into the distant future.

It is non-rational to destroy a living species or to shatter the last remnant of a living community in order to make way for some marginal expansion of some already abundant crop or a misplaced suburb. But what is non-rational for society in the long run may seem entirely rational to an individual or to a social group with short-term objectives. Furthermore, ignorance of the interrelationships among living things and their environment may often lead to unexpected damage when a resource is exploited in a superficially rational way.

The term quality of living is more elusive, since people differ in their wants and aspirations. Conservation, however, seeks to maintain the highest quality of environment, meaning an environment that is healthy, esthetically appealing, and diversified.

It is a goal of conservation to maintain wild species and natural communities on earth, so that man will always find present the natural variety that accompanied his own long course of evolution. Conservation's goal is also to encourage the building of diversified and pleasing man-made environments, from farmlands to cities, so that nobody need live in a monotonous and ugly world. Another goal is to use the living resources of the earth in such a way that they will continue to yield, as well-cared-for farmlands have yielded, through the centuries to come. Conservation seeks also to avoid those uses that lead to the degradation of the earth, through pollution, poisoning, or the loss of productive capacity. It is a responsibility of those concerned with conservation to seek to maintain human populations at such a level that all may enjoy a rich and varied life, and not to allow human population increase to endanger the future of mankind.

ECOLOGY AND CONSERVATION

Life on earth exists in a thin layer of soil, water, and atmosphere near the surface of the planet. This layer and the life it contains, form the biosphere,

Dr. Dasmann is Director of Environmental Studies for the Conservation Foundation, Washington, D.C. This article is excerpted from Public Affairs Pamphlet No. 421, the Public Affairs Committee, Inc., 1968.

the sphere of life, upon earth. As our knowledge of the biosphere grows, our knowledge of the intricate ways in which all parts of it are related to one another also grows. Thus air pollution from California's coastal cities affects the health of pine trees in the distant Sierra Nevada. Radioisotopes from atomic explosions in central Asia can appear in alarming concentrations in Alaskan caribou. Pesticides from the factories of America or Europe appear in the tissues of Antarctic penguins. A decision made in Washington, D. C. , can affect the conditions of life for creatures in remote Amazonian jungles. Security and prosperity in the United States may depend on food and population in southern Asia.

We are unaware of all of the consequences of our activities. We depend for oxygen upon the activities of green plants on the land and in the ocean. We produce carbon dioxide through combustion of fossil fuels and many other activities that promote oxidation. When do we reach the danger point in the oxygen-carbon dioxide balance of the atmosphere? At what point does the accumulation of atmospheric carbon dioxide bring about potentially disastrous changes in the earth's climates—melting polar ice caps perhaps and raising sea levels dangerously high? Our activities proceed faster than our knowledge of their consequences.

The great numbers of living species on earth, hundreds of thousands of kinds of animals and plants, are arranged over the planet, not at random, but in organized and structured communities of living things, the biotic communities. Each community is distinct. The species within each are tied together in intricate networks of energy flow or pathways of chemical raw materials from soil, air, and water through various plants to various animals. Disturbance of any part of a community affects all parts.

Each community in turn forms the living portion of ecosystem, built up of soil, air, water, the energy from sunlight, the physical characteristics of earth and atmosphere, all interacting with life. The resistance of ecosystems to disturbance varies enormously. Some, the more complex systems of the warmer and more humid regions, show a strong ability to rebound from outside interference: the forest clearing is soon grown over and reclaimed by forest. Others, the more simple systems of air or cold regions may be easily shattered by man's influence or natural disturbance, and take decades or even centuries to recover. Complexity adds stability to natural communities. Simple communities tend toward instability.

Man's tampering may produce unexpected side effects. In the tropics it may seem common sense to control a crop pest with an insecticide. Yet such common sense can lead to new and more destructive pests previously held in check by predators or parasites that the insecticide has destroyed, which call in turn for new insecticides that may in turn produce greater damage. Simplification of complex natural systems has been the basis for man's agriculture and cannot be abandoned. Yet extreme simplification, as exemplified by single-crop cultures (monocultures), leads always to a precarious balance between crop plant and an unstable ecological system. Perhaps a general guideline for man's use of the natural world, based upon our present knowledge would be: The disturbance of any natural environment should not exceed the minimum needed to accomplish its rational use for worthy human goals.

It is difficult to know to what extent man's future may depend upon the continuance on earth of some other species. Many of our great gains in science and medicine have come from research upon some previously unnoticed species of plant or animal. The rhesus monkey brought us greater understanding of human blood groups. Foreknowledge of the Rh (rhesus) factor in blood has saved countless lives. The sea urchin brought new knowledge of problems of growth and development. A simple mold gave birth to our families of antibiotics. Thus, for our own welfare, if for no other reason, we ought to maintain on earth adequate samples of all of the profuse diversity of living things, unmodified by man.

POPULATION AND ENVIRONMENT

Without control over human population increase, all other efforts at conservation must inevitably fall short. The concept of "standing room only" for man on earth has been raised as a nightmare to call attention to the dangers of our present rate of population growth. This is, of course, a level of population that cannot be reached since catastrophe would intervene long before such a level had been attained.

Unfortunately, at present levels of population, catastrophe has already intervened. Thousands die of starvation each day. Still more are killed in riots and revolutions, major and minor wars, waged by or on behalf of people who are dissatisfied with their share of the earth's blessings. With present levels of population we are as yet unable to provide anything approaching "quality of living" for all. As inevitable growth occurs, our environmental problems and human problems grow less easy to solve.

A major question of population policy must be faced in every community and nation: how many people can be supported without loss of the quality and diversity in the human environment? Some nations and regions behave as though their policy was to maintain maximum numbers of people at a minimum subsistence level. Technologically advanced nations seem to feel that no problem exists so long as economic gain exceeds population growth. But the growth of gross national product can conceal loss of those qualities in living that add color and meaning to existence, that give hope for the future and joy to daily living. The question of how many people can have an opportunity for living a full and satisfying life, is one we have hardly begun to explore. Yet in area after area, growth is proving disastrous, whether it be growth of subsistence populations in an impoverished country or the unplanned spread of middle class suburbs in a wealthy land blotting out natural diversity and creating a world of uniformity and discontent.

The question of what kind of an environment people do prefer is one that deserves far greater and much more searching study than it has yet received. One knows that people will differ and can hope that these human differences can be maintained and satisfied in a world that still has room for diversity.

"The effort to do something about problems that arise out of conflict between man's need and capacity to engineer his environment for economic use, and the need and capacity of natural systems to adjust to the consequences."

THE ECOLOGICAL VIEW

Gordon Harrison

OF ALL THE creatures who over the eons have inhabited this planet, man has been unique in his ability deliberately and massively to alter the environment. One striking way in which he has done so has been to reduce disease by making the man-occupied world less hospitable for parasites and their insect transport. Technological success here has lowered death rates much faster than society could adjust to the implications. Hence to simplify slightly, the world population began to grow cancerously.

In the unindustrialized world this sudden imbalance faces millions with starvation. Family-planning programs cannot achieve results quickly enough to avert the food crisis. Technical efforts to increase food supplies, despite some dramatic successes, are too meager to do the job, and it is not certain that even an all-out effort could succeed. The typical conservationist approaches, to warn of a developing imbalance between resources and consumption while trying both to save the resource and rationalize the patterns of consumption—these have little relevance at this late hour. Many observers believe that millions of people will starve in the 1970's, victims of our failure to recognize that we are not masters of the living system on which we depend for our life but parts of it, just as much as cells are parts of a body.

That lesson of folly is infinitely more tragic than any we face immediately in the developed world. We here are nevertheless pursuing a course that is similarly at odds with our circumstances aboard a small planet, similarly heedless of natural constraints on consumption, and therefore finally catastrophic as surely as if a man were to spend his days gorging himself without stopping.

The most obvious symptom of our own approaching crisis is pollution. By pollution I mean not only the poisoning of air and water by the wastes of production but equally the splurge of metropolis, the needless engrossment of some of our most produc-

tive farmlands for suburban housing, and the cavalier destruction of landscape by strip mines, highways, power lines, billboards, as though man did indeed live by these alone. Pollution in this sense is often regarded like famine as another direct consequence of over-population, and there is no question that increased numbers of people and especially their concentration in urban areas have made pollution critical and highly visible. Pollution, however, is not caused by too many people: It is the result of human disturbance of the cycling of energy and materials in natural systems.

That cycle in outline is well known: Primary producers (chiefly green plants) with energy from the sun synthesize their own organic food out of carbon dioxide, water, and minerals. All other living creatures feed on these plants either directly by grazing or indirectly by grazing the grazers as carnivores or parasites. A part of the food eaten is excreted; all of it is returned in one form or another to the environment. The organic discard passing through a variety of scavengers is eventually broken down by bacteria into its inorganic components which are thus made available to the plants as raw materials once more.

Man's intervention is radically disruptive. When a farmer clears a wood and plows a field he functions with respect to nature like a natural catastrophe—indeed generally more effective than fire, earthquake, or tornado. He exterminates a system of interrelated plants and animal life which over a long period of time had become mutually adapted to the physical environment and to each other in such a way that each creature was just making a living.

In a natural system, fully developed as a primeval forest, for instance, the input of sunlight is used to maintain the community of organisms. While individuals come and go within it and populations of species fluctuate so that at times there may be more oak and less hickory or more mice and fewer owls, the total quantity of living matter remains constant; that is to say the system ideally yields no net biological

---

Mr. Harrison is the Ford Foundation's program officer in charge of Resources and Environment. This statement is taken from the 1968 pamphlet, Ford Foundation Grants in Resources and Environment.

product. Net biological product—a crop—however, is just what the farmer wants. He therefore destroys the balanced system and creates a deliberately unbalanced one whose cycle from plowed field to seed to crop to harvest and back to plowed field is completed in a single season. He does this essentially by simplification, suppressing on his farm as many of the living things as possible that would compete with his planted crop for energy and minerals. He weeds; he fences; he sprays against pests.

The result is a system that in nature's terms is disturbed. The excess product—the developing crop—represents unexploited environmental opportunities, or in the ecologist's jargon, unfilled niches. Pests arrive on the scene to take advantage of these unusual opportunities. Unlike men they cannot cart away the crop; they can only multiply in numbers to consume it. If left alone they would make off with the feast and then move on, or starve down to numbers adapted to lower supplies of food, or provide a bonanza for predators who obeying the same law of nature might increase in their turn to exploit it. By many complicated interactions over time, populations feeding on each other would come once more into balance. Balance of course is never a static condition but rather a moderated pattern of ups and downs around a mean, much like temperature fluctuations in a thermostatically controlled room, although immensely more complicated.

It is clear that the simpler a natural system is the more unstable it must be. Consider a three-part food chain: grass, rabbits, and lynx. Suppose drought destroys the grass crop. Then rabbits wholly dependent on it will die off and so will lynx who are wholly dependent on rabbits. But if among the grass were drought-resistant plants and rabbits were adapted to eat them, then as least a proportion of plants, rabbits, and lynx would be likely to survive prolonged dry spells. The system would be made hardier still if chipmunks were added to feed on nuts and could be caught perhaps by more skillful lynx who would then not entirely die out for lack of rabbits but might produce a cleverer strain better able in the future to handle environmental adversity. In any event the more alternative ways there are of eating and being eaten the better the chance a living system has to avoid massive fluctuations in the birth and death of species. Variety thus appears to be nature's grand tactic for survival.

Man is the only creature who values wealth because only he can achieve it. An important consequence of the farmer's productive system is that it enables him to capture excess produce from the soil, more than he needs at once to consume. He can exploit wealth by storing it and that leads to the settled life, to villages, and at last to cities. It is in permanent human settlements that off-premise consumption produces the specifically human problem of garbage and wastes. Waste is in fact only a symptom that geographically the metabolic cycle has been split: Production has occurred at one place, consumption and excretion at another. The byproducts of human use that would in nature return immediately as food for other organisms in the cycle are, as it were, left high, dry, and a nuisance out of their natural context. Civilization so far has been more impressed with the nuisance than with the anomaly that processes which on the land sustain life, in town can poison it.

Currently this nation devotes a lot of energy and money (though not nearly enough) to seeking a technological fix for the waste problem. So long as this technology explores essentially for more sophisticated holes in which to throw things away, it may be immediately useful in changing the locus of the nuisance—garbage is after all more tolerable on the town dump than in the bedroom—but in the long run it is doomed. Let it be noted again that all the materials by weight extracted and processed for human consumption are breathed away or end up as waste. The concepts of use and discard therefore are simply irrelevant to the facts of life within a system that is closed so far as materials are concerned. The traditional focus on production and consumption looks at only one segment of the indivisible circle: Consumption, if it is to continue, must be tied to production at both ends, accepting the product and giving up the raw materials for new products.

The problem of waste disposal is not the focal or even necessarily the most important issue for conservation, but it serves as well as any to illustrate the principles of interdependence that make it necessary for man in all regards to pay more attention to his impact on his environment and vice versa. The concept of the natural system, along with the recognition that nature has a tactic realized by maximum stability while man embraces an opposite tactic aimed at maximum production, provides the essential philosophic context within which it becomes possible to see what conservation can and cannot, should and should not do.

The environment and the quality of political life.

CONSERVATION COMES OF AGE

Grant McConnell

WHAT IS significant is that today there is a conservation movement and that it is grounded firmly in both popular support and principle. It is no longer a matter of a handful of scientists and other enlightened individuals quietly influencing key statesmen to slip actions through which will have genuine public support only at a later time. This is the sense in which it is appropriate to agree that conservation " has come of age ".

What accounts for this development? A full explanation would be complex. On the face of things it might seem that the values of great numbers of Americans have changed over the years. In the sense that values are really testable only by choices actually given effect, this is plainly true. But this is to say very little. There is a genuine possibility that recent generations have wanted different things than their predecessors, but in view of the possibility that the political system may have had a bias in validating some preferences instead of others, casting aspersions on our ancestors as a wholly materialistic lot is not justified. If current Americans show more signs of caring for the nonmaterial aspects of their environment, it may well be because the political order has evolved sufficiently to allow such concern to have occasional effect.

There are good grounds for believing this is the case. Very briefly, the United States is much more of a nation than it has been in the past. It is knit together with roads, airlines, telephones, television, magazines to a degree difficult to have foreseen even a relatively few decades ago. The horizons of the average American have vastly expanded so that the inhabitants of Sauk Center and all its real counterparts now share a national culture as never before. Inevitably, this has been reflected in the workings of the political system. Many decisions that were formerly within the exclusive provinces of states and localities are now made in larger arenas, arenas in which an inevitably greater diversity of citizens participate.

Formerly, choices on the allocation of values, as for example between natural beauty and resource exploitation, were largely in the hands of localities and, in fact, were regarded mainly as a private matter. Insofar as the choice lay in the hands of a lumber or mining company, the choice for exploitation was preordained. But the situation was more complex than this suggests. If the choice were in the hands—as it usually has been—of a locality or state in which the lumbering or mining industry bulked particularly large, the support of the community or state would flow to the narrow interests of such an industry. Some local citizens would be aggrieved at the costs in natural beauty and wilderness but their voices would be so weak in the face of the seemingly monolithic determination of their neighbors as to be beneath the threshold of hearing. Indeed, the feeling of powerlessness would generally lead them not to speak at all, given the inevitability of failure and the necessity of living with those neighbors.

Thus, it has generally been true that fights for conservation have taken on an aspect of outsiders against locals. The appearance has been false in that almost any locality contains some individuals concerned for conservation. Nevertheless, these individuals could only be heard in chorus with like-minded fellows drawn from a larger constituency. The exploiters of commodities, understanding the situation at least intuitively, have persistently appealed to the strong American tradition of decentralization as a supposedly democratic principle and have sought to retain the power of decision in local hands. There have been contests in which localities have lined up for conservation, establishment of the Gila Wilderness, for example, but these have been rare. Conservation, and conservation of wilderness and scenic values especially, have depended on creation of larger constituencies. Thus it is not difficult to imagine what would have happened to the Grand Canyon if its future had been decided by Arizona instead of the nation. The American people as a whole have a far smaller per capita money stake in damming the Canyon's potential kilowatts than do the people of Arizona. It is also understandable why officials of Humboldt County resisted creation of a Redwoods National Park, while a strong drive for the park came from San Francisco, and why opposition to the North Cascades Park was loudest in Bellingham and Wenatchee and weakest in Seattle.

The change that has come about is far from total. It is in degree only. It is, moreover, a change of some complexity. It involves a new awareness and knowledge of people in New England, the Midwest, and California about the North Cascades, many miles distant from their homes. It involves the increasing urbanization of Americans and the drift of political power to city dwellers. It involves the changing economic base of cities like Seattle, with the relative decline and position of the lumber industry. Thus, it is not inconceivable that the success of the Boeing Company may have been the essential factor in preserving the North Cascades. The change also in-

Dr. McConnell is professor of Politics and Academic Assistant to the Chancellor at the University of California at Santa Cruz. This is an excerpt from his prologue to Congress and the Environment, edited by Richard A. Cooley and Geoffrey Wandesforde-Smith, University of Washington Press, 1970.

volves the development of national conservation organizations. All of these have c o n v e r g e d in the creation of a larger and more diverse constituency, with a consequently growing power supporting wilderness, scenic values, and environmental protection. [1]

Second, a deep and general change has occurred in our national political life. This is now a rich and prosperous nation. We now have a large generation of youth that has no memory of depression. At long last, we are generally free of the incubus of fear that tomorrow the economy will collapse. This has a very profound meaning—that the substance of political a n d moral life is no longer almost wholly economic. Economic matters have, in the past, been highly preoccupying, simply because hitherto we have never been out of the shadow of potential famine or other economic disaster. It is highly unlikely that men have ever really believed that economic affairs are the m o s t important department of life, but it is true that so far we have always had to give first thought to that d e - partment simply because it has had a prior urgency. As a result, our political system has been formulated to adjust economic claims, and it has worked peculiarly well. The reason for this is that economic claims are bargainable; it is almost always possible to split the difference somewhere in an economic contest so that each side is reasonably satisfied. When we respond to the injunction, "Come, let us reason together," it is to bargain and to split differences.

As the nation has become richer, however, economic values have lost their old urgency and other more important matters have emerged and taken the foreground. The values of natural beauty and wilderness are critical examples here, but they are really not bargainable. The sort of "reasoning" which has been characteristic of politics on the economic model does not apply. It is faintly conceivable, f o r example, that by offering a sufficiently high price to the National Museum in Amsterdam to acquire its treasure, " The Night Watch," one could get that great painting away from the Dutch; but it is absolutely inconceivable t h a t o n e could make a deal to get a 2-foot square cut out of the lower left-hand quadrant of the picture for any price. This is just not a possible bargain.

So it is with supposed bargains offered on natural beauty and wilderness. To bargain over the G r a n d Canyon, the redwoods, the North C a s c a d e s , may seem eminently sensible if you are interested in kilowatts, lumber, or copper, but it is nonetheless immoral if your concern is with scenic beauty and wilderness. Such a bargain might be possible i f t h e value of scenic beauty and wilderness could be stated in the same dollar measure as kilowatts, lumber, and copper. It would, alternatively, b e bargainable i f the economic developers were able to o f f e r a new Grand Canyon, some new 2,000-year-old redwoods, or some new North Cascades in the exchange. Unfortunately, however, this alternative has practical difficulties. The fact of the matter is that any such bargain is completely one-sided—to take away more or less of the Grand Canyon, the redwoods, or t h e North Cascades. The brute power of the opposition may conceivably win, but such an outcome will not be a bargain in the sense of being mutually acceptable.

This fundamental characteristic of the politics of conservation is deeply involved in what has occurred with the conservation movement. There is much evidence that Americans today have moved beyond the conception that everything of meaning in life can be stated in either dollar or head-count terms. It is evident, for example, that many Americans are willing to go to extreme lengths in their principled opposition to the Vietnam war. It is plain that many individuals are willing to lay their lives on the line for simple human dignity. And many of our best young people are going to extremes to assert their rejection of the material calculus. Both moral and aesthetic principles are emerging everywhere as the fundamental material of politics and common life. In this setting, i n - creasing numbers of individuals are declaring themselves for what they really believe. It i s h a r d l y surprising that many are declaring the values of scenic beauty and wilderness; there are hardly any values less uncertain and ambiguous than these. Formerly, the sort of ridicule offered by spokesmen for firms such as the Kennecott Copper Corporation, that concern for these values is "sentimental," was effective. We were once half persuaded that such concern was soft-headed, and that these values w e r e inferior. It is beginning to emerge that the r e a l l y soft-headed sentimentalism is that attached to money.

The striking evidence of growth in the conservation movement since 1954 is directly related to the clarity with which the conservation leaders of today have perceived the strategic nature of conservation issues. A telling incident on this score is one related to the Echo Park controversy. When the Upper Colorado Project was put forward, nearly everyone believed Echo Park was necessarily doomed. But a small group of individuals got together and decided that the principle involved was simply wrong and that they should say so. This was to be a gesture, but the declaration struck such a chord of public response that ultimately it became possible to save Echo Park by sheer mass support.

The style of the conservation movement is intransigent. It is often shrill and strident. It gives rise to internal controversies of much intensity. However distressing those controversies may be, they a r e themselves strong evidence of the degree to which participants r e - gard their cause as serious. By the same token, today's movement is principled. This very feature is responsible for the great current growth of t h e conservation movement, and, in fact, is why there is a genuine movement today where there was none before. To the degree that it stands by its principles, it will continue to grow and frequently to succeed. To the degree that it seeks to compromise and make deals, it will fail and wither.

The leaders of the modern conservation movement must expect to be told that they are unreasonable. They must expect continued demands to enter into "bargains" in which they can only lose and never gain. They may be told that they should go back to the old reliable way of quietly finessing things through men of influence. But those days are gone, and with all gratitude to the notable men who managed those coups of influence, their coups cannot now be emulated. Henceforth, the conservation movement will have to succeed as a movement, enduring all the committee meetings, the endless work of organization, and, most of all, hammering out the principles and the applications of those principles.

FOOTNOTE

1. Regarding the general principle involved, see my Private Power and American Democracy, Alfred A. Knopf, New York, 1966, Chapter iv. ∎

"The ability to perceive beauty may, in the long run, prove man's salvation."

A REPORT ON THE AMERICAN ENVIRONMENT

The President's Council on Recreation and Natural Beauty

AT A TIME when science and technology have raised the human condition to unprecedented heights and feed the mind of man for incomparably greater adventures, man is perplexed by a growing sense of insecurity in the natural system that has always been his home. For man brought with him into this world not only the brilliant promise of a higher order of life, but also the threat that he will wrest from the earth a victory that is destructive to the victor.

At a distance, this seems an enormous paradox. Nature, having produced man, seems equipped to support him lavishly. As evolution proceeds, the mind of man displays a growing capacity to shape a world hospitable to his fullest development.

These harmonious prospects are imperiled, however, by the accelerating pace of change. In the technologically advanced portions of the earth, there have been greater changes in the lives of ordinary men within the past century than in all previous history. But the immense powers that man has acquired over nature have not been matched by an equivalent growth of wisdom in their use. In his single-minded pursuit of particular aims—evolving into the intensive specialization accompanying technological advance—man has often been oblivious to unintended side effects of his actions. As change is introduced on an increasingly larger scale and at an ever swifter rate, these unplanned consequences of man-induced change have coalesced to create an extraordinary crisis. To be understood, this crisis must be taken apart like the pieces of a puzzle. Some of the present dilemma was set in motion ages ago.

From observing and experimenting with the processes of nature, man discovered that he could manipulate them to serve him. He invented agriculture—and learned to drain, plow, fertilize, and terrace the land. He changed the courses of rivers, made gardens of deserts, and reshaped mountains and coastlines. But in his haste to exploit the wealth that lay in the earth, he also deforested mountains and valleys, destroyed the ground cover, and exposed the soil to destruction.

The result was to fill the streams with silt and the marshes with debris. Man's alterations of the landscape caused the waterways to flood and further devastate the land. These alterations of the landscape also disturbed the habitats of other living things, resulting in the depletion and extinction of entire species.

Technological civilization opened unlimited new vistas to man. It made possible cities larger than ever before, offering the benefits of urban life to ever greater numbers of men, and bringing a diversity of social life and cultural and intellectual exchange never before known. But now, in the center of most of these cities, malignant cores of decay have developed. The residents of city slums know little of the rich variety of choice and quality that exalts human life. More frequently, their lives are encompassed by filth, ugliness, and squalor.

Man learned that his knowledge could be used to provide him with an enormous range of goods and services. He developed vast industries with energy borrowed or captured from nature. The wastes inevitably generated by industrial processes are poured into the water, released into the air, buried in the soil, or scattered about the landscape. Harmful substances have thus been freed to find their way into the cells of plants and animals throughout the earth.

Unlike most species of life, man has roamed the earth building a home for himself in every climate. Human survival has even been accomplished beneath the sea, at the poles, and now far out in space. Intricate systems of roads and highways have been constructed to speed the transport of man and his goods across the land. In America, the idea of the road leading on to better things is part of the national heritage.

Yet, as roads, houses, factories, and commercial centers spread across the landscape, the distinct forms of the land and the profuse features of plant and animal life that have always been part of man's habitat are obscured or obliterated.

In pursuing survival and greater security, man has tampered with the careful balances in natural systems, sometimes with unintended consequences that endanger his security. He often overlooks the elaborate relations between predators and prey that exist in

---

This statement is taken from the <u>Introduction to From Sea to Shining Sea,</u> the Council's 1968 Report.

nature. Frequently, he has waged successful w a r against one species only to see the resulting unnatural gap filled by disastrous proliferation of another species.

Man has learned to inoculate himself against deadly plagues, and diseases that once took a dreadful toll have been almost banished from the more advanced societies. Yet simultaneously there has been a tremendous increase in the diseases of urbanization and high-pressure living— heart disease, ulcers, arteriosclerosis, hypertension, and others. Man is a part of nature and cannot with impunity separate himself from the natural rhythms that have given him nurture during all his previous millenna on this planet.

One of the most ominous threats to the environment lies in the failure of man thus far to provide humane solutions to the problems posed by the spread of his own numbers. No major urban center in the world has yet demonstrated satisfactory ways to accommodate growth. In many areas expanding population is outrunning the readily available supply of food, water, and other basic resources and threatens to aggravate beyond solution the staggering problems of the new urban society. A limitless proliferation of the species would eventually condemn man himself to a termite existence.

There are elements of tragedy in man's abuse of nature and of his own promise. Yet the increasing recognition of America's environmental crisis constitutes abundant ground for hope. There is still opportunity to repair the damaged fabric of life if Americans begin to consider themselves part of the earth's interlocking, interdependent natural system. Americans who learned in the frontier era to "conquer" nature now need to learn new techniques of cooperating with nature.

Cooperation with nature can lead to new forms of creative expression. Man has traditionally found expression in music, poetry, painting, the performing and plastic arts, in the sciences, in industrial technology. Only recently has he begun to give this impulse expression on a large scale in the art and science of designing his environment.

Basic to intelligent adaptation of design to the environment is the science of ecology—a word derived from two Greek words meaning "the study of t h e home." It is the study of the relation of an organism to its total environment. No man is an island, and no creature of any kind is independent of its habitat. Changes cannot take place in one part of the complex web of life without affecting the whole. Every proposed human change in the environment must be considered for its total effects. Ignorance of the long-term, indirect consequences of human activities is the root of the contemporary crisis. Ecology helps to reveal nature as a laboratory offering the guidance man sorely needs in his efforts to restore and e n - hance the quality of his environment.

Ecology has a counterpart in the field of technology with the development of systems analysis. A space missile, for example, is a combination of systems— each composed of sub-systems—for propulsion, guidance, enclosure of passengers, and communications. The effects of all activities within each system and sub-system must be measured not only by the effi-

ciency of the single system but also by their effects on other systems.

Similarly, a human environment is composed of various systems and sub-systems, including a residential system, a park system, an educational system, a commericial system, an industrial system, an agricultural system, a communications system, and a transportation system. The goal of all these systems should be a total environment capable of satisfying the broadest range of human needs. The effects of activities within each of these systems must be evaluated for their influence on all other systems consititing the environment. A transportation system, for example, should be measured not merely for its efficiency in moving people and goods, but for its effect on residential neighborhoods, parks, schools, the distribution of commercial and industrial facilities, the total development of the community and of the individuals who compose it. Sophisticated methods of evaluating these effects have yet to be developed, and therein lies a major contemporary challenge to science and technology.

Yet, whatever knowledge science can bring to bear on the problems of these times will not be sufficient. The adaptation that the future demands will require the efforts of a whole people. Will that effort b e made? The beginnings of a response may be found in the widespread enthusiasm for the natural beauty movement. It is almost as if Americans, confronted with the staggering consequences of nature o u t of balance, have fallen back on the one faculty that can somehow judge it and respond: the esthetic sense. If something is beautiful, it is likely to be functioning properly and in good health. The ability to perceive beauty may, in the long run, prove man's salvation.

The natural beauty movement has from the start meant far more than "beautification." It means a vigorous expansion of traditional concepts of t h e American conservation movement started by John Muir, Gifford Pinchot, and Theodore Roosevelt. It means turning also to the problems of the cities, where most Americans live. It means the control of pollution and litter and the elimination of public eyesores. It means a resurgence of civic pride in the neighborhoods and towns of America. It means a new emphasis on amenities in the man-made environment such as grass, flowers, trees, parks and open spaces, fountains, art in public places, and design excellence in buildings and streets. It means broadening t h e process of decision-making by public agencies to include humane and esthetic considerations. The natural beauty movement implies a faith in the capacity of technology to solve the problems it has created and an imaginative determination to f i n d innovative solutions. Finally, the idea central to t h e natural beauty movement is the belief that exposure t o nature in some form contributes to the renewal a n d fulfillment of every human being, in body and in spirit.

The ambitious aims of the natural beauty movement will not be quickly achieved. The effort requires hard thought, difficult decisions, and a reappraisal of some habitual standards and values. Success will ultimately depend on the willingness of the individual to accept the responsibility of environmental stewardship.

"The quality of the environment confronts man with his most serious difficulty."

SOME CRITICAL ISSUES TODAY
IN THE FIELD OF NATURAL RESOURCES

Irving   Fox

A COURSE in natural resources given 50 years ago, 20 years ago, or even if it had been given 10 years ago, would have emphasized substantially different issues than those we now consider important. From, let us say, about 1910 to 1950, the problems and issues remained much the same. During that 50-year period you would have heard about the growing scarcity of resource commodities and the terrible threat that this scarcity posed for our future welfare. You would have heard about the importance of resource programs as a stimulant to economic development and the regulation of monopoly, especially in the power and transportation fields.

These issues remain today, but they are a faint echo of what they once were. In part, the resource problem has changed from what it was. In part, a new sophistication has arisen with regard to the nature of resource problems and issues. But these old ideas persist, and many people, if not most, have been indoctrinated with a concept of resource problems that is now passé. Thus, my first task is to explain why the preservation of the resource base to supply food, fiber, energy, and minerals is an oversimplification of the resource problem and no longer should be considered a central resource issue. After this is done, we can turn to the critical issues in the field of natural resources as we proceed through the latter part of the twentieth century.

THE RESOURCE SUPPLY - DEMAND OUTLOOK

Since the days of Malthus, the doctrine of scarcity—the fear of running out of resource commodities—has dominated much of our thinking about natural resources. The theme is familiar today. Most of us have been victims of it. We've heard that we're running out of water, that our mineral resources are being depleted, that the world will soon be unable to feed itself; soon there will be no petroleum, and in another generation we will lack timber.

In 1962 a book was published by Resources for the Future, entitled Trends in Natural Resource Commodities. It deals with the production, prices consumption, and employment, as related to resource commodities from 1870 to 1957. It reveals that per capita, as well as total consumption, has been increasing with regard to resource commodities. It indicates that employment per unit of output has sharply declined in the natural resource industries. And it indicates that the cost of production, with the exception of forest products, has remained relatively constant.

What does this mean? It means that in spite of a tremendous increase in the use of resource commod-

ities, in spite of the need to mine less accessible deposits of coal and other minerals, to use lower-grade ore, to produce much more food on the same land, to drill deeper for petroleum, it is as easy and it costs no more to provide resource commodities today than it did in 1870. Stated another way, because of advances in science and technology of production, we have no greater shortage of natural resources in America today than we did nearly 100 years ago. In 1963, Resources for the Future published another book. Its title was Resources in America's Future, and it consisted of 1,000 pages, dealing with a projection of economic growth of the U.S. from 1960 to 2000, estimates of the demand for resource commodities and a comparison of this demand with the supply outlook. Its findings are also revealing. It concluded that in the face of a prospective doubling of population and a quadrupling of economic activity over the 40-year period from 1960 to 2000, no significant resource commodity shortages could be envisaged in the United States.

Resources for the Future also published another book entitled Scarcity and Growth, by Barnett and Morse. It is a scholarly inquiry into the doctrine of scarcity as originated by Malthus. This analysis contained some significant conclusions. One conclusion was that:

The transformation of materials into final goods is becoming increasingly a matter of chemical processing.... The natural resource building blocks are now, to a large extent, atoms and molecules. Nature's input should now be conceived as units of mass and energy, not acres and tons. Now the problem is more one of manipulating the available store of iron, magnesium, aluminum, carbon, hydrogen, and oxygen atoms, even electrons. This has major economic significance (1:238).

These gentlemen go on to say:

It is by no means necessary to reduce produce today in order to increase production tomorrow. If, instead, current production is maintained and consumption is reduced in favor of research and investment, future production will be increased. Higher production today, if it also means more research and investment today, thus will serve the economic interest of future generations better than reservation of resources and lower current production (2:247).

In short, these gentlemen are saying that the limitation upon our resources base is not the supply of

Formerly an executive of Resources for the Future, Professor Fox is now Chairman of the Department of Urban and Regional Planning and Associate Director of the Water Resources Center, The University of Wisconsin, Madison.

natural resources as we think of them usually, but
the supply of atoms, energy, and human ingenuity;
that it's not necessarily wise to reduce production
today to have resources available for tomorrow.

THE MAJOR RESOURCE PROBLEMS

You are mistaken if you feel that these conclusions
lead to the conclusion that there are no resource problems. There are, in my judgment, three major problems in the natural resources management field today, and these create five major issues.

Environmental Quality

The first major problem is that of environmental
quality. There is clear evidence that the most serious general resource problem in the world today is
that of preserving and enhancing the quality of the
physical and biological environment. This, in my
judgment, is one of the three or four most serious
problems confronting mankind.

What is the nature of this problem? One aspect
is environmental contamination; contamination from
nuclear radiation, from chemicals used for the control of pests, fertilizers, food preservatives, and
from the wast products of our cities and our industries. These threaten human health and well being.
A second aspect is the destruction of critical elements
of our ecological system. These may be destroyed
by contaminants or more directly by the hunting and
killing of animals and agricultural practices which
destroy all but a few species of plants produced for
agricultural markets. Many of these threatened biota
are sources of medicinal drugs. Ecological imbalance
leads to the emergence of pests, bacteria, and viruses. Species such as the bald eagle, the mountain lion,
and the wolf, which are threatened with extinction,
add to the richness of life. A third aspect is the degradation of the aesthetic character of the landscape.
Urban concentrations often are ugly to look at as well
as noisy and dirty. Rural landscapes may be marred
by unsightly billboards, litter, and crude structures.

A fourth aspect may be termed crowding, which
evidently has unfortunate social and psychological
consequences. We appear to be losing our opportunities for privacy, to be relatively alone when one
wants to be. An increasingly larger percentage of
our people are being concentrated in urban places.
Today we have crowded parks, and we are crowding
into the wild places. In short, we are generally creating a less happy and less attractive physical environment than we once had. We face a general decline
in the richness and beauty of mankind's surroundings.

And why do I characterize this as our most critical problem? There are several reasons. First is
its complexity and the uncertainty this complexity creates. We simply do not understand the consequences
to mankind of what we're doing through nuclear radiation, contamination of the air and water, chemicals
in our food, and urban crowding. The nature of these
problems are such that early answers are unlikely.
Your children are unlikely to suffer from hunger, lack
of clothing, or lack of shelter. But they may be the
victims of environmental contaminants, which we do
not now understand and which we may not understand
until it is too late. A second reason that this is a serious problem is that some of the actions we take in
the resource field constitute irreversible decisions.

It is a very solemn thing to extinguish a form of life
because once a species is destroyed, it cannot be
brought back to life. Once a valley is inundated by a
reservoir, it is next to impossible to restore it. Once
a lake is seriously polluted, it may be impossible to
make it once again a productive and useful water area.
A third reason this is a serious problem relates to
the fact that man does not live by bread alone. A large
part of our income is the well-being we derive from
our physical and biological environment. This sort of
income does not appear in our national income accounts.
We could continue to have high, even increasing money incomes, and suffer a net decline in human welfare.
If we could measure environmental values, it is possible that we would find this happening today. In considering the seriousness of environmental quality problems, it is sobering to realize that our traditional
economic and political institutions tend to foster the
destruction of the quality of the environment. This
situation creates one of the major issues which will
be discussed and illuminated later in this paper.

Managing the Resource Industries

A second major resource problem is that of managing the resource industries to serve best the overall public interest. These are agriculture, mining and petroleum extraction, fishing, forestry, water development,
and the provision of outdoor recreation opportunities.

Simply stated, an unregulated private enterprise system for these industries simply does not serve the public
interest. The reasons are complex, and it would not be
possible to describe them in any detail in a short presentation of this nature. However, a few of the reasons may
be cited. First is what the economist refers to as the
price inelasticity of demand for many resource commodities. This is the reason that agriculture tends to be faced with periodic instability. Supply simply cannot adjust
readily to changes in price and as a result in a free market the prices of agricultural products tend to fluctuate
wildly with, at times, disastrous effects to consumers
as well as producers.

A second reason an unregulated sector of resource industries does not tend to serve the public interest is the
common property nature of some resources. A good example where everyone is free to use the same lake, river, or ocean area is fisheries. But there are others.
The air, the seas, the radio spectrum, and outer
space are the common property of the people of the
world. When no one owns the resource, there is no
motivation to manage it to optimize benefits from it.
Thus there is a tendency toward over-exploitation.
This is the case of the blue whale, which is almost ex-
tinct. This is the cause of a serious problem in the
management of fisheries all over the world. If we
fail to develop international institutions to manage
common property resources, over-exploitation and
conflict almost certainly will result.

A third reason that the resources industries do not
tend to serve the public interest if they are unregulated is that some of these industries tend to be natural monopolies. Water supply, electric power, and
navigation are classic examples. A fourth reason is
that for some resource development activities we must
have long-term horizons, longer possibly than a farmer or a forester can afford to have in terms of his
own economic interests. This means that the ordinary individual or small private enterprises are in-

hibited from dealing with these resources in terms of the long-range needs of society. And finally, there are what might be called the collective goods nature of a good many of these resources. That is, if you have a beautiful scenic valley, that scenery is available to all, and the private individual may or may not be motivated to preserve the scenic area.

Over the world, governments have intervened to deal with these limitations, but serious problems remain. There are large sectors of poverty in American agriculture while many prosperous farmers in the United States receive large subsidies. There is good evidence of gross inefficiencies in petroleum extraction. We are faced, as in Alaska, with the depletion of fishery resources and an over-investment of capital in the fishery industry. The small forests of the United States are in economic trouble, and their potentialities are not being realized. It is charged— and I think with some justification—that we make uneconomic investments in water projects. And today, we're struggling—and I think with some degree of success—with the management of our outdoor recreation resources. In brief, one of the major problem areas in the resource field is the large question of how to manage the resource industries to serve present and future generations both efficiently and equitably.

Realizing Scientific and Technological Opportunities

A third problem area is that of making world resources available to serve best the needs of mankind generally. Even in the most congested areas of the world it is technically possible for people to be well fed, clothed, and housed if the resources of this planet are utilized effectively. There are vast under-utilized resources in Asia, Africa, South and North America. The technology is available to develop and utilize these resources to serve mankind. To support this view your attention is invited to the recent experience in India where this past year a bumper crop of grain was grown. Because of scientific advances in rice and wheat genetics, production has skyrocketed and for the first time in several years a surplus exists. The technology is there; the resources are there, but there are serious problems in realizing the opportunities that are available, not only in the underdeveloped countries of the world, but also in countries such as our own.

THE CRITICAL ISSUES

These three problem areas—the problem of environmental quality, the problem of managing the primary industries, the problem of realizing scientific and technological opportunities—lead to five critical issues. There may be more, but these five interrelated issues are the ones we will be most concerned with in dealing with resource problems in the years ahead.

Population Control

First is the question of population control. How rapidly and to what extent should population growth be controlled to aid in solving the problems of environmental quality and in meeting the demands for goods and services produced from resources? We're hearing a great deal about this, and we will hear a great deal more about it in the years ahead. There can be no doubt, if one looks at the statistics and examines what has happened in the past, that population limitation in some form or another will eventually be neces-

sary. We merely have to project what is going on now into the next century to see (whether we want it or not) that some sort of limitation on the natural growth of population will be essential. This simply cannot be avoided. There is considerable evidence that slowing the rate of population growth would aid in bringing the supply of resource commodities in to better balance with demand today and in the next few years. This is quite apart from the question of having a doubling of population or a large increase to deal with 50 years from now. There is no doubt, also, that population growth complicates the problem of preserving environmental quality. The issue then that all the countries of the world face, is how, when, and to what extent should population control be introduced.

Extinction of Plant and Animal Species

The second critical issue relating to resources (and in a sense this is an ethical issue raised by such people as Albert Schweitzer and Aldo Leopold) is the issue of to what extent man is justified in continuing through his action to modify and extinguish plant and animal species. Man's welfare, we know, is inextricably interrelated with the ecology of this planet. How and to what extent is imperfectly understood. Yet through the use of pesticides, the extension of agriculture to more and more land, and in a variety of other ways, we are modifying and destroying species at a rapid rate—a rate heretofore unknown. The question is whether it is time that this be viewed not as a scientific problem alone, but essentially as an ethical issue. In my judgment, it is extremely dubious that early advances in science can unravel all of the consequences of what we are doing. In the face of such uncertainities in the past, man has adopted ethical norms to govern human behavior. Should we not view the destruction of any species of life as a very solemn act—something that mankind should accept as being contrary to the basic rules of a civilized society. The issue deserves careful but urgent attention.

The Application of Knowledge to Resource Potentials

The third major issue is that of how to improve communications and apply knowledge so that resource potentialities can be realized more effectively than they are at the present time. This is a critical problem in dealing with environmental problems in North America and Europe. In the low-income countries, this issue must be confronted and solved if the supply potentials are to be realized and environmental problems are to be dealt with to meet the needs of the populations that are there today and the populations that certainly will be there over the next couple of decades.

Let us examine a little more deeply the situation in North America and Europe. The complexity of environmental problems has been mentioned. There are two other problems that merit attention here. First, private institutions are not motivated by a market economy to reduce many of the adverse environmental consequences of their activities. Since they do not bear the cost of such actions as pollution of the air and water, private organizations are not encouraged to take these effects into account in the calculus of their operations. The second problem relates to research public institutions sponsor or undertake on environmental problems. Decisions as to what research to support are dominated by the scientists who are supported by the research. Scientists are well qualified to judge the prospects of advance and determine appropriate research methods. But they have no special qualifications to judge what research is most important to mankind. There is a growing uneasiness that our research programs are designed to serve the interests of researchers rather than the public generally. One of the most urgent needs we face in the field of environmental quality is research strategy to get at our environmental problems in a systematic way. It is doubtful that such a strategy is developing today.

In the low-income countries, the problem is somewhat different. The advancement of knowledge and application thereof to resource problems is much more important than it is in North America or in Europe. The potential, as noted earlier, is there. It's not the lack of resources that causes famine today. It is the inability to apply modern science and technology to food production. If the supply problems of the low-income countries are to be met, over the short run, over the next 10, 20 years or so, this problem must be overcome. It will require capital to support research and education and especially new institutions to provide motivation to advance and apply knowledge. This problem, of dealing with the application of knowledge and communication in cultures quite foreign to our own, is one of the most difficult problems faced in the world today.

Policy Design

The fourth issue is the question of public policy design in the resource field. Government is here to stay. Government intervention in the natural resources field is essential if public interest is to be served. No other recourse is available. In theory, since government represents all of the people, one would expect governmental agencies to weigh all costs and benefits in deciding what programs to undertake and what policies to impose on private individuals and organizations. As you are well aware, the problem is not that simple. An important point is that the benefits from environmental contamination are concentrated, but the damages tend to be diffused. This is evident in water and air pollution and landscape deterioration. If one looks at the programs that affect the resource industries and seeks to make them more effective organizations, a similar situation exists. Subsidies and public programs concentrate the benefits while the costs are widely shared by the people of the country. The result is that there are strong political and economic forces which support the destruction of the environment and strong political forces that say programs must be provided to aid the resource industries. At the same time the political forces, which aim to preserve and enhance the quality of the environment and which are concerned with the effect of programs of aid to the resource industries upon people, generally have tended to be weak. The outlook today is a continuing decline in environmental quality unless there is a substantial strengthening of public institutions that deal with environmental quality matters. In addition, the erosion of confidence in the foundations of our society will continue if some of the glaring inequities in governmental treatment of resource industries are not remedied. We have a long way to go to develop resource policies which on the basis of objective criteria can be said to serve satisfactorily the public generally.

International Flow of Capital and Resource Commodities

The fifth issue is the question of how can there be achieved a good balance in the flow of capital and re-source commodities between the high-income and low-income countries of the world? For both developed and low-income countries, this is one of the critical issues relating to the exploitation of resources. This applies to food products, timber, minerals, energy, and the fibers. Why is this such an important issue? First, the low-income countries urgently need capital in order to develop. One of the best ways available to many of them to secure capital is through the production and sale of resource commodities. Second, many of the smaller countries are not nearly self-sufficient in natural resources. The future welfare of these countries, especially such countries as we have in Africa, is dependent on their ability to secure resources from abroad through trade. Many countries, both developed and low-income, can produce some resource commodities only at a high cost. The economic growth of such countries will be advanced if they can trade the commodities they can produce economically for commodities which are costly to produce. And fourth, unfortunately the low-income countries associate the exploitation and shipment abroad of natural resource commodities with colonialism and the empires of the last century. Thus, they tend to discourage the entry of foreign capital for such purposes and the export of resource commodities. In short, there is a need to develop the resources of these low-income countries. The capital is in the developed countries of Europe and North America. The use of these commodities today takes place preponderantly in the high-income countries. How are we to achieve an appropriate balance in the use of the resource commodities of the world in the interest not only of the developed countries, but of the low-income countries as well?

It now appears that long before population and economic growth in North America and Europe encounter serious problems of resource supply, the quality of the environment that man is creating will confront him with a much more critical difficulty. We will continue to be faced, as we have been in the past, with the problems of managing the resource industries to serve the overall interest of the public. We will also face, in the kind of international world we have today, the problem of making world resources available so as to best serve the needs of mankind. If these problems are to be met, we must realize a new type of policy design which is capable of weighing environmental values and other considerations with which we are concerned, and we must develop a research strategy which will assure an adequate advance in knowledge about the relationship between man's activity and his physical and biological environment. Here critical issues arise with regard to population and to the preservation of species. In the developing countries, the most critical problem relates to the advancement and application of science to resource management tasks. Internationally, our major challenge lies in aiding scientific advancements in the developing countries, in encouraging the free flow of resource commodities in international trade, and in finding ways and means of managing amicably and efficiently the common property resources of the world, including the air, outer space, the radio spectrum, and most important of all, the resources of the sea.

REFERENCES

1. Barnett, Harold J. and Morse, Chandler, Scarcity and Growth, Resources for the Future, 1755 Massachusetts Avenue NW, Washington, D.C. 20036, 1963. ∎

Man and his environment are on a collision course.

THE POPULATION-POLLUTION SYNDROME

David Archbald

ARE MAN and his environment on a collision course? Yes—according to most environmental scientists and many statisticians. But where, when, and how great the collisions are still partly up to man. In addition to our exploding population, we must recognize we have become a geological force. We are converting over a million acres a year from farm and wild lands to highways and building sites in the United States alone. We can literally move mountains and poison rivers, lakes, and ever-increasing portions of the oceans and atmosphere. So the best we can expect is that we learn to direct this force and to develop and implement effective controls to check the population-pollution spiral to minimize the future man-environment collisions.

HISTORY

Actually a series of local or regional collisions have already occurred dating back to the time when man moved out of the Mesolithic into the Neolithic or Stone Age, about 10,000 B.C. At this point he walked out of the " woods " and left behind over a million years of natural evolution, of natural interaction with all the other plants and animals on earth. Man had " arrived. " He had become a farmer. He turned from simple wild food gathering to agriculture—domesticating animals and raising crops. Rats, which he formerly ate, became competitors for his grain. His gardens promoted unnatural concentrations of single-plant species and permitted certain insect species to build high populations, too. These insects no longer had to expend much time and energy on foraging for food over a diversified plant community. Native plants also competed by attempting to naturally revegetate man's croplands, formerly ignored, now they were weeds.

These competing animals and plants had not really changed, but nevertheless they were now pests. It was true then, as is usually is today, that we see things not as they are but as we are.

Thus, agriculture was man's first attempt to modify his local ecosystem. He replaced naturally evolved complex stable ecosystems with unnatural simple unstable ecosystems and in so doing set himself apart from his natural environment. Consequently, he experienced his first minor collisions with his environment.

By about 6,000 B.C., man had learned to irrigate his crops and the world's first civilization developed—the Sumerians of Mesopotamia. Further population increase created cities like Nineveh and Babylon. Lumber came into demand and the forests on the upland slopes of the Tigris and Euphrates were cut to fill the need. Soon thereafter, the denuded mountains relinquished their soil to rains which eroded the denuded uplands, washing a sea of mud into the irrigation ditches. The Sumerians removed silt until it was piled 50-feet high along the banks. With the primitive tools of that age further dredging became impossible. The irrigation systems began to breakdown. This, with man's new-found enemies—plant and animal pests, caused crop failure. Fish died in the muddy river waters. Starvation ensued. Sumeria began its decline. Once again, man had modified his ecosystem, won temporary benefits, and destroyed his environment in the process.

This drama, with the same leading character, can be recounted over and over. Only time and place change: the locust swarms of ancient Egypt which were mentioned in Exodus in the Bible; epidemics such as bubonic plague which killed a fourth of Europe's population in the 1300's ; the draught-caused famine of 1877-79 in China where 9 million died; and the global flu which killed 25 million in 1918-20.

POPULATION: BIRTHQUAKE

Thomas Malthus correctly predicted in 1798 our current population dilema (see Table 1). From Table 1 we can statistically figure that there are 1,300,000 additional mouths to feed around the world every week. Increase in any population occurs when the birth rate exceeds the death rate. Man, through his technological discoveries over the past few centuries has sharply reduced death rates. Through this same technology, he also has been able to increase the production and distribution of food—but not fast enough, as indicated by the following quote from the May 31, 1970 issue of the Caracas newspaper.

Dr. Archbald is President of the Man-Environment Communication Center, Madison, Wisconsin.

Today General Da Fonseca mobilized all units of the 4th military region of Brazil to ship food and other materials to sections of the Northeast ravaged by severe drought. The order to mobilize came while 200, 000 hungry men, women, and children were migrating from the interior to the Atlantic coast in search of food and water. Starving northeastern peasants have ransacked many businesses in different cities of the region and have assaulted at least six freight trains carrying food supplies   (4).

The July 17 issue of the same paper reported, "Brazilian President, General Garrastazu Medici, has declared all townships of the Northeast region a disaster area because of the severe drought. It has been estimated that about a million people have been affected."

POPULATION: IMPACT ON ENVIRONMENT

The Prodigal Population

Man, in his eagerness to rush toward an unknown destination, has been prodigal indeed '. When the Pilgrims stepped ashore on Plymouth Rock, North America was an unending wilderness, seemingly inexhaustible yet hostile—a challenge to the settlers' very survival. Consequently, a cultural pattern of natural resource exploitation and building developed which h a s continued down to the present day. In Table 2 we can see a f e w of man's "triumphs" in his "battle with nature."

It is a tragic irony that the U. S. , the world's most affluent country, has been able to afford to preserve so little of its wilderness. The tiny percentage of the natural resources we have today was preserved by default, not by foresight. Either the particular resource became too scattered or too inaccessible to exploit profitably. Virgin eastern white pine forests or bits of prairie are such isolated remnant resources. Many of our natural areas are hardly virgin, having been subjected to some grazing, selective lumbering, fire, erosion, chemical invasion, and other forms of abuse. We are presently converting over one million acres of farm and wildlands to highways and building sites every year.

True, natural resources made possible the phenomenal development of the U. S. But why did so many resources have to be 98-100 percent depleted? This same story holds for each continent, only the chronology is different.

TABLE 1

WORLD POPULATION (10) IN MILLIONS OF PEOPLE BY "DEVELOPED" AND "UNDERDEVELOPED" CONTINENTS

	1965	2000	% increase
South America	240	624	160
Africa	306	768	118
Asia	1,800	3,300	83
Total "underdeveloped"	2,346	4,692	100
North America	213	354	61
U. S. S. R.	231	353	53
Europe	440	527	20
Total "developed"	883	1,234	40
Total for world	3,229	5,926	184

TABLE 2

SOME NATURAL RESOURCES: THEN AND NOW

Natural Resource	Original Acreage	Now	% of Original Resource Remaining
Wisconsin prairies	2, 000, 000	Less than 20, 000	Less than 1%
California Redwoods	2, 000, 000+	(Redwood Park 58, 000)	3
Passenger Pigeon	5, 000, 000, 000	0	0
Bison	50, 000, 000	6, 000	1/100 of 1

Population - Pollution Syndrome

In recent decades, man's chemical assault on his environment has surpassed even his physical attack. The "effluence of his affluence"—municipal and industrial wastes, vehicular exhaust, atmospheric dust, chemical pesticides used on crops, lawns and gardens—is staggering.

Air. Air pollution now costs every American $ 65 per year in property damage. Moreover, it takes thousands of lives prematurely by aggravating bronchial ailments. Yet, the total 1969 Congressional outlay for air pollution control is about 45 cents per person.

The relative increase in world population and combustion of fossil fuels (coal, liquid hydrocarbons, natural gas, and lignite) is described in the Report of the Environmental Pollution Panel of the President's Science Advisory Committee (8). The carbon dioxide increase is presented as an indication of man's ability to release long-stored energy into his environment, energy that throws the environment into ecological disarray. With more and more energy available, man is able to plow, cut, net, mine, or bulldoze for the quick dollar. We are accumulating waste by-products roughly at the rate the CO_2 curve is ascending. So, environmental degradation is progressing considerably faster than the population is increasing.

The climatologists are not in complete accord in their interpretation of the significance of atmospheric CO_2 accumulation. It has been suggested that atmospheric warming due to an increased CO_2 "greenhouse effect" could melt the Antarctic ice cap and raise sea level 400 feet. If this takes 1, 000 years, and it could occur sooner, the seas would still rise 4 feet every decade and in 30 years many of the world's great seaports would be largely inundated. Indeed, between 1885 and 1940 the average surface temperature over the entire earth showed a rise of . 9° F. But between 1940 and 1960 the temperature dropped . 2 °F. Some scientists attribute this decrease to the abrupt increase in the atmospheric dust (1). Unfortunately, it is nowhere near as simple as one injection negating the effects of a second. Atmospheric dust and CO_2 have quite different effects on such important factors as light quality and intensity, photosynthesis, plant and animal respiration, wind velocity and direction, and water acidity. One estimate of the various pollutants being released into the air is presented in Table 3 (2).

TABLE 3

ESTIMATED U. S. AIR POLLUTION TONNAGE PER YEAR

Source	Millions of Tons	% of Total
Cars, trucks, and buses	85	65
Manufacturing industry	22	17
Electric power plants	15	12
Heating of homes and buildings	8	6
Total	130	100

Water. Certain lower forms of life survive without oxygen. All forms of life, at least on this planet, require water to survive and reproduce. Man can go many weeks without food but only a few days without water. Clean air and clean water are man's two most important natural resources. Yet look at what we have done to Lake Erie, one of the world's great freshwater lakes. Through mismanagement and abuse, we have converted a clean, blue lake into an aquatic desert, listless and murky green.

In 1900, the whole U. S. sewage system discharaged less than 10 million pounds of phosphates annually. By 1964, the discharge totaled 250 million pounds, with synthetic detergents being a major contributor. The Nation-al Research Council warned 2 years later that by the mid-1980's the nation's municipal wastes are expected to have a biological demand equal to the oxygen available in the entire summertime flow of the nation's river systems. In other words, if the nation's mid-1980 municipal water were uniformly dumped into the country's streams and rivers the water's dissolved oxygen would be completely depleted and all aquatic life exterminated.

Finally, the so-called clean power from nuclear energy has two potentially harmful waste products: discharge of heated water used in the cooling process and radioactive wastes. Thermal pollution reduces dissolved oxygen levels and encourages algae growth—illustrating again that we cannot get something for nothing.

The story of DDT accumulation through both aquatic and terrestrial food chains is now too well known to be recounted. But what about the half-million chemicals the FDA estimates we are now exposing ourselves and our environment to? FDA estimates the number is increasing by 400 to 500 per year. We are begging the question of how these chemicals directly affect us and all other organisms. But what are the possible effects of various chemicals in combination? We just do not know.

Aldo Leopold (5) wrote 20 years ago: "A thing is right when it tends to preserve the integrity, stability, and beauty of the biotic community. It is wrong when

FIGURE 1 [2]

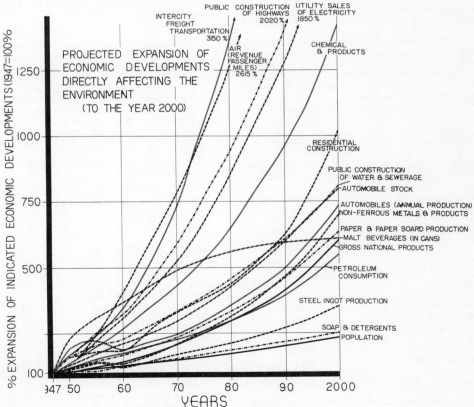

it tends otherwise. " Many of the chemicals we are using are destroying or dislocating biotic communities.

Figure 1 indicates the extent to which Americans will pollute our environment in the next 30 years unless broad protective measures are adopted. What comfort can we derive from the fact that our gross national product (GNP) is expected to double in the next 20 years? After comparing the socioecologic environment in the U. S. and the world in 1950 and 1970, I see little cause for optimism for 1990 unless our national and world values change. When a GNP is sufficient to meet its people's basic biological and social needs, the value of a growing GNP depends on the values, wisdom, and goals of the nation producing it. We are still selling our virtue to buy wealth. For our own long-term survival, we must chart and follow a course designed ". . .to preserve the integrity, stability, and beauty of the biotic community. "

WHAT SIGNIFICANCE: ECOSYSTEMS?

Man is clever in adapting but also brazen and arrogant. He has insinuated himself into the forefront of the biotic community. And in his scramble to dominate, he has broken nearly every ecological principle of energy flow, isolation, community interaction, and population control. He is trying to rule without knowing nature's rules. The more he manages, the more managing he has to do. If he extirpates a natural predator, then he has to assume that predator's role or risk being overrun by the now uncontrolled prey. Can he poison the pest plants and animals without poisoning the pollinating insects, honeybees, earthworms, or the ocean diatoms which produce 70 percent of the oxygen we breathe?

The extent to which all species are "hooked in" to each other is remarkable. This interlocking of species moved Leopold to comment: " How do we know but when we pick a pasque flower but what we change the course of a star. " That we have been unrestrained in picking pasque flowers is evident from—

MAN'S HAND ON THE LANDSCAPE

Before	After
Natural ecosystem	Man-dominated ecosystem
Chipmunk and mink	House mice and rats
Butterflies and luna moths	Houseflies and house moths
Orchids and trilliums	Ragweed and thistles
Gamebirds and Song-birds	Housesparrows, starlings and pigeons
Game fish	Bullheads and carp
Earthworms and fire-flies	Termites and cockroaches
Prairie community	Corn monoculture
Blue skies	Brown haze
Blue water	Green? Black? Brown?
Tens of thousands of species interacting in a stable, dynamic self-perpetuating community	Man-controlled, man driven community
" Underdeveloped" Quality environment!	"Developed" ?????????

OUR PROBLEM (S)

The problem is multi-faceted. It involves an explod-

ing population, ignorance of ecological principles and exploitation of the world's limited resources. We have unleashed superpowerful forces which we may not be able to check: a runaway population, poverty, and pollution—chemical, physical, thermal, and biological.

As these forces continue to gain momentum, our ability to control our destiny diminishes proportionately. Given our present anti-pollution programs and laws, we cannot possibly even hold the line at the present level of pollution, let alone reserve it. If, in the next 15 years, we can muster the know how and money to rid the U. S. of the equivalent of the total 1970 effluent, we will still be polluting the environment at today's rate. Our effluent will have doubled by then because of increased population and increased per capita consumption of apparently indispensable creature comforts.

Why do we find ourselves in this bind? Primarily because of our money-making drives—dollars and drachmas, rupees and rubles, pounds and pesos—money takes precedence over all other values. Minimize costs and maximize benefits. This is fine if we consider the input of all the costs, monetary, and environmental, and output of all benefits, short and long-term.

In this milieu, the environmentalist is often hampered by cumbersome legal machinery. Civil and criminal laws have been evolving over the centuries, whereas the body of anti-pollution law is relatively new and very incomplete. A party or chemical suspected of polluting is innocent until proven guilty. In some cases of pollution, years may slip by before enough scientific proof of damage can be gathered. By this time irreparable damage may have occurred.

Government is a balance of conflicting interests. Until a need is clearly demonstrated, in some cases "over-demonstrated, " little is done. Hence, the term " government by crisis. " This is especially true of the natural environment where man is so woefully ignorant of its extreme intricacies and delicate balances. Because of our lack of understanding, by the time scientists suspect environmental deterioration it is usually far advanced. Moreover, because it usually costs the polluter more money initially to quit polluting or to adopt precautionary measures, he is unlikely to act on his own. The 1968 Santa Barbara oil slick mess illustrates government-by-crisis, yet isn't as critical as the slow degradation of Lake Erie.

TWO CASES OF ENVIRONMENTAL POLLUTION

Atypical	Typical
Santa Barbara oil slick	Lake Erie
Sudden	Relatively slow
Visually dramatic	Visually undramatic; one year was much like the previous
Instant property damage	Property damage, but not as obvious
Responsibility easily fixed	Responsibility difficult to fix—thousands of polluters
Biological recovery: 5? 25? years	Biological recovery centuries, if ever

Lake Erie points up several aspects of man's role as despoiler of the environment, aspects of which society is usually unaware. The despoiling process is usually gradual, in man's own time scale. Total property and esthetic damage may be staggering but rarely fully appreciated because the loss is not abrupt. There is difficulty in assigning blame. Too often the stupid response we get is "that's the cost of progress." Little or no heed was given to the cost of environmental degradation when the cost/benefit ratio was considered for the various economic ventures in the Erie basin.

The adage " an ounce of prevention is worth a pound of cure" takes on special significance in resource management because so often there is no cure for environmental pollution. We hear about " cleaning up " L a k e Erie, chemically perhaps. But we will be about as successful in the Lake's biological restoration as all the king's horses and all the king's men were with Humpty Dumpty. We are convinced technology is waiting in the wings to rescue mankind from himself. Nonsense. That's wishful thinking and specious reasoning. Our unbridled faith in our own technological ability—reinforced by the Apollo space shots, heart transplants, etc. —is simply a relative thing. Comparing such accomplishments with the complex chemical, physical, and biological interrelationships of Lake Erie is like comparing the complexity of a single leaf with that of a whole forest. Killing an organism is infinitely easier than bringing it back to life. It appears this will remain so in the forseeable future.

Another instance of our over-confidence in our technology concerns the world's food crisis. We hear how we will farm the unlimited resources of the sea. First, the sea's resources are as limited as our knowledge about how to farm it. Let us look at the record. In 1955, the world catch of marine food would have provided enough calories to support 23 million. A decade later, enough calories for 46 million. But during this same decade when the seas yielded food for just 23 million more, the world population increased by 500 million. Hardly encouraging. Moreover, to cause considerable damage to the seas, all we need to do is pollute coastal waters. This would prevent the reproduction of many species harvested at sea.

Famine is here: 15,000, and many more by other estimates, are dying from starvation daily and millions are suffereing from malnutrition. And, apparently, regardless of our technology and ambitious programs, the crisis is worsening. Projected dates of widespread famines vary from 1975 (6), 1975-80 (9), and according to the U.S. Department of Agriculture as late as 1984.

During the summer of 1970, a new virulent strain of southern leaf blight swept through the midwest states from the Gulf resulting in an estimated national corn yield loss for 1970 of 8 percent. Tons of corn were flown to Hawaii to assure a seed source for next year. Mass simplification of ecosystems, in this case from hundreds of prairie species, to one species, corn, followed by further genetic purification of this one remaining species is true ecological brinksmanship.

The other side of the coin here is, of course, expanding populations which divert capital from improving the lot of those already on earth and aid and abet man's oldest enemy—disease. A case in point, is the new strain of cholera sweeping across Asia towards Europe.

Typically, the disease is contracted from food or drinking water contaminated by human excrement or vomit. Clearly, the greater the population and the greater the mobility, the greater the opportunity for spread of the disease. Health officials are still uncertain how the epidemic got its start. But according to Time magazine, September 14, 1970, " Perhaps the most disturbing aspect of the current epidemic is the refusal of many governments to face up to the presence of the disease within their borders." Why? One main reason was to avoid scaring off tourists. At any rate, at this writing Paris hospitals have begun to ration cholera vaccine.

We Americans must check our population growth. " Saying that the population explosion is a problem of underdeveloped countries is like telling a fellow passenger your end of the boat is sinking," asserts Paul Ehrlich (3).

Another critical part of our problem is that we are daily inundated with a torrent of " facts," often apparently conflicting, about racism, Vietnam, the generation gap and even population-pollution problems. We must, however, keep these issues in perspective. Is it not to be expected that with more people going in more directions, there will be more social conflict? The real danger lies in wasting our energies in fruitless nation-to-nation and man-to-man conflict, which only keeps us from facing the universal challenge—mass famine in a degraded environment.

That Americans are not alone in their pollution problem is evident from the following two excerpts from Soviet publications.

Pravda recently asserted (7) " Every violation of hygienic rules and sanitary norms, large or small, has a direct effect on the people—their mood, their attitudes, their health. We have received many letters protesting water and air pollution. The working people propose the adoption of a number of legal measures to put an end to instances of this barbarous attitude toward nature."

" The problem of geohygiene (earth hygiene) is highly complex and closely tied to economic and social problems. This problem can therefore not be solved on a national and especially not on a local basis. The salvation of our environment requires that we overcome our divisions and the pressure of temporary, local interests," says Andrei Sakharov, the Russian Nobel prize winner in physics (10).

Harrison E. Salisbury comments on Sakharov's new book, " There is roughly a quarter century left before the year 2000. Sakharov does not claim universality for his thoughts. But he would agree that unless his blueprint—or some reasonable variation—is adopted by the principal societies of the world, the prospects of survival into the second millennium are virtually nil."

CONCLUSION

The natural environment is shared by every individual. We all use the environment. We all pollute the environment. It is, therefore, the social responsibility of every individual to help preserve environmental quality for others here today, tomorrow and the days after—because, the chances of mankind's survival tomorrow can be measured directly in terms of mankind's efforts to preserve a quality environment today.

FOOTNOTES

1. This paper is now available as a 26-minute, 16mm, color, sound film entitled " Spaceship Without a Skipper." Contact Man Environment Communication Center, 545 West Dayton Street, Madison Wisconsin 53703.

2. Data for this chart comes from Resources in America's Future, Landsberg, Hans L.; Fischman, Leonard L.; Fisher, Joseph L., Johns Hopkins Press, Baltimore, Maryland, 1962.

REFERENCES

1. Bryson, R.A., " Climatic Effects of Atmospheric Pollution," paper presented at National Association for the Advancement of Science meeting, Dallas, Texas, December 27, 1968.

2. Dixon, J. P., " The State of Our Atmosphere," Proceedings: The Third National Conference on Air Pollution, Washington D.C., December 12-14, 1966 pp. 18-22.

3. Ehrlich, P. R., The Population Bomb, Ballantine Books, Inc., New York, New York, 1968.

4. El Nacional, Caracas, Venequela, May 31, and July 17, 1970 (translated news articles).

5. Leopold, Aldo, A Sand County Almanac, Oxford University Press, New York, New York, 1949.

6. Paddock, W.; Paddock, P., Famine—1975! Little, Brown and Company, Boston, Massachusetts, 1967.

7. Pravda, June 21, 1965, Moscow, U.S.S.R., p. 20.

8. Report of the Environmental Pollution Panel President's Science Advisory Committee, 1965, pp. 114-120.

9. Sakharov, A.D., " Progress, Coexistence and Intellectual Freedom ", W.W. Norton and Company, Inc., New York, 1968.

10. World Resources Inventory, Southern Illinois University, 1965, p. 8. ■

"In attempting to 'sell' conservation today, it is especially important to know something of the national taste in environment."

THE POTENTIAL OF CONSERVATION HISTORY

Roderick Nash

LOOK OUT the nearest window (if there isn't one, that too is revealing about attitude toward the environment) and consider the face of the land. What you see is a human creation. The tree or shrub or patch of grass is there, in other words either because men put it there or because they allowed it to remain. Is the vegetation beyond your window carefully manicured, farmed, or growing wild? If the last, is it from choice or neglect? Such questions probe deeply into public tastes, values, and ambitions. Perhaps your glance meets only concrete and asphalt; this exclusion of nature tells something else about a people's preferences. And what of the buildings, utility installations, and other accouterments of civilization? Are they constructed with aesthetic considerations in mind, related to each other, to the landscape, and to human needs, or erected haphazardly?

The point is that any landscape is an artifact—an object made by man. Its condition, rightly seen, reveals a society's culture and traditions as directly as does a novel or a newspaper or a Fourth of July oration because today's environment, the "natural" part included, is synthetic. Especially since the advent of modern technology, man has shaped the face of the earth. He has, in fact, been the primary agent of change. In an hour, a bulldozer performs the equivalent of thousands of years of erosion—perhaps more. And the choice not to alter the earth, in most regions, now also involves a conscious exercise of human will. The landscape as a result, either developed or wild, is an historical document. The bulldozer, as well as the pen, makes a record that the historian would do well to study. And the realization is growing in regard to the environment that today's choices will in large part determine tomorrow's experiences. So the land, in the last analysis, is not only a document revealing past thought and action but also a slate upon which the present outlines the kind of life it bequeaths to the future.

When consideration of the environment is broadened to include what people have thought about it as well as its actual condition, the potential of conservation history is increased. Indeed a new interdisciplinary field concerned with man's understanding of the environment seems imminent. Geographers, psychologists, anthropologists, and ecologists are combining with intellectual and cultural historians and students of literature and speech to investigate the many levels of man's relation to the land. We are only beginning to learn how and why men react to the outdoors. Often such knowledge is buried beneath intertwined layers of custom, symbol, and myth extending back to prehistory. Untangling the meaning of concepts such as garden and wilderness or determining the significance of the color green have astonishing possibilities.

It follows that conservation history may be studied as something more than past politics or economics to the record of resource management. Inextricably involved are ideas about national identity and purpose as well as a society's aesthetic, religious, and ethical convictions. The history of American conservation, in particular, can be made to bear on some of the basic issues in American life. Natural resource policy, for example, is one of the best places to examine the tension between individual freedom and social purpose. Enlightened use of the land demands a limitation on the action of landowner because the easiest, or most lucrative, method of exploiting a resource is seldom in the best long-term interests of the nation as a whole. But in a society that covers individualism and free enterprise, especially as it concerns the land, how can conservation principles be instituted? The profit motive will not suffice although the payment of bonuses and extension of tax advantages to those who practice conservation has been tried. And, public lands aside, legal coercion is difficult since it means interfering with a man's relationship to his property. Telling an individual, or a corporation, how to manage his land is close enough to telling him how to furnish his house as to make most Americans uneasy. Consequently, conservationists have argued that some kinds of property are less private than others: specifically, those which everyone shares—in the environment. What one does inside one's home is truly private, but when individual action affects rivers and soil and scenery that other people use and see, individual rights must be redefined.

Faced with this problem, conservation leaders have endeavored to secure the voluntary cooperation of landowners and the sympathy of the citizenry. This explains the frequent justification of conserva-

Dr. Nash is Associate Professor of History at the University of California, Santa Barbara. This is the foreword to his new book, The American Environment: Readings in the History of Conservation, Addison-Wesley, Reading, Massachusetts, 1968.

tion in terms of patriotism, prosperity, national strength or greatness, democracy, and efficiency. Such ends, it is argued are worth the extra cost and effort of intelligent custodianship of the land and its resources. But this line of reasoning evades the idea that land health and beauty are desirable ends in themselves. The relatively small, but increasing, number of American conservationists who have taken this position believe that land has rights which men should respect as part of their ethical code. The same restraints that, in theory, prevent a man from killing his neighbors, they assert, should prevent him from exterminating a species or destroying a forest. To be sure, such advocates of a land ethic as Aldo Leopold and Stewart Udall are under no illusions about the difficulty of its acceptance. Yet they insist that such a fundamental shift in values is a prerequisite for the success of conservation. Securing the public's cooperation is as big a problem as devising the techniques for managing the land.

Framed another way, this issue involved the relationship between the expert and the people. Frequently planners and scientists know what to do to further conservation, but persuading the people to apply this knowledge is a different matter. It is the horse-and-water problem in classic form; communication is the key. How does the expert, whose understanding of a situation is often built on years of technical research, convince the nonspecialist and secure his approval for instituting a program of land reform? In a totalitarian state, this is relatively easy: appropriate use of resources is simply decreed. The king's forest will not be clear-cut. But the democratic assumptions and institutions of American civilization as well as its pervasive anti-intellectualism (especially in regard to land, common sense is difficult to displace as the source of authority) complicate the matter. Policy decisions concerning the environment must be hacked out of a thicket of contending often directly contradictory, interests. And once a course of action is set, there is no assurance, given the vagaries of public favor, that it will be continued. This is particularly unfortunate in the case of resources since the land responds slowly to threatment Political leadership changes much more quickly than the environment.

The record of conservation in the United States has direct relevance to assessing the significance of the concepts of the frontier and of abundance in the national experience. A number of scholars have followed Frederick Jackson Turner in suggesting that if we have a national character, it is due to these formative influences. Conservation may be interpreted as an effort to extend both the frontier and abundance beyond the point at which they might otherwise have ended. Clearly, the desire for an easy way to a full stomach is not the only relevant factor here. At stake, many believe, is the perpetuation of American traits and ideals: democracy, individualism, independence, and even the nation's youth and confidence are being "conserved" along with resources. Nor can we discount as a factor in the American conservation movement the vague feeling that there is something special about the New World environment worth preserving—a certain freshness, a chance for a new start and for progress that inspired the transplanted Europeans with messianic expectations. The national sense of pride and identity, in sum, are

closely connected to the history of conservation.

Another way conservation serves the study of basic issues in the American experience is in its ability to focus the chronic controversy between utilitarian and aesthetic interests. Obviously a particular natural object, such as a tree, can be claimed by both interests—as lumber or as scenery. The same is true of a canyon that could be dammed for use as a reservoir or preserved as wilderness. The fact that neither tree nor canyon can satisfy both demands simultaneously has given rise to violent altercations. In the context of allocating resources, Americans have been confronted with basic questions of value and ultimately with choices about the nature of their civilization. Frequently the issue reduces to the question of whether the nation, with its well-known material abilities and appetites, also possesses an aesthetic and spiritual sense.

Conservation history is important for the way it illuminates the advantages and limitations of our custodianship of the land. Anyone professionally concerned with resource policy or involved in a citizens' crusade can benefit from knowing how his predecessors formulated ideas, secured the public approval necessary for their institutionalization, and evaluated their results. In attempting to 'sell' conservation policies today, it is especially important to know something of the national taste in environment. Such information is perhaps best derived from an examination of how this task was formed.

Two pitfalls are commonly encountered in the teaching and writing of the history of resource management. The first is to speak of "conservation" as if it denoted a single school of thought. In fact, as some of the statements in this volume will reveal, conflicts among conservationists are as frequent and bitter as those between them and the parties they seek to restrain and reform. Pronounced differences in ends separate those who would preserve the environment for recreation from those who would develop its resources, albeit wisely, in the public's economic interest. Yet both factions (best represented today by the dam-building Bureau of Reclamation and the wilderness-minded Sierra Club) vigorously insist that they are conservationists. Even those in closely related fields often find themselves at odds: the optimum conditions for ducks are not the most conducive for the propagation of fish, and "outdoor recreation" ranges from wilderness backpacking to roadside picnicking. Yet in spite of evidence to the contrary, politicians, journalists, scholars, and the public at large usually refer to 'conservation' as a unified interest. Part of the difficulty stems from the fact that nobody today is really against conservation any more than they are against peace or freedom. But when more specific definitions are demanded, the rhetorical similarity disappears.

The second common mistake is to approach the history of the environment with a manichean orientation. It is easy, in writing about the landscape, to fall into the rhetoric of moralism—the 'good guys' versus the 'bad guys.' Most accounts of American conservation contain at some point an elegiac description of the 'unspoiled' continent: once the country was beautiful and rich in resources, but then came the 'greedy exploiters' who 'raped' the 'virgin' land. Such a representation unjustly uses the emotions of the present to describe the actions of the past. It fails to employ historical sympathy, to understand the past in its own terms. Neither the pioneers nor most subsequent resource developers considered themselves unthinking spoilers or were regarded as such by their contemporaries. Instead, they acted in a manner consistent with their environmental circumstances and intellectual heritage. When the forest seemed limitless, cut-out-and-get-out was an appropriate response. Certainly early Americans made mistakes in using the land, but they became such only in the opinion of later generations. Rather than shaking moralistic fingers, conservation historians would do well to attempt to understand why men acted as they did toward the environment.

Readings in the history of conservation not only concern natural resources; they also reflect distinctive traits of the American character. Almost uniquely among modern peoples, the emigrants who settled the New World had the opportunity and the responsibility to make their own environment. Nothing was inherited in this respect but wilderness. Asians or Europeans of the same era, however, had no alternative but to live in a physical setting shaped by thousands of years of occupancy. Except in a limited way, the landscape could not express their preferences. North Americans, on the contrary, had, and to some extent still have, the chance to make fundamental choices about the character of their environment. Attitudes toward the past, contemporary tastes, and ideals for the future combine to influence such decisions. There are, in sum, few richer lodes than conservation history from which to mine an understanding of American culture. ∎

"What is needed is leadership toward redirection of our way of life."

ENVIRONMENTAL POLLUTION: AN ECOLOGICAL PERSPECTIVE

Durward L. Allen

ANY REALISTIC appraisal of the influences of waste products on human life must take place in an ecological context. That is to say, it should consider characteristics of the human habitat, the dynamics of human numbers, and the kind of life we want to live. Such an evaluation might logically suggest expedients in the husbandry of people that could lead to desirable goals. Those goals cannot be strictly defined, but we can indicate them in a general way. It probably is fair to say that our long-term objective in mediating the relationships of mankind to this earthly environment is to improve the life of the individual. We must assume, ingenuously perhaps, that time will reveal the solid values on a basis of trial and error—provided the critical errors are not irreversible.

CULTURE: ANOMALY OF THE AGES

There can be no doubt that many of the logistic and social conditions affecting humanity are deeply rooted in our biological past. Studies of the ecology and behavior of other forms of life can contribute to an understanding of the human species, and unquestionably we have reached a stage in the development of environmental problems that calls for all the enlightenment we can muster.

It would be helpful indeed if it were possible to interpret reliably what can be learned from laboratory populations of certain animals or from natural communities and to judge thereby our own status and estate. Major difficulties arise in the fact that both innate behaviorisms and basic environmental relationships are masked and complicated by a great array of cultural developments. We are well removed from that primate ancestor who lived, presumably, as a well-adjusted component of a natural and a self-sustaining ecosystem. Development from hominid to human took place over at least a million years, and even in the recent past, progress from a hunting and gathering culture to a modern industrial way of life encompassed at least 10,000 years. It is not strange that we have difficulty recognizing homologies among many analogies or that people are inclined to regard their own species as something apart from nature.

As George Gaylord Simpson (14) effectively propounds, it is proper to recognize man the creature as a part of nature and at the same time to contend realistically with the fact that he is totally unique as a product of evolution. It is likely that primordial food gathering and scavenging, and later hunting, activities disturbed the environment relatively little. For this kind of life, the social unit had to be small and foraging was commonly restricted to the most favorable sites (13). However, it probably was true that with the earliest use of fire the influence of the innovating biped was seen extensively in certain vegetation types. In climatically favorable regions the primitive arsonist helped along the regime of natural burning that expanded grasslands into forested areas. This probably did not materially impair the biological productivity of the land, especially in terms of the hoofed animals that were human food.

The next instar of the man-culture was a different matter, for sedentary peoples with livestock and cultivated grains were able to commit heavy aggression against their immediate habitat. The denuding of land and the spreading of the earth's deserts is an old story amply documented by Harroy (5), Shantz (15), Lowdermilk (8), and others.

While human settlements were scattered and relatively small, environmental pollution was not a major problem. When people concentrated in too great a degree and fouled their environs, they were subject to the same limitations as other living things. Epidemic disease reduced their numbers. Biologically we can recognize pollution as a characteristic density-dependent mortality factor that acts as a natural check on the expansion of populations of most animals.

After the advent of the industrial era and the development of modernized technologies—principally within the past century—human relationships to the earth were vastly changed. Medical science upgraded sanitary standards, reduced death rates, and extended life expectancy. Populations grew more rapidly than ever before. Increasing mastery of physical and engineering sciences permitted the large-scale exploitation of resources, radical modification of natural conditions on land and water, and the use, if not occupation, of practically every major habitat.

SUCCESS AND JEOPARDY

In a period so brief as nearly to preclude the updating of mores or the development of an ethos of resource use, man has extended his dominion over the earth—all of it. The very fact that man can do this may turn out to be less than a blessing. In his overflowing

Dr. Allen is Professor of Wildlife Ecology, Department of Forestry and Conservation, Purdue University, Lafayette, Indiana. This paper was presented at the Conservation Leaders' Forum on Environmental Quality, Cornell University, Ithaca, New York, October 29, 1969. It is Journal Paper No. 4020 of the Purdue Agricultural Experiment Station.

numbers and in his ubiquitous presence, this creature has lost his place in any natural ecosystem. That should be disturbing, since it is invariably true that the organisms of this world live in communities, of which the plants and animals are interdependent. If one creature becomes too successful, it will destroy the community and its basis of livelihood.

Most other kinds of life are adapted to a fairly limited spectrum of environmental conditions. Thus, with their living and dying, their nibbling and defecating, they affect only certain areas of the earth's surface. In terms of effects on water, atmosphere, and land, there are dilution factors and regeneration periods. But man the generalist, the omnivore, the cosmopolite, the technocrat, has managed to find some kind of grist from the mountaintop to the ocean, and he builds his mill on every falling water. Unless he engenders a wisdom to match his ingenuity, he could commit costly errors.

The state of world overpopulation, as a result of widespread public health programs and declining death rates, is so well known and so much discussed as to be almost commonplace. Predictions are that the accelerating increase of human numbers will convert the present world population of 3.5 billions to more than 6 billions in the next 30 years. The year 2000 is a popular chronological benchmark, and by that time our U. S. population of 200 millions may well be more than 300 millions. The major burden of human increase is in the underprivileged two-thirds of the world, which is to say that segment of humanity little changed by our own mass-production technology.

Cultural differences in various regions create wide variations in the impact made by humans on their environment, and this applies particularly to the nature and rate of pollution. In many tropical countries teeming rural populations have long lived under primitive sanitary conditions and used the much subdivided land intensively, especially under a night-soil regime of fertilization. In their forthright book, Moment in the Sun, Robert and Leona Rienow (12) describe this disease-ridden habitat as a "septic world" where waters, soils, and even deep aquifers bear the inoculum of universal plagues and contaminants. Travelers from the Western World know well the precautions to be taken by those from regions of higher sanitary standards. This is biologically degradable pollution—that much can be said for it. The return of organic waste products to soils and waters is natural, and below certain thresholds it is the means by which nutrients are recycled and the productivity of ecosystems maintained. But in this case excessive population density produces a major disease potential held in abeyance to some degree by endemic resistence and nonendemic public health measures. At least, the population remains ruinously high.

In the so-called Western World, we also have had a problem with organic pollution, but there are major differences. In large areas, population levels have been much lower than in the tropics, and our agriculture does not make use of human wastes. For the most part cities are served by sewage systems that remove the burden of defilement from the immediate habitat. This burden has been placed directly on our waterways, with the result of widespread overenrichment and the degradation of waters for wildlife production and recreation. The contamination of beaches, tidal zones, and estuaries has steadily made more and more such areas unfit for human use and necessitated the condemnation of shellfish and similar resources.

We have a technological cure for this problem, since we do know how to treat sewage. We also recognize what is needed, since in the Clean Water Restoration Act of 1966, the Congress authorized an annual federal cost-sharing for grants to construct locally needed sewage treatment works. As planned, under that program the national government should by now have contributed some two and a half billion dollars. Actual appropriations have been slightly more than a billion—less than enough to meet the matching funds now available in local communities.

The delays in doing the job on domestic sewage have much in common with our other failures in the field of pollution abatement. In any case we will pay for pollution. We will pay by cleaning it up, or we will pay in the quality of our habitat. Thus far, in major degree, we have chosen the latter course.

In the long view, our visible plans for sewage disposal are inadequate and improvident. We still have the wastrel attitudes of our first three centuries when our population was building toward an optimum (which we undoubtedly have passed) and when our exploitation of every kind of natural wealth was an open-ended free-for-all. We are not in the habit of "saving" things, least of all products that are waste almost by definition. But the year-by-year transfer of nutrients from the land to fresh waters to the ocean is not an enduring system. Organic wastes need to be accumulated, refined, and put back on the land. The sooner this operation is planned in its entirety, the faster we can get on with the job of upgrading our resource base.

PROBLEMS AT COMPOUND INTEREST

The growth of human numbers has been at geometric rates as open spaces of the world (e.g., North America) were occupied, as medical science mitigated natural checks, and as the resource base of the population was broadened through extractive technology. As Mayer (10) has pointed out, men of the industrialized countries, armed with mechanized might, have far greater impact on their environment than similar numbers of people in agrarian cultures of the world. The strength of the human arm has been multiplied many times over, and scientific enterprise is tireless in devising new ways to recover and use the products, natural features, and spaces of the earth.

Modern technology is said to be elaborating on an exponential curve, and many of its manifestations certainly are growing even more rapidly than the population. Electric power production, and with it thermal pollution of waters, is doubling in 10 years. Automobiles, with their attendant noise and fouling of the atmosphere, are increasing twice as fast as people. On another plane, the demand for outdoor recreation is expected to quadruple in 30 years. Elsewhere (2) I have cited evidence suggesting that as people aggregate in high densities their social, economic, and biological problems proliferate on a scale far greater than the growth of numbers. The striking upsurge of interest in social and environmental problems—a phenomenon of the past several years—indicates that we are being overwhelmed by what Abelson (1) called "the inexorable exponential."

There appears little doubt that our rapidly mounting levels of pollution, both organic and industrial, manifest rates of increase that are accelerating. Stewart (18) has noted that the population of the United States has multiplied five times over since 1870. But the effect of pollution is aggravated out of proportion because the wastes of today's population are going into the same area of land and water. Locally, the problems are even greater because of the steadily increasing concentration of people in cities. Domestic waste disposal in a scattered population is largely a do-it-yourself operation. In cities the individual is dependent on public services—services that must be increasingly efficient as the space occupied by the individual is reduced.

Significant to the above is Martino's (9) discussion of equilibrium growth rates. He notes that "it should be clear that no component of society can long continue to grow at a rate greater than the rate of growth of the society as a whole."

Actually, waste disposal is only one of the pressing dependencies of city dwellers. No doubt a great deal can be done for our cities through technical studies and improved planning. But thus far efforts at rehabilitation and easing the ills of social stress do not appear to be self supporting. Inevitably the large cities go back to the federal government for financing. There we do not seem to collect enough taxes either, as the mounting public debt witnesses. The indications raise a suspicion as to whether truly adequate service to great concentrations of humans can ever be self-supporting. Thus far the only visible trend that could alleviate many problems would be an orderly regression in human density.

WASTAGE ON THE GRAND SCALE

In an ecological system the outputs of substance and energy must equal the inputs. This is essentially true of what is happening in our great industrial complex that converts resources of the earth into things that, immediately or ultimately, become items needing disposal. Over millions of years, organisms evolved in earth and water that were capable of breaking down every component of living things. But our latter-day chemistry has produced a welter of compounds new to the world, and for which no natural degrading process exists. An estimated half a million substances are being dumped into our waters eventually to accumulate in the oceans. Facing up to the degradability question has become a major issue. In the case of detergents, the transition has been made, which constitutes a small start on the total problem. Long and costly effort went into the development of an immortal beer can. Now we find that what we really need is a degradable beer can.

In both quantity and quality our industrial pollution is becoming an embarrassment that witnesses the carry over of primitive habits to modern times. The middens left by early human settlements attest to a simple, over-the-shoulder kind of waste disposal. This is still the basic procedure in our modern industrial plant. It has been a prevailing practice simply to discard our leavings in ways that were easy and cheap. This made profits higher, and what was done to the environment in which people had to live was considered one of those things. Clouding the sky with smoke, littering the countryside with junk, destroying every kind of recreation water, establishing pig farms or cattle feed lots under conditions that produce an olfactory horror downwind, designing vehicles that steadily increase the level of auditory harrassment on our thoroughfares—this has been considered a part of "using" resources, creating jobs, and how do you spell environment anyway? A social ecologist (6) tells us that a major difference between the human species and other animals is that man is capable of "an extraordinary degree of flexibility and refinement in behavior." Of course, that same felxibility makes possible an extreme degree of unrefined behavior.

Profit-taking at the cost of habitat conditions has been so universal and so firmly established it is evident that legal innovations of a drastic nature are called for. There is growing support for a constitutional amendment that would affirm the right of the individual to reasonably salubrious living conditions. It would require a semantic genius to word such an amendment, but it is worth the effort.

We probably are on the verge of important changes in our standards of biological decency. In our society many people have found it immoral to interfere with purely animal rates of procreation, even though the new generations could not be adequately supported. They have remained strangely aloof to the vulgarity of human swarming and spoliation of our world. Our principal motivation in the use of natural wealth has been, how fast can we convert it into something that can be used, worn out, and thrown away. Senator Muskie has commented (U. S. Congress, 1968) that "thus far the so-called natural resource policies have been designed not to work toward enhancement or protection of these resources, but to indicate the maximum levels of exploitation which we will permit."

It is evident that we have a limited but socially responsible citizenry who are becoming aware of what the run-away population spree is costing and what it portends for the future. It should be obvious by now that, like every other species of this biosphere, humanity will depend for its actual survival on population limitation. This containment of numbers may be through "internal" controls, as in the case of the effective behavioral responses of many carnivores, or it can be through environmental checks, as frequently happens for a wide diversity of creatures. Obviously, in our own case it would be degrading and disastrous to allow habitat conditions to deteriorate to the point of limiting the population. A planned limitation is the only choice, and there is particular futility in attempts to estimate the maximum number of people our earth could support. Above an optimum level additional numbers are accommodated only at the expense of living standard and by damaging the resource base. It is also unrealistic to accept a doubling of the population by the year 2000 as inevitable and to develop every resource to meet the prospective "need." The availability of new usable space and material would guarantee the anticipated increases in number.

On this basis I postulate that there is no acceptable alternative to a balanced steady-state society in which resources are used only as rapidly as they can be renewed, recycled, or substituted for. In this kind of system waste disposal and pollution control would take their place as intermediate benefits in a chain of processes that would use organic residues to renew land productivity and employ other byproducts as industrial raw materials.

For the present, in this country we undoubtedly are many billions of dollars in arrears on the job of cleaning up existing messes and reworking our industrial establishment to avoid the pollution abuses that now are rife in cities and open spaces alike. As Chauncey Starr (17) said recently, "Many of our environmental pollution problems have known engineering solutions, but the problems of economic readjustment, political jurisdiction, and social behavior loom very large. It will take many decades to put into effect the technical solutions we know today."

One might well be restive over the fact that, if we are confronted with exponentials to the extend indicated, our time for effective action may be short indeed. The truth is that the costs of controlling pollution to tolerable levels may well be prohibitive. We are dealing with an already overburdened environment. Too many people armed with an inconceivably powerful and ecologically unaware technology have little chance of enjoying a clean, comfortable, and inspiring world.

THE UNKNOWN HAZARDS

In the haphazard release into the environment of thousands of substances new to the biological world, men have taken a heedless risk. Highly persistent substances accumulate, and infinitesimally low concentrations may have effects on specific organisms. Even the great dilutions do not stay that way, for in progressive transfers through trophic levels of the food chain, a dosage may build up that is lethal or damaging to a high-ranking consumer. The insidious effects of organochlorine pesticides are showing up in the impaired reproduction of many fish-eating and raptorial birds, to cite one example. Even more obscure relationships could become critically important. A recent environmental report of a task force of the American Chemical Society (4) deprecated our almost total lack of knowledge regarding the ecological effects of long exposure to low levels of pervasive chemical pollutants. It remarked, "If man were to destroy any of at least half a dozen types of bacteria involved in the nitrogen cycle, say, life on earth could end."

In terms of ultimate consequences and the need for reliable studies and projections, one of the most challenging pollution problems of our time concerns the carbon dioxide content of the atmosphere. In their report, "Restoring the Quality of our Environment," the Environmental Pollution Panel of the President's Science Advisory Committee (19) brought together information pertinent to this situation:

The panel noted that over the past century more than 122 million metric tons of coal, lignite, petroleum, and natural gas have been removed from the earth, oxidized, and liberated as carbon dioxide. About half the CO_2 produced in this way remains as a residuum in the atmosphere. Measurements in a recent 5-year period indicate that the concentration of carbon dioxide in the atmosphere increased by 1.36 percent. The outlook is that by the year 2000 this steadily increasing combustion of fossil fuels will build up the atmospheric content of carbon dioxide by at least 25 percent. Neither the exact level nor its effects can be reliably predicted at present, but it is likely that a change of this magnitude would cause a significant alteration of the earth's climate. This would come about through more efficient trapping of the radiant energy of the sun, bringing increases in temperature and a melting of the

Antartic ice cap. With certain assumptions, the report speculated that this process might produce a rise in sea level amounting to 400 feet in 400 years.

Cole (3) has described the events of geological history that tied up huge amounts of carbon in the form of fossil fuels and thereby created a reservoir of oxygen in the atmosphere. He points out our heavy dependence on the replenishment of that oxygen by green plants and also on the proper cycling of carbon, nitrogen, phosphorus, and other major constitutents of living things.

It is quite possible that the concentration of such toxicants as DDT, which is now accumulating (with a half-life of 10-15 years) in water, air, and every kind of organism over the entire earth, could pass a critical threshold. A change for the phytoplankton of the oceans or little-understood microflora of the soil could bring on disastrous alteration of the atmosphere. Monitoring operations are being developed, and computer modeling of complex ecological systems offer hope that some of these trends could be predicted. But many problems are hardly being investigated, and out permissiveness in the face of poorly understood pollution hazards could be inconceivably costly.

It goes without saying that through our food, water, the air we breathe, and radiation possibilities, we ourselves may well be vulnerable to the effects of long-term exposure to widespread contaminants. Yet in discussing the need for cross-disciplinary research, Walter Orr Roberts (U. S. Congress, 1968) remarked that "only modest efforts have been made . . . to mount a sustained research program on the medical effects involved in slowly-developing health impairments–like aging–that result from low-level but long-persistent alterations of the atmospheric environment... through pollutants added in the form of trace gases, liquids or solids that result from industrial activity or urbanization. This is an area of biometeorology that has significance to every living person, and yet we have not seen the first beginnings of an adequately sustained research effort in this area."

As one investigates the ramifications of pollution problems, he inevitably concludes that men in haste and ignorance have been extremely lucky in their meddling with only sketchily understood relationships of the biosphere. In effect, they have carried out bioassays on the entire human race. It is an ominous thought that, the scale of operations being what it is, the statistics could easily go against us.

THE BEGINNINGS OF CHANGE

Here in America, we are deciding whether it is the birthright of a few overbreeding generations of men to devastate a continent. Of course, there has long been an opposing view, but the conservation concept has in some quarters been discounted as an ideology garrisoned by malcontents–obstructionist reactionaries who could not face progress. The truth is that the idea of management for the future as well as the present–the essence of the conservation policy– is the only course available if the human race is to avoid self-destruction. Ideally, conservation should be a part of our guiding folk-wisdom, with moralistic implications. Unfortunately, one does not develop this in a frontier boom-town atmosphere, which is the kind of air Americans breathe. We are under extreme pressures, and there is no time to await the results of extensive trial and error.

For those attuned to the resource management field, we have had plenty of trials and also abundant errors. What is needed is leadership and an authoritative re-direction of our way of life. There is no question that a statement in a recent congressional "white paper" (7) was correct that "the Congress is the only insti-tution having the scope to deal with the broad range of man's interactions with his physical-biological sur-roundings. We therefore believe that leadership toward a national environmental policy is our responsibility."

Increasing numbers of our representatives in Con-gress are joining action to protect and improve our mishandled environment—to clean up pollution, guard public health, preserve the scenic beauties of our country, and defend dwindling samples of primitive nature from the on-rush of development. Recently 41 Senators, led by Senator Muskie of Maine, sponsored a bill that they hope will become the "Environmental Quality Act of 1969." In both houses of Congress there are statesmen of this neglected cause fighting its battles, often with a minimum show of interest from their public. As their knowledge and under-standing grows, so grows their awareness that this drive for a decent world must not be allowed to fail.

There has been some discussion of the need for a "Council of Environmental and Population Advisors" to be created by law in the office of the President (16). Such a council might be of major benefit if is were able, through the authority of the President, to place a re-straining order, pending further review by Congress, on activities of the federal government that threaten further damage or deterioration of the environment. Some such mechanism is most urgently needed to change our longstanding practice of permitting far-reaching plans to be made by specialists in single-interest agencies, then carrying them out until some-thing goes radically wrong.

The extent to which environmental issues are com-manding attention in the public press—including the challenge of population control, which must be our first concern—provides a basis of hope that we actually can do the things that are so urgent, despite the roadblocks of ignorance and self interest. The key to that hope lies in Admiral Bickover's (11) perceptive statement that making "wise use of technology in the future is perhaps the paramount issue facing electorates in all industrial democracies." For it is true that the sci-entific know-how that has shown such vast potential for environmental damage has the same potential for healing and improvement. The deficiency lies not in the knowledge of how to do things, but in how it is ap-plied. With the truly fantastic degree of scientific enlightenment now at our disposal it would be possible to make this world a realm of beauty and comfort for a reasonable number of human inhabitants.

Our concerns over an unending variety of pollution problems must be a part of our calculations in the entire field of population-resource strategy. As if this were not broad enough, the complex of challenges is world-wide. The bulk of DDT we produce is going to tropical countries as their cheapest method of malaria control. Sweden, a socially conscious nation much concerned with pollution, is finding that a substantial portion of the sulfur dioxide in their atmosphere is coming from outside their borders. No doubt, this is an area in which international understandings and action will be

necessary. We will need to look at that, but there is an immediate and critical job much closer at hand.

REFERENCES

1. Abelson, P. H., "The Inexorable Exponential," Science, 162:(no. 3850)222, 1968.

2. Allen, D. L., Population, Resources, and the Great Complexity, 34th North American Wildlife and Nat-ural Resources Conference Transcript, 1969.

3. Cole, LaMont C., "Can the World Be Saved?" Bioscience 18:(no. 7)679-684, 1968.

4. Cooke, L. M. and others, Cleaning our Environ-ment—the Chemical Basis for Action, American Chemical Society Report, 1969, 249 pp.

5. Harroy, J. P., Afrique, Terre qui Meurt, M. Hayez, Bruxelles, Belgique, 1944, 557 pp.

6. Hawley, A. H., Human Ecology, The Ronald Press, New York, 1950, 456 pp.

7. Jackson, Henry M. and others, "Congressional White Paper on a National Policy for the Environ-ment," Senate Committee on Interior and Insular Affairs and the House Committee on Science and Astronautics, 1968, 19 pp.

8. Lowdermilk, W. C., Conquest of the Land Through 7,000 Years, U. S. Department of Agriculture, Agricultural Bulletin 99, 1953, 30 pp.

9. Martino, J. P., "Science and Society in Equilibrium," Science, 165:(no. 3895)769-772, 1969.

10. Mayer, Jean, "Toward a Non-malthusian Popula-tion Policy," Columbia Forum, 12:(no. 2)5-13, 1969.

11. Rickover, H. G., "Can Technology be Humanized—in Time?" National Parks Magazine, 43:(no. 262) 4-7, 1969.

12. Rienow, Robert; Rienow, Leona T., Moment in the Sun, The Dial Press, New York, 1967, 286 pp.

13. Sauer, C. O., "Early Relations of Man to Planets," Geographical Review, 37:(no. 1)1-25, 1947.

14. Simpson, George G., Biology and Man, Harcourt, Brace, and World, New York, 1969, 175 pp.

15. Shantz, H. L., "An Estimate of the Shrinkage of Af-rica's Tropical Forests," Unasylva 2:(no. 2)66-67, 1948.

16. Smith, A. W., "Washington Needs a Council of En-vironmental and Population Advisors," National Parks Magazine, 43:(no. 261)10-11, 1969.

17. Starr, Chauncey, "Social Benefits Versus Techno-logical Risk," Science, 165:(no. 3899)1232-1238, 1969.

18. Stweart, G. R., Not so Rich as You Think, Hough-ton, Mifflin, Boston, 1967, 248 pp.

19. Tukey, J. W. and others, Restoring the Quality of Our Environment, Environmental Pollution Panel, President's Science Advisory Committee Report, 1965, 317 pp.

20. United States Congress, Joint House-Senate Col-loquim to discuss a national policy for the envi-ronment; Committee on Interior and Insular Af-fairs, U. S. Senate; and Committee on Science and Astronautics, House of Representatives, Hearing, 1968, 233 pp. ∎

"The high standard of living we talk about appears to be for this generation only."

PEOPLE AND ENVIRONMENT

Lamont C. Cole

I AM SURE you have all been hearing a good deal about what we are doing to the environment—it's suddenly become a good "in" topic. In fact the College of Home Economics has changed its name to the College of Human Ecology; this show that it is certainly popular. Still our environment continues to degenerate at an alarming rate. The United States has less than 6 percent of the world's population, is using something close to 60 percent of the world's resources that are being consumed, is talking about industrializing the rest of the world to match U.S. standards, and these standards may leave some things to be desired.

If you take seriously the United Nations' vital statistics: the U.S. has slipped from seventeenth to twenty-third place among the world's nations in terms of infant mortality within the last year. We are imposing on our environment something like over half a million kinds of different chemicals—practically none of these have ever been tested in advance, singly or in combination, to see what they may be doing to the living things in the environment. In fact, all of these half-million chemicals eventually wind up in the oceans which are necessary for the continuation of life on earth. I think it is very surprising to see how few people recognize that our atmosphere is a biological product. Ninety-nine percent of the atmosphere, neglecting pollutants, consists of just two gases: nitrogen and oxygen; both of these are put there by living forms. If it were not for denitrifying bacteria in the soil and water and especially in the marine sediments, there would not be any nitrogen in the atmosphere.

It was surprising to me to see that the astronomers were so surprised when they could not detect nitrogen in the atmosphere of Mars. Well, you would not detect it here either, if we should happen to poison the denitrifying bacteria, because nitrogen is a scarce element on earth and it is their activities on earth that maintain the balance of the atmosphere. The oxygen is put into the atmosphere by green plants carrying out the process known as photosynthesis. By far the most important of these green plants are the microscopic ones floating in the oceans, the phytoplankton. It is perfectly true that a field of grass or a woods can produce tremendous amounts of oxygen, but when these plants burn, decay, or are consumed by animals, they use up as much oxygen as was produced in their formation. So, the only way to compensate for the oxygen we are using in burning fossil fuels, which we are doing at an increasing rate every year, is to have green plants produce the oxygen and then have the remains of these plants sequestered away somewhere without being oxidized. This happens in swamps, bogs, and lakes—there is an awful lot of oxygen demand buried on the bottom of Lake Erie—but the big and important reservoir of this unoxidized organic matter is the marine phytoplankton, because they sink into the sediments without being oxidized—and this compensates for the oxygen used in burning fossil fuels.

So, if one of our half-million chemicals should turn out to be a deadly poison for the marine phytoplankton or for the denitrifying bacteria, the composition of our entire atmosphere would begin to change very rapidly. In fact there was an alarming paper by Charles Wurster at the New York State University at Stony Brook. He showed that for phytoplankton in Long Island Sound, at least, very small concentrations of DDT, as little as a tenth of a part per million, was strongly inhibitory of photosynthesis. If this should turn out to be a general phenomenon, we may already be in trouble. Even if we stopped all use of DDT tomorrow, it would still continue to wash into the oceans for a number of years, and most of it would go into the coastal waters which are much more productive of life than the open ocean. We are just playing Russian roulette with our whole environment.

We are talking about industrializing the rest of the world. You have probably noticed how the clearness of the atmosphere is changing everywhere. Denver used to be noted for its clear air. I was in Denver last month, and driving in I noticed a nasty, yellow cloud hanging over Denver—it might as well have been Buffalo. This atmospheric pollution is quite general. Vincent Schaeffer, the head of the

Dr. Cole is Professor of Ecology at Cornell University. He is president of the American Institute of Biological Sciences and past president of the Ecological Society of America. This paper is taken from the Proceedings of the 1970 Extension Conference at Cornell.

atmospheric laboratory at New York State University at Albany, summarized in a 1969 paper some of the conclusions from his more than 25 years of monitoring the U.S. atmosphere. I think his most striking finding was the increase of air pollution upwind from our cities. I don't think, even 10 years ago, that Syracuse could have been taken seriously as a regional source of air pollution; and yet now we read in the papers that Cortland is threatening to sue Syracuse for polluting its air. What is happening, apparently, is that the air that Syracuse receives from the west has already been to Buffalo and Rochester and doesn't have time to become purified before Syracuse adds its contribution. So how far do we have to go to get Asia industrialized to the point where its air pollution is coming over to add to California's problem? Or, how long will it be before air pollution from our east coast megalopolis is drifting over and adding to Europe's problems? As a matter of fact Reid Bryson of the University of Wisconsin has made some very sophisticated measurements tracing the movements of air pollutants from Japan into California. They are not where you can follow them with the naked eye, yet, but they are where they can be detected. If we do try to industrialize Asia in general, this is going to be a much more general phenomenon.

This is happening all over the world. The British are talking about how they have cleaned up the air in London. This was done partly by putting high stacks on the factories. Now in Scandanavia they are complaining about the air pollution coming from London. We in this country cause fully a third of all air pollution in the world, and it is going to be an awful mess if we try to make the rest of the world like we are.

We are doing other things, too. I published a paper in which I attempted to answer the question, "If we've got to keep our use of energy doubling every 10 years the way most people say we have to, how are we going to be able to get rid of all this heat?" Well, you can make some simplifying assumptions that let you apply rather simple physical theory to this question—and unfortunately in my paper I made a terrible arithmetic error that made the results come out much too optimistic. I thought it was going to be on the order of 800 years before the earth would become uninhabitable, simply from the high temperature that would be necessary to radiate all of this heat energy. I was wrong. The correct figure is 130 years if we go on doubling the production of the use of energy every 10 years.

At a UNESCO conference on the environment in San Francisco, I think I got an indication of how we are going to have to proceed to get action on some of these sources of pollution. Just as I was about to go on the program, a friend handed me a reprint from the Journal of the American Medical Association and I just had a chance to glance at it. The paper was entitled something like "Hazards of Automobile Exhaust Gases on the City Streets," and in it the authors quoted the secretary of one of the largest automobile manufacturers. I can quote that statement verbatim: "Our business is to produce and sell automobiles; we'll worry about the public health aspects . . . when the public demands it and legislation enforces it." Now this is a more forthright statement than you are used to hearing, but I'm sure you know the attitude and have heard it before. What is surprising about this particular case is that the

paper was published in 1923. Years ago we had our early warning about automobile exhaust. Since that time the manufacturers have made cars larger and more powerful; they have increased the compression ratio so that it has added nitrogen oxides to the inventory of pollutants; they have added lead to the gasoline, then boron, and most recently, nickel; and I would not predict what Madison Avenue will think of next for a gasoline additive. I think it is high time that the public started demanding—and government started enforcing.

For the first time, in the summer of 1969, we lost the entire catch of a marine fishery to water pollution. You saw a lot of publicity about the coho salmon in Lake Michigan. I don't know why that got so much publicity, because the same thing happened off the southern coast of California with a jack mackerel catch. The entire catch was declared unfit for human consumption because of pesticide residues and had to be destroyed. So we are dumping all these complex pollutants around. You may have read that the mustard gas England disposed of by dumping it in the Baltic Sea in 1945 has now reappeared, injuring fishermen and causing alarm about the Baltic resorts in Scandanavia. I remind you that we dumped mustard gas ourselves: into the Atlantic Ocean, and more recently than 1945. We do not know just when it's going to reappear.

In some cases we force the polluters underground. There are something like forty deep wells operating in the United States where the hazardous materials are shot down into the rocks and it is hoped that they will not reappear at some later date. I think this is a doubtful assumption.

Right up to this year, the military has been taking all of our production of certain herbicides, 2, 4, 5-T and Picloram which is a much more persistent material. They have been taking much of the production of 2, 4 D and they have been shipping these to Vietnam for the purpose of defoliating the rain forest to make the enemy more visible. There are lots of reasons for an ecologist to be worried about what happens when you defoliate a rain forest; but I'm also worried about what happens if some of these tankers, carrying the concentrated herbicides, sink in the Pacific Ocean. What will they do to the phytoplankton?

I made calculations sometime back on the amount of oxygen we consumed burning fossil fuels in 1966 in this country. Then I made what I think is a very good estimate of the amount of oxygen produced in that year inside the borders of the coterminous 48 United States. It turned out that the amount produced was not quite 60 percent of the amount used. In other words, we are absolutely dependent upon atmospheric circulation to bring in oxygen produced outside of our borders and, in our case, mostly in the Pacific Ocean.

I am quite sure that a similar study would also show that industrial Europe is dependent upon the Atlantic Ocean and the Mediterranean for much of its oxygen and yet we are willing to play Russian roulette with this source. The Navy and various companies are making noises about exploiting the ocean bottom. Sometimes the Navy talks as though it is going to turn it into an armed camp and mount each sea into a fort. I don't know how this is going to come out, whether the countries are going to embark on another colonial type race for the ocean bottoms, or just what is going to happen. I do know that the Navy sought appropriations on the grounds that American industry would be unwilling to invest in exploitation of the ocean bottom unless they could be assured of protection from piracy and foreign intervention. This was a self-fulfilling prophesy, because a company that would like to mine manganese from the ocean bottoms has asked the Navy that it be protected from foreign intervention and piracy.

It begins to look as though the carrying capacity of the earth for human life is going to be governed not so much by its ability to produce food as by its ability to degrade wastes. Frederick Smith, a Harvard ecologist, recently estimated and testified before a Congressional committee that the rate of deterioration of the U.S. environment appears to be approximately $30 billion per year. This is an estimate of what it would cost to stay even—to keep things from getting any worse. Dr. Smith is a very capable person to be making such an estimate and I think it's quite clear if we assume that about a third of this can be allocated to water pollution; $10 billion a year might enable us to stay even. The $2 billion that President Nixon is talking about to clean up our bodies of water cannot possibly do anything more than slightly reduce the rate at which things get worse.

New pollutants keep coming to light. I served on Secretary Finch's Pesticides Commission where we became acutely aware that mercury is a serious problem in the environment—mercury used in seed dressings, and such things. There have been a number of cases of food poisoning from shellfish in Japan from mercury pollution; in this case from plastics factories. Sweden has recently closed 40 bodies of water to fishing because of accumulation of mercury in the fish and has announced that these will undoubtedly have to remain closed for at least 100 years. The United States is using much more mercury than Sweden did—both on an absolute basis and on a per capita basis, so it may be that the problem has not yet gotten to where we have noticed it. Also, it was just last summer that I became concerned about another class of compounds: the polychlorinated biphenyls (PCB's). These are very widely used in industry: in the plastics industry, in the packaging industry, and in the rubber industry. The wear of tires in the streets is releasing PCB's into the environment.

Our original concern with PCB's was that they interfere with the chemical testing for chlorinated hydrocarbon pesticides, which is DDT and its relatives, and we looked at them as just an annoyance. Now it turns out that they are serious pollutants in their own right. They are going all over the world. They undergo this biological magnification where each animal that eats another animal accumulates a bigger dose than the prey had. Dr. Pettingill of the Cornell University Ornithology Laboratory after a trip to Antarctica informed me that PCB's have now been found in Antarctic life. They have gone everywhere, and yet we have been unable to find out even what the quantities produced are, because these are industrial secrets.

The high standard of living which we talk about appears to be for this generation only. We are bequeathing our descendants dying lakes and rivers;

soil that is decreasing in fertility; exhausted mineral deposits; polluted oceans; and such things as the high-level radioactive wastes that we have buried at Hanford, Washington, in South Carolina's Savannah River, and elsewhere. These wastes are so hot that it has been estimated that they would boil spontaneously for at least 300 years if they were not kept cooled. The Atomic Energy Commission (AEC) has them in stainless steel and concrete tanks. AEC says this stuff must be kept from contaminating the environment for at least 600 years—I say 1,000 years. But, AEC's own survey a couple of years ago showed that about 5 percent of the tanks are already leaking after only 20 years. Each year they have items in their budget request for new tanks to replace some of those. Look what we are giving our descendants: this stuff—billions of gallons of it—with directions that you must keep this refrigerated for at least 600 years and spend your resources to produce new tanks every 20 years or so. And then we are talking about greatly expanding the use of nuclear energy, without knowing how to dispose of the wastes.

Our trouble here is that all of the decisions are made on the basis of short-term economic gains. We are now seeing a spread of the no-deposit, no-return bottle. In fact, the Ithaca grocery stores have signs on the doors saying they will not accept deposit bottles. Statistics show that the deposit bottle makes an average of 20 round trips. So, by this one decision, we are increasing this particular solid waste disposal problem by a factor of 20. Our legislation gives depletion allowances to industry for mining, and mining has many detrimental effects on the environment, as you know. But if they repealed these depletion allowances—if they made it as expensive to mine and refine new ore as it is to reclaim used metal—then these automobile graveyards that are plaguing us would disappear, and empty beer cans would be much less in evidence around the country.

Even our agricultural practices have changed drastically. My grandfather was an Illinois farmer. He never bought synthetic fertilizers of any sort. The manure from the animals was sufficient. But now they say this is uneconomical. The animals are fattened in feed yards—sometimes as many as 2,500 to the acre. The synthetic fertilizers are put on the fields, so you then have this problem of animal waste. Some 2 billion tons of animal waste per year as a disposal problem is second in amount only to the sediment that we must dispose of.

The basic problem, without which the others cannot be solved at all, is the population explosion. But even in principle, the others cannot be solved if the population is going to continue to grow indefinitely. I have heard many times that we do not have a population problem in this country, but in some ways ours is the worst in the world. In terms of the resources he is going to use in his lifetime, the amount of pollution he is going to cause, the impact on the environment, one American is equivalent to approximately 80 Indians. This is the most serious of all our problems, and yet former Secretary of the Interior Stewart Udall testified before a Congressional committee that the amount of money the U.S. spends on population regulation each year, at home and abroad, would run the Pentagon for 3 hours. I mentioned this to a man who is very knowledgeable in the inner circles of our government and he said he was confident that the 3 hours must refer to a Sunday afternoon. Yet, in his "State of the Nation Message," Mr. Nixon asserted that 100 million children will be born in the United States between now and the turn of the century. I hope this is not a self-fulfilling prophesy because it presupposes continued population growth at just about the present rate. I am no sociologist, but feel confident that many of our other problems are also related to this crowding, this increased density of the population. I am sure it has something to do with the violence in our cities; the rise of mysticism, where everybody wants his own guru; the multiplication and expansion of the astrology columns in our newspapers; and the attempts to get away from it all through the use of drugs. People are uneasy about the future; they recognize that something's wrong and I think the population explosion is the thing that underlies all of this.

I have been going around to some of the environmental teach-ins and have gotten a little feel for some of the directions in which the discussions may go among the young people. You can be pretty sure of one thing that is likely to come up, and that is blaming our troubles on the private enterprise system and the profit motive. I tell these young people that I hope they will not accept any such simplistic explanation. In the first place, I know something about Russia's environmental degradation, and their problems are identical with ours. Second, one of the very worst sources of environmental deterioration in this country is our own government. I could spend a lot of time telling you what I think the public ought to know about the Army Corps of Engineers, the Bureau of Reclamation, the Atomic Energy Commission—and, yes, some segments of the Department of Agriculture. Our basic problem, I think the most fundamental of all, is this passion for growth—the thing that I have been calling the Chamber of Commerce syndrome. Mr Nixon, for example, promised to maintain a healthy growth of the gross national product. I cannot think of any worse measure that one can design for the health of anything than the GNP. Every automobile accident adds to the GNP. If vandals would stop breaking school windows, the glass companies would have to cut back a little on production. Glazier's unions would have to lay off a few people. All this would hurt the GNP; yet we want to keep this growing. Walter Heller, former head of the Council of Economic Advisors, was quoted in Time as speaking for most economists when he said that he could not conceive of a viable economy without growth. I think this is our basic problem and this is why Russia's problems are identical with ours. Because like us, although theirs is a planned economy, they are committed to continuous growth and expansion. ∎

Only by being our own sternest taskmaster can we keep from being our own worst enemy.

CAN TECHNOLOGY CORRECT ITS WASTELAND?

Irwin Hersey

WATER pollution has been defined by Robert T. Eckenrode, president of the System Sciences Division of Dunlap and Associates, Inc., as "the presence of toxic or noxious substances or forms of energy in natural water resources. Water pollutants may be noxious or toxic to people where the water source is used for drinking water, transportation, or recreation; to industry where the source is used for industrial processes or cooling; or to nature where the pollutants disrupt the desired b a l a n c e. Heat manifests itself as a water pollutant where w a s t e water is returned to the source with thermal characteristics so different as to upset the natural or desired fauna and flora balance of the source."

So much has been written during the past few years on the extent of water pollution today that little useful purpose would be served by reviewing the matter in detail. However, the National Academy of Sciences—National Research Council (NAS-NRC) report on "Waste Management and Control," published in 1966, gives some idea of the scope of the problem, and particularly of how rapidly it is growing.

The report notes that any assessment of the magnitude of water pollution must consider the relationship between the total available supply of fresh water and the quantity of waste-carrying water. The former—the average annual stream flow that discharges into the oceans from the continental U.S. —is essentially fixed and amounts to about 1,100 billion gallons a day. The latter is the quantity returned to the stream flow after use by man, with its quality altered in one way or another.

A few past and projected ideas point up the scope of the problem. In 1954, some 300 billion gallons of the total were withdrawn daily, of which 100 billion gallons were consumed and thus represented depletion through use, and 190 billion gallons w e r e returned to the streams. Corresponding values for the year 2000 are 889 billion gallons returned. Thus, in 1954, withdrawals amounted to less than a third of the total and waste-ridden returns less than a fifth, in 2000, withdrawals will be a little over four-fifths and polluted returns about two-thirds of the total stream flow.

WATER USE IS INCREASING

Five categories of use were included in these data: irrigation, municipal consumption, manufacturing, mining, and steam-electric power generation. The projected increase for irrigation is very small, the principal change in returned irrigation water being an increase in the amount of dissolved mineral salts and some added contamination from chemicals used in fertilizers, pesticides, and herbicides. Municipal sewage returns are expected to more than double, since more than 95 percent of the estimated U.S. population of 280 million will be living in urban areas. A sevenfold increase is expected in industrial wastes and the residues will be varied in character, containing oxygen-consuming ingredients as well as industrial chemicals of every kind.

The major withdrawal of water will be for power generation, and this water will be returned almost undiminished in quantity but at appreciably higher temperatures. As already noted, this "thermal pollution" can have a shattering effect on the ecology of streams into which it is introduced.

Pollutants entering water sources have been broadly classified into eight categories: domestic sewage and other oxygen-demanding wastes; i n f e c t i o u s agents; plant nutrients; organic chemicals such as insecticides, pesticides, and detergents; other minerals and chemicals; sediment f r o m land erosion; radioactive substances; and heat from power and industrial plants.

All pose different problems. F o r example, b y 1980 it is estimated that the oxygen required to reduce sewage to stable compounds through the action of arobic bacteria will be large enough to consume the entire oxygen content of a volume of water equal to the dry-weather flow of all 22 of the U.S. river basins. A health hazard is posed by the incomplete elimination of infectious agents, while problems from excessive growth of algae blooms and plants h a v e cropped up in many large lakes and remedial measures are largely lacking. Organic chemicals have already caused spectacular kills of fish and wildlife,

The author is Contributing Editor of Engineering Opportunities, in which this article appeared in June 1969.

and we know very little about the effects of long-
term sublethal exposure. Methods of removing other
minerals and chemicals, many of which are toxic,
are poorly developed. Sedimentation fills stream
channels and reservoirs, necessitating expensive additional purification measures. While intense public
concern has led to the development of techniques to
prevent radiation contamination under present conditions, the increase in nuclear power reactors by the
year 2000 poses a serious challenge. And, since the
amount of oxygen water can contain is reduced when
the water is heated, the consequences for fish and
aquatic life may be quite serious.

So much for the extent of the problem. The immediate reaction to all this is to throw up one's hands
and give up. However, there are indications that
something can be done about it, the prime example
probably being Sweden, which is making a concerted
effort to solve its water pollution problems.

SWEDEN IS ATTACKING THE PROBLEM

One particular problem that has concerned the
Swedes is what has been done to many of the lakes
near population centers into which unprocessed or
incompletely treated sewage has been released over
the years. While this is a temptingly cheap waste
disposal method, it eventually destroys the lakes by
adding large quantities of phosphorus and other nutrients, encouraging the growth of algae, which reduce the amount of oxygen in the water and eventually kill all fresh-water life. Sweden is today dotted
with such "dead" lakes, many formerly prized recreational areas and now deserted.

A number of projects aimed at reviving these lakes
are now under way. One is at Lake Trummen, near
Vaxjo, which suffered from the injection not only of
raw sewage, but also of waste from a local textile
plant. While the pollution was stopped, the damage
had long since been done. The lake is strangled with
plant growth, making swimming impossible, and all
the fish have died. A 16-foot-thick blanket of dead
matter coats the lake bottom and the maximum water
depth is now only 6 feet. Left alone, the polluted
lake would eventually disappear.

Scientists from the Limnological Institution at
Lund University, however, have launched a long-
term project to bring the lake back to life and at the
same time to gather data which may help in other
such cases. The first stage of the project, a 1-year
research period, was just concluded, and the second
stage, begun in fall 1970, consists of pumping up the
relatively loose top layer of the sediment blanket,
which contains most of the pollutants. Prof. Sven
Bjork of the Limnological Institution says this layer
contains from 10 to 20 times more phosphorus than
the lower, more densely packed sediment. Various
ideas for disposing of the rich mud will be tested—
spreading it in forest areas and on farm land, and
using it as filler in old gravel quarries in the area.

LOW BUDGET—BUT RESULTS

The pumping will take several months and, after
it is completed, studies will be made of the lake's
progress over the next 9 or 10 years. While this
study period may appear to be unduly long for a lake
with less than 10,000 square feet of surface area, it

is intended primarily to gather experience that will
be useful elsewhere, and the $200,000 price tag on
the entire project does not seem high. As Professor
Bjork has noted, "it is still possible to do rather
much with small investments" in the water pollution
fight.

Other approaches to the same problem are being
tried. One is a variant on the bubble technique used
to pump air into submerged, perforated plastic hoses
to keep harbors free of ice during the winter months.
The method is being studied as a possible means of
bringing lakes back to life. The injected air adds oxygen to the water near the bottom of the lake and also
agitates it in such a manner that the water near the
bottom of the lake comes into contact with air at the
surface, thus providing a double dose of oxygen. There
are some problems involved in using the technique.
If, for example, the air is injected too rapidly, all
the "dead" water may rise to the surface at the same
time and possibly suffocate surface life. One aim of
the project is to work out precise methods for applying the technique.

Another phase of the same project involves pumping up water from the bottom of a dead lake, running
it through an artificial stream to aerate it, and then
pumping it back to where it came from, thus adding
oxygen and evacuating sulphurated hydrogen, which
kills off fish life. These studies, covering 4 lakes
and scheduled to last 4 years, will cost about $220,000.

A third project is focused on the potential of aluminum sulphate for curing lakes which have an excessive nutrient content. In the spring of 1969, two
badly polluted lakes near Stockholm were sprayed
with the substance, which combines with phosphorus
in the water, flocculates, and then settles to the floor
of the lake, producing a harmless blanket on the bottom. A preliminary check the following fall showed
that algae formation, usually quite heavy in the summer, had dropped to nearly zero and pollution had
been cut down considerably. However, there is still
some question as to whether the improvement is permanent, and only time can answer this question.

A LAKE DRAINED OF LIFE

Another project involves the famous Lake Hornborga in south central Sweden, at one time a world-
renowned bird sanctuary which formed part of a chain
of rest stops along the north-south route traveled by
many migratory birds. Most birds now avoid the area although this is not because the lake has been polluted, but rather because it has almost disappeared
due to attempts by local farmers to create more ara-
ble land by sinking its water level 5 times, beginning
in the 19th Century. The lake's area has shrunk from
about 15 square miles to the present 4 1/2 square
miles in the process and, as Lennart Vilborg of the
Swedish National Nature Conservancy Office says
"to call it a lake today is somewhat pretentious."

The accuracy of Vilborg's comment is indicated
by the fact that only about one-fifteenth of the area
was open water when the field investigation was started
in 1967. The rest was a vast sea of reeds, birch
trees, and a relatively small amount of other forms
of plant life. Maximum depth is only 2 1/2 feet and
in the summer most of the "lake" is completely dry.
In winter, the lack of oxygen is so great after the first

freeze that the fish remaining in the lake die. The current attempt to restore Hornborga involves cutting the reeds and raising the water level.

That Sweden is particularly conscious of the pollution problem is indicated by the fact the country has formally asked the United Nations to sponsor an international conference in 1972 to combat the increasing tide of pollutants. The proposal drew 54 cosponsors in its original form, and was adopted without opposition. In fact, it was, as one cynical UN observer put it, "the most acceptable international topic this side of motherhood."

CONTROLLING THE POLLUTERS

The Swedes hope the conference will not only dispel public ignorance and apathy, but also enable researchers in this area to persuade their governments to take whatever measures are necessary to combat pollution, and produce a common outlook and direction in the consideration of environmental controls. Meanwhile, Sweden has passed a new law requiring all pollution-causing industries, as well as local councils, to conform to specified pollutant levels. Companies must apply for concessions to operate so that the harmful effects may be weighed against the economic benefits.

Evidence is beginning to appear that the U. S. is also becoming concerned over water pollution. For example, the Food and Drug Administration, reacting to growing public pressure for stricter enforcement of pesticide control laws, seized some 28,000 pounds of processed Lake Michigan coho salmon infected by pesticide residues. It is interesting to note that no one really knows today how many of the fish caught in U. S. lakes by commercial and sport fishermen every day are contaminated. A classic example is Clear Lake, California, where DDT, at the minuscule concentration of 2 one-hundredths part per million, was used to kill off a troublesome insect that hatched its eggs in the lake. As a result, plankton accumulated DDT residues at the rate of 5 parts per million, fatty tissue of fish feeding on lake-bottom was found to contain several hundred to 2,000 parts per million of DDT, and grebes and other diving birds died from eating the fish.

The New York State Health Department reports high concentrations of DDT in the state's central and northern lakes, and frankly admits its concern. As John Gottschalk, director of the U.S. Bureau of Sport Fisheries and Wildlife, puts it, "What is happening in Lake Michigan is an indication of what to expect elsewhere. There will be a day, and it may not be until the year 2000, when we are the coho salmon."

Concern over DDT led Sen. Gaylord Nelson (D. —Wis.) to commemorate the fifth anniversary of the death of Rachel Carson (who in the book Silent Spring 7 years before first exposed the pesticide threat) by introducing a bill to create a national commission on pesticides. Although federal regulatory legislation is on the books, it is rarely enforced and, in fact, there has been no criminal prosecution under the statute for some 13 years. As a result, the chemical industry is currently producing pesticides at the rate of better than a billion pounds annually, and their use is virtually uncontrolled.

It has been estimated that water pollution control is now costing about $6 billion annually, and this figure is expected to double by 1980. While it is difficult to come up with a figure on how much it would cost to do away completely with water pollution (and that's probably impossible), the NAS-NRC report on "Waste Management and Control" indicated that "the total cost of meeting all projected needs will undoubtedly run into tens of billions of dollars."

REMEDIES ARE COSTLY

The report pointed out that one proposed system to separate all present combined sewer systems would cost $20 to $30 billion, and alternate solutions would also be very expensive. "An investment of tens of billions of dollars will be needed just to eliminate the backlog," the report went on. "For the future, it becomes clear that a major investment will be required to keep the quality of the waters in our streams, lakes, and estuaries at reasonable levels."

What exactly can be done? The report suggested some possible areas for future technology which could contribute to water pollution control. One hope is that industrial techniques will be developed which would completely eliminate water transportation as a means of waste disposal. This would involve the replacement of liquid-based cleaning or plating techniques by mechanical or other methods, and by changing the raw materials used for certain processes in order to eliminate pollutant discharges.

In addition, synthesis, typified by the present conversion of some "hard" detergents to "soft" biodegradable detergents, could be made into a design criterion for new products. Although it is impractical to expect all products destined for eventual water disposal to be non-polluting or easily treatable, this general technology is deserving of major emphasis, particularly in the control of non-point sources.

CONTROL AT THE SOURCE

Perhaps the most prominent area for a major breakthrough is the control of pollution from point sources by means of new waste treatment techniques. It could conceivably produce effluents as good as, or even better than, the original water supply. If treatment techniques could be developed which would permit the recycling of treated waste water for reuse, and the ultimate disposal of the waste concentrates, it might be possible to completely control pollution from municipal and industrial wastes.

The distribution of waste over a larger area or into a larger volume of water has some utility but cannot effect major improvements in the total pollution picture. Detention or dispersion with time similarly hold no great promise for the future, although all these techniques could provide an immediate solution in some areas.

DIVERTING WASTE MATERIALS

Diversion of waste out of areas of use is somewhat similar to elimination, at least with respect to the use region. Although there is some question as to whether this technique would be competitive with other methods from the cost standpoint, the approach seems deserving of more attention than it has had in the past. In particular, the practicability of a 2-pipe system for water supply and waste disposal appears worthy of study. Another technique, dilution, or low-flow augmentation, has broad applicability for both point and non-point pollution sources, and also appears deserving of emphasis.

Perhaps most important, the report concludes, the complementary application of several or all of these processes, together with increased water conservation and reuse of treated water, warrants review. Re-engineering the home, and use of knowledge gained in developing the closed-cycle system found on the Gemini and Apollo spacecraft, could conceivably minimize the amount of waste leaving the home. Collection of non-point source pollution, or blending two streams of different qualities to provide a product of intermediate quality, could be helpful in some areas.

In addition, pre-concentration of waste concentrate could lead to the use of more economic disposal methods. The concept of dual use of existing facilities, such as adapting existing sewer systems for new treatment techniques, or grouping industries or municipalities to achieve the economies inherent in large-scale treatment, and even combining facilities for treating both waste water and solid waste, all may hold a practical answer to pollution abatement, and all are worthy of serious attention.

One thing is becoming more and more clear as time goes on and that is that the overall pollution problem cannot be attacked piecemeal. Unfortunately, that's what we have been doing. The present war on pollution (in this country, at least) has been and is being hampered by its fractionation, not only at the local and state levels, but also at the federal level, where more than 80 different commissions, offices, agencies, administrations, corps, and services are concerned with, and spend money on, pollution control.

This is especially frustrating because pollution control, even more than most urban problems, is a systems problem, since disposal of solid waste can cause air and land pollution, reduction of air pollution can lead to land pollution, and sewage disposal can cause water and air pollution. Systems techniques can be used to analyze the overall problem and yield insights to solutions, while preventing the use of specific solutions which could generate new and unexpected problems.

This systems approach has frequently been advocated before Congress, and has been used in a few projects by Aerojet-General Corporation for the state of California and by Dunlap and Associates. The NAS-NRC report also indicates that the systems approach offers the best possibility for devising a successful pollution-control program.

FREEDOM FROM THIRST

Lord Ritchie-Calder, who has long been concerned with ecological problems, recently wrote that the pollution of our sweet-water lakes and rivers has increased so much during the past 25 years that a "Freedom from Thirst" campaign is rapidly becoming as necessary as a "Freedom from Hunger" campaign.

"Polluting the environment," he went on, "has been sufficiently dramatized by events in recent years to show the price we have to pay for our recklessness. It is not just the destruction of natural beauty or the sacrifice of recreational amenities which are crimes in themselves, but interference with the whole ecology—with the balance of nature on which the persistence of life on this planet depends. We are so fascinated by the gimmicks and gadgetry of science and technology, and are in such a hurry to exploit them, that we do not count the consequences."

However, the consequences are rapidly catching up with us, as even a glance at our seas and inland waterways will indicate. It is long past the time for liquidating our dirty-water problems, or we may all too soon be "drinking today the water our neighbors drank yesterday." ▪

A popular interpretation of the ecological crisis.

WHY THE WORLD IS NOT OUR OYSTER

Robert I. Standish

IN THE current widespread burst of interest in our urban and rural surroundings, I am sure there is a vast amount of public confusion. We generalize about the problems and grope for solutions, knowing only that something has gone wrong. Even the terms are vague, and often carelessly used. The word en vironment, for example, has no equivalent in some languages. Ecology is a favorite term liberally sprinkled throughout most articles, as is the phrase, quality of life.

What we badly need are clear definitions and a clear understanding of relationships. Fortunately, certain aspects of our present condition are common to all, and are simple enough to be understood (if not agreed to) by everyone. In this paper I would like to try to sort out some of these things, to give you, if I can, a perspective and a deeper appreciation of the terribly important job ahead in which all of us are involved.

Let us look first at ecology. This is a science of natural relationships and interactions of all elements and all life. In practice, one generally deals with segments of this vast field, such as forest ecology, wildlife ecology, or human ecology. Within these segments are even smaller units which are termed ecosystems. Food chains, the cycling of elements, energy transfers, and so on, are the basic fabric of the system. Everything is prey for something else. To have life, there must be death.

John Muir, founder of the Sierra Club, described it very well. "When we try to pick out anything by itself," he said, "we find it hitched to everything else in the universe." That's ecology: the hitching of everything to everything else.

Although this is an ancient field of study, predating the Greek, surprisingly few people outside professional ranks have any real idea of what it is all about, why it is important, or why scientists are so alarmed right now by what is happening in the world around us.

Let me try to explain, very simply, how all this works. It all starts with the minerals in the rocks and soils of the earth, in the waters, and in the air. These, plus sunshine, and the ability of plants to change elements into the stuff of life, are the essentials in the living process we call ecology.

For billions of years, creatures in fantastic variety and countless numbers, have existed together in an interrelated, balanced kind of water-soil-biological society. The waters nourish the soils, and the soils bring forth green things in which sunlight through the miracle of photosynthesis, creates oxygen and carbohydrates. Herbivores find plants good to eat, and carnivores find the herbivores good to eat. And the remains of all three—and humans too—decompose to nourish the earth to permit the process to go on and on and on. The same general kind of system functions everywhere, in the waters of the world as well as on land, and even among forms too small to see. Bugs, worms, yeasts, molds, fungi, and bacteria— all play essential parts, and without them you and I and all the so-called higher forms of life would soon perish.

As the ecologists say, everything has its niche, each helping make possible the existence of something else and ultimately the whole body of life. This relationship of creatures is especially visible in ecosystems where certain species control or are controlled by other species. When the balance is interrupted through some natural disaster, or far more often by the interventions of man, the results are usually plain to see.

The story of a spruce forest illustrates this point. You have probably heard of pine beetles, or bark beetles. These insects attack conifers, feeding on the succulent inner layers of tree tissues and microscopic living things which invade their tunnels. They spend most of their lives hidden beneath the tree's protective shell. Bark beetles would make short work of all the pine trees except that woodpeckers find them extraordinarily tasty. In a natural forest there are plenty of beetles but there are plenty of woodpeckers too, so the beetles rarely multiply fast enough to be a damaging factor in forest ecology. They cannot get ahead of the woodpeckers. There is an ecological balance.

Mr. Standish is Public Information Officer, International Union for Conservation of Nature and Natural Resources, Morges, Switzerland.

Sometimes things get out of hand. For example, in the White River National Forest in Colorado, a bad storm blew down several groups of trees. (They might also have been felled by some irresponsible person with a chainsaw, but in this case the weather was at fault.) Here, under the bark of these fallen trees, protected by crushed branches where the woodpeckers could not get to them, the beetles feasted and multiplied, producing too many new generations of beetles for the local woodpecker crops to handle. As a result, the entire forest of several thousand acres was eventually killed, and along with it went its great dependent community of other living things.

In the natural world, balances are usually achieved in communities of plants, and in communities of animals, and between them both. Forests, for example, will support certain varieties of trees, certain undergrowths, and brush, grasses, ferns, lichens, mosses, and so forth. Animal and bird life adjust to the food and shelter this environment supplies. Insects, worms, snakes, lizards, and all manner of things play essential roles too, as pollinators, predators, parasites, or scavengers, so the forest can support a certain number of birds and animals that feed on these forms. There will be a population of seed and nut eaters, a smaller number of herbivores such as rabbits, deer, or elk, and a few predators such as coyotes, bears, wolves, owls, hawks, and so forth up to the top of the food chains.

There will be fluctuations, of course. Populations rise or fall in number, depending on the food supply and habitat. But as we saw with the beetles and woodpeckers, these balances can be easily upset. If someone thoughtlessly poisons the coyote, the rabbits may get out of hand. Or if the mountain lion or wolf is eliminated, the deer will soon eat and breed themselves into trouble.

I like the woodpecker-beetle story because it illustrates another principle—that when living things become too successful, they destroy the source of their livelihood and disappear, along with the community on which they depend. This happened to the bark-beetles in our forest example. And unfortunately, it could also happen to mankind. Man is so successful in the business of producing children and controlling death, that he is very very rapidly destroying the source of his livelihood, through carelessness, greed, ignorance, and insensitivity, bolstered by a blind belief that science can fix any problem he creates, a capacity not yet demonstrated in any real way. One could go on citing examples to illustrate elements of ecology, but I think one or two more will be sufficient to fill out this brief and simplified look at certain basic facts of life.

This science involves all living things, including the molds, fungi, bacteria, and other microscopic organisms, all of which play important roles in the web of life. There could be no life without the several kinds of microorganisms, which take nitrogen from the air and convert it by several steps to nitrate, which is used by green plants in building proteins. All animals, including humans, directly or indirectly get raw materials for building their own proteins from the proteins of plants.

There could be no life, at least as we know it,

without the bacteria which cause decay and carry out the complex business of breaking down animal and plant remains into substances plants can use again. Nor could we live without other kinds of bacteria which can convert nitrate to molecular nitrogen—to replenish the atmosphere. As you know, there can be no life without oxygen. The air is full of it, but only because plants keep putting it there, taking in carbon-dioxide, and giving off the vital gas. A mature beech tree, for example, gives off enough oxygen to keep five people breathing. But most of the world's supply of free oxygen—about 70 percent—comes from microscopic plants—the planktonic diatoms in the oceans, and in freshwater too. These tiny plants are also the indispensable base of all marine food chains.

If 1969 was notable for anything good, it probably was the developing awareness that mankind is upsetting the world's ecological balance, in massive ways, and to an extent that has most of the world's biological scientists gravely concerned. It seems terribly ironic to me that presumably intelligent peoples could live almost 2,000 years into the Christian era without any general awareness that our supposedly enlightened societies have been frightfully unintelligent—and aggressively ignorant—in our use of the biosphere, and the resources of the earth. But there are some glimmers of light. A few people are at last becoming aware that our environment, our own ecological habitat, which of all species only humans take for granted, as theirs to play with or freely alter to suit any whim or purpose, is in serious trouble.

Scientists fear that some tragic, stupid error or miscalculation, or simply the overwhelming accumulation of evil consequences, might trigger an ecological catastrophy that could do to mankind what the windstorm did to that spruce forest in Colorado. In a highly technological age, when men still play with pathogenic viruses, deadly chemicals, nuclear explosions, and massive changes to the face of the earth, it could happen. Historically, men have been too careless to believe otherwise.

Our environment bears terrible scars and open wounds still unhealed. Air in some cities—and even in great areas—is not fit to breathe. Most of the world's major lakes and streams are foul, or have long since been killed by pollution. Food is contaminated by such poisons as Strontium 90 and residues of many lethal chemicals. Even mother's milk now contains 2 to 6 times (11 + ppm) the amount of DDT considered a safe level (5ppm) in cow's milk. It was pointed out that if mother's milk came in any other container, it wouldn't be allowed to cross state lines.

Have you been to New York lately? New York and many once great cities, in substantial part at least, are becoming madhouses of confusion and social decay. Our once abundant open space—living space—is shrinking at alarming rates. Wildlife has been destroyed. Forests are cut recklessly. Precious mineral resources are being squandered. Mountains of waste still accumulate—hundreds of millions of tons each year in the U. S. alone. And on top of all these horrors, proudly, complacently, and smugly, sits the naked ape, the human species, the most successful breeding animal of all the higher forms.

Is it any wonder that some people are beginning

to wake up? Is it any wonder that youth all over the world is searching for new value systems and standards? Plainly, we will have to change our ways if we are to survive and have the kind of life we all want to have. We must restore our environment, and maintain it, as a safe, decent, and hopefully pleasant place to live—not just for our own self-centered few remaining years, but for all generations to follow us, for all time. We must realize that the earth is a closed system into which nothing enters but sunshine. Adlai Stevenson called it "spaceship earth," an apt simile. There is no new source of supply, no new frontier, no new continents to conquer. With the exception of an occasional meteorite and some moon rocks, nothing has been added to the earth since the beginning of time, and nothing more will ever be.

What must we do to ensure our survival? Very simply, here are some of the main things environmental scientists believe human society must do. First of all, because people consume resources and destroy their environment, the world's population must be stabilized in relation to its resources. Virtually every expert agrees that this is of the highest priority. This is urgent, because the children have already been born who, without any encouragement whatever, will push the human mass to double its present size—from about 3 1/2 billions to 6 or 7 billions—in approximately 30 years. This matter is not only the most urgent problem, but the most complex because of the profound social, political, and economic changes needed for stability. Birth controls alone are not enough, but in my judgment they must come first, and they must be pushed vigorously and enthusiastically by every means and every device and at every pressure point for if the millions of unwanted children who arrive each year were not born, we would be well on the road toward achieving stability. It is plainly silly to think that because there are some unoccupied areas, and a few improved sources of food, that the world can accommodate more and more billions. It is thought that we could survive with 8 billions—just barely. But the world cannot feed its present 3 1/2 billions. Clearly, we have exceeded optimum levels.

Second, I'd say some kind of reform in distribution of the world's food supply, and the handling of food resources, needs to be developed. One hears a great deal of nonsense on the subject of food abundance. The facts are that three-fifths of the present world population—or more than 2 billions people—are perpetually hungry. These are the people living in much of Latin America and in older parts of the world, in Africa, Asia, India, and China, areas now critically short of water, soil, forests, and resources of all kinds, where there is little hope that food supplies can be increased significantly. What is worse, their populations are increasing at double the rates of the Western World's. According to Dr. George Borgstrom, professor of Food Science at Michigan State University, if all the food in the world were equally distributed, and each human received identical quantities, we would all be malnourished. And if all the food were distributed at the U.S. dietary level only about one-third of the human race could be fed.

India is taking great risks to bring enough land under cultivation to try to feed her present population, while Europe and America have a food surplus.

Millions of people are starving for proteins, yet the richest protein supply, the fisheries of the Humbolt current off Peru, goes mainly to feed cats, cattle, and chickens—not in South America, but in Europe and North America, which are already fat with food.

Obviously, and sadly, such basic inequities can only mean great trouble ahead. It boggles the imagination even to try to think of the measures that will be needed if the world's present population is to be fed—but what is to be done to feed the 75 millions new people being added every year? I won't try to answer that one. But I will say that the facts of the human condition demolish any of the pious arguments I have heard against trying to limit human fertility.

Next, pollution of all kinds must be controlled. This is a deeply rooted economic and social problem, involving industry, agriculture, housing, public health, forestry, foreign aid, war, marketing, urbanization, transportation—and even you and me, individuals whose inconsequential personal contributions of empty cigaret packages, or automobile exhaust or household waste add up to an almost inconceivable mountain of litter, filth, and poison.

The cost of control must be built into production costs, and our cherished habits of thinking simply must change, not only about our own rich societies, but also about the kind of aid and advice we give to those parts of the world which have not yet learned how wonderful electric toothbrushes and throw-away beer cans can be. Critical decisions bearing on the general environment, in my view anyway, should no longer be permitted on the basis of an individual's self-interest, or the profitability interest of a manufacturing company, or the tax load interest of a community, whether it is in Kansas or Canton Vaud. These things must come, and are coming, whether we like them or not.

Certainly, before too long I think we will be forced to give up conspicuous consumption, whether for war material, 100-story buildings, 300-horsepower road monsters, 16 suits in our wardrobes, or whatever. I think we must stabilize our economic life along with our populations, and stop going so heavily into debt to the future. I think we must learn to be frugal, to recycle materials and to conserve energy sources. I believe in the old slogan "waste not, want not," for myself and for my country. Until we learn to do these things, in my view, the proliferation of junk products, and planned obsolescence in marketing are not only idiotic, but morally wrong as well.

Lastly—although this must be concurrent and continuing—is the education of our children and our young professional people and businessmen to understand and respect nature and her unchanging laws. Francis Bacon said it succinctly: "We cannot command nature except by obeying her." We cannot poison the planktonic diatoms with pesticides, radioactive garbage, or surplus nerve gas and still expect them to produce 70 percent of our oxygen, or function as the initial source of all life in the sea.

Every action has a counter action. This must be taken into account by some means more sensitive and more realistic than by figuring cost benefit ratios for projects that benefit a few rather than many, for the short-term rather than the long-term. ∎

II Defining Environmental Education

ALTHOUGH the mass media may only just then have delineated it, environmental education did not spring full-blown from the head of any ecological Zeus on April 22, 1970. Its antecedents are many. Various aspects of a concern for interrelations between man and his environment have been recognizable in American education for at least 70 years. One of the oldest root-stocks has gone under the broad rubric of natural history or *nature study*. The goal of nature study has been to increase our understanding of the ways of the wild and thus to heighten our appreciation of "nature's vast, pulsing harmony." Nature study has been the province of many informal educational agencies, and has been found in schools and colleges principally in biology courses.

Conservation education has attempted to add to nature study the concept of a concern for the wise use of natural resources. But society—and the schools—have had trouble defining "wise use." Where it has been interpreted to mean rational development, conservation education has found a base in departments of geography and in social studies courses. Where it has been interpreted to mean preservation of vanishing wonders, conservation education has been carried forward most effectively by a number of voluntary organizations.

Outdoor education has been a mixture. To the extent that it is focused in departments of physical education, it is oriented strongly toward the theories and methods of outdoor recreation. Some educationists, however, have given outdoor education a broader domain, saying that it applies to all outdoor experiences that cut across the entire curriculum.

Then there has been an eclectic thrust which could be called *citizenship education*. From one perspective this genre has been concerned with a cultural and esthetic appreciation of the American endowment and the American mission. From another perspective, citizenship education has sought to generate a commitment to social action, which in recent years has found its particular emphasis in a concern for the rehabilitation of the cityscape and its poor. From a third perspective, citizenship education has involved consumer education- an orientation to the shortcomings and excesses of the economy.

Resource management education has represented the professionalization of certain distinct man-land relationships: soil conservation, water management, game management, park management, urban and regional planning, landscape design, architecture, environmental engineering, metropolitan management, and so on.

All these antecedent forms of environmental education have certain things in common. First, they tend to take an "egg-crate" approach to man-environment relations. That is, they carve up the natural and physical environment into compartments like woods, water, inner core, and wilderness. This is so, on the one hand, because societal approaches to resource management have been assigned to various discrete bureaus, each with its own gospel; and on the other hand, because of the rather rigid departmental organization of knowledge in schools and colleges. Second, the antecedent forms of environmental education tend to be rather long on rhetoric and short on both ecological principles and practical guidelines to public action. Third, with some exceptions, the training of environmental educators has grown up outside the mainstream of American teacher education. College courses for the training of planners, interpretive naturalists, conservation educators, social workers, and resource management specialists have frequently developed quite independent of schools of education.

Overall, pre-environmental education has lacked compelling theories of content and methodology. Its concepts and materials have been rooted in an agrarian era. It has lacked practitioners of adequate background and scope. It has been oriented to particular "users" of the environment rather than to the overall environment itself, and it has had no clear-cut federal or foundation impetus or funding.

Enter environmental education. Some might say the term has sprung into being merely at the whim of phrase-makers, or to put a new label on an old bottle. On the contrary, there are real and significant differences between the old conservation and the new environmentalism.

In terms of its *scope*, the new environmentalism attempts to be all-encompassing. Whereas yesterday we tended to treat soil conservation, architecture, water conservation, art, forest conservation, wildlife conservation, urban engineering, and so on, as separate units, today we try to understand and explain the ecological unity of all man-land relationships. In terms of its *focus*, then, the new environmentalism is man-centered. That is, our primary concern has shifted from the survival of remnant redwoods and raptores to the survival of nothing less than the human species itself. At the same time, we are not so much concerned about quantities of natural resources as we are about the quality of the human experience.

In terms of its *locus*, while the old conservation conjured up images of open country, the new environmentalism incorporates the pressing problems of the city. In terms of its *emotional underpinnings*, the new environmentalism is based more on fear for man's tomorrow than on a love for nature's yesterday. In terms of its *political alliances*, the old conservation was linked to such orthodox causes as depression pump-priming, national defense, and outdoor recreation; the new environmentalism, on the other hand, encompasses population control.

It is, however, in its *basic cultural orientation*, that the new environmentalism differs most strikingly from its principal antecedent, conservation. The latter, in the words of one patron saint, stood clearly for economic development, for the infinite goodness of American "progress." But environmentalism reflects a growing suspicion that bigger is not necessarily better, slower can be faster, and less can be more. If anything surely marks this revolutionary nature of the rationale of the new environmentalism, it would be the recent words of a Republican President of the United States, telling us that "wealth and happiness are not the same thing," that now is the time to "make our peace with nature," and that we must "measure success or failure by a new criteria."

From nature study, environmental education draws an emphasis on an understanding of our ecological system—man, culture, natural environment. From conservation education, environmental education draws a concern for the husbandry of the system. From outdoor education, environmental education borrows the concept that such issues should cut across the entire curriculum. From citizenship education, environmental education draws social dimensions and a commitment to action. From resource management education, environmental education draws a technological point of entre to public policy change.

In turn, the environmental impulse is energizing changes in its antecedents. Nature study is becoming less taxonomic and anthropomorphic and more ecological. Furthermore, biology departments that leaned heavily in a molecular direction in the post-Sputnik era are switching back to a science-and-society orientation. The American Institute for the Biological Sciences, for example, has a special committee at work under a distinguished ecologist, Dr. Edward Kormondy, on a review of courses and materials such as the BSCS series.

Conservation education, as practiced by lay groups particularly, is taking on a broader context. For example, a new brochure for schools, put out by The National Wildlife Federation, opens with these words: "Conservation is no longer just the story of vanishing wildlife and vanishing wilderness areas. There is a new urgency in the word today. Suddenly, as we stop and look at our total environment, it has taken on the meaning of human survival."

Project ME (Man's Environment) is also diagnostic of change: "Alert man to his environmental problems and the need for solution. . . . Communicate to pupils that clean air, water, and land are essential in man's survival kit." These are the underlying aims of the new outdoor education program sponsored by the American Association for Health, Physical Education, and Recreation.

Citizenship education is discovering the intimate and essential relationship between "people problems" and the problems of the environment—natural and man-made.

The National Environmental Education Development (NEED) Program is a National Park Service effort in curriculum development to foster environmental awareness and involvement in school children. The Forest Service, the Bureau of Sport Fisheries and Wildlife, the Soil Conservation Service, and other agencies long concerned with resource management education are adjusting their programs in a frank recognition of the fact that swelling population, rampant technology, and fragile biosphere are on a collision course, threatening the quality of the human experience if not the very survival of man.

Environmental education programs themselves are emerging largely from a new college and university configuration, commonly called an "environmental studies center." Each such center tries to be multidisciplinary in its posture and multi-process in its programs. By multi-process is meant a university program concerned with the production of new knowledge and new knowledge-seekers, of more and better resource managers, of citizenship education, and of technical counseling and services. By multidisciplinary is meant a concern with the total environment of man: its social, cultural, economic, and esthetic, as well as its physical and biological aspects.

In essence, then, specific new educational programs are either already underway or are on the drawing boards. Springing from various roots, fostered by various movements and agencies, what is being called environmental education is undergoing definition, as the articles that follow attest. ∎

A report on an environmental education seminar series.

IDENTIFYING NEEDS, OBSTACLES, AND SOLUTIONS

Mario Menesini

OUR ENVIRONMENT and its resources are a major concern of mankind today. That concern can be voiced, legislated for, and exercised, but the one most positive means of creating concern for—and intelligent management of—our world is through the environmental education of those who will inherit it.

There is no better way to integrate and establish people relationships than through recognition of mutual environments shared by total populations. A series of environmental education seminars were concerned with education of people to the total environment and, particularly, with the relationships of individuals within their natural and technological environmental structures. Another purpose, from a pragmatic approach, concerns the fact that environmental education is now a curriculum requisite in California, as provided by Senate Bill 1 passed in the 1968 legislative session. Many other states and districts have or are adopting similar requirements. The seminar goals were:

1. To give all students, including the culturally different, the disadvantaged, the exceptional, and the handicapped, an opportunity to develop an environmental awareness through education.

2. To provide and coordinate environmental/ecological education ideas for the curricula.

3. To develop operational or logistical skills so that participants could implement environmental education programs.

4. To provide a platform for discussion and understanding of the term "environmental education."

5. To exchange information about what is needed to implement environmental education, the specific obstacles which prevent implementation, and the problem solutions which have been tried.

SEMINAR BACKGROUND

The seminars were sponsored by the U.S. Office of Education EPDA (Education Professions

Development Act) Grant No. 45 4174 to John F. Kennedy University, Martinez, California. The seminars were produced in cooperation with Boston University, Boston, Massachusetts, the Morton Arboretum, Lisle, Illinois, and Educational Consulting Service, Orinda, California.

As a preliminary planning step, outstanding educators were named to an advisory group. Within the framework of the proposed seminar structure, the advisory group suggested various activities and methods of operation for the seminars. Each of the seminars conformed to a basic series of lectures and panel discussions. The individual reactions of the participants, however, which followed the formal presentation gave rise to a number of findings which are the essence of this seminar report. While there are some minor differences in the reactions of the participants from one part of the country to another, the significant findings presented here were basically found to be common concerns relative to environmental education throughout the educational community.

SMALL GROUP DISCUSSIONS

The participants were provided an opportunity to meet in small groups with colleagues. This enabled each participant to meet with a cross-section of educators in various stages of environmental education work: those who had established ongoing environmental education programs; others who were experiencing the developmental stages of establishing programs and those who were interested in beginning a plan for environmental education in their schools. The groups were arranged so that discussions took place relative to the participants' varying interests. For example, the educators were grouped according to grade levels in the San Francisco Bay area and Chicago area so that participants interested in secondary, intermediate, and primary grades could discuss common problems. In the Boston seminar, those interested in curriculum development, environmental law, population problems, and urban ecology met together. Leaders were identified for each group to organize discussions and report on their

Dr. Menesini is Director of the Educational Consulting Service, Orinda, California.

results. Participants were asked to discuss the following:

(1) to evolve the needs which could be met within their school districts by implementing environmental/ecological education;

(2) to describe the problems which they faced in establishing such ecological programs; and

(3) to describe what solutions they could derive or were presently using to implement environmental education in their school districts.

The needs, problems, and solutions most frequently mentioned in the group discussions follow.

(1) NEED: FINANCES

It goes without saying that the most frequently mentioned need is that of finances. Most school districts report a desire to be involved in environmental education. Often administrative support is either negotiable or well-informed and favorable to a program. Yet the need for immediate implementation is thwarted by the financial problem.

Problems

Previous priorities and satisfaction of the public often dictate that other school activities receive the budgetary appropriations. Costs of transportation, materials, and housing of students for on-site visits can be high and environmental education is often in competition with such programs as driver education, music, and athletics. Unfortunately the more immediately visible programs receive the benefits.

Solutions

Sometimes the financial problem solves itself. When the program is well presented, districts indicate their willingness to support environmental education by providing funds from district resources. Other districts rely on service clubs and PTA contributions to produce the program. A third, and perhaps more educationally sound, concept is for students to organize activities and work projects that will supply funding for their own environmental education on-site experiences. Recently several government agencies (such as the National Park Service, Fish and Game, and Forestry Departments) have become aware of environmental education needs and problems and have contributed toward implementation of on-site programs.

(2) NEED: FACILITIES

The second largest deterrent to providing environmental experiences is a lack of on-site facilities.

Problems

Despite the fact that the nation has a large system of national and state parks, educators have no way of knowing where sites are available for educational use now or in the future. For districts with limited funds, or with no available government site, educational use of local areas (small parks, playgrounds, streets) is often obstructed by limited imagination. Many are unable to envision the possibilities near at hand.

Solutions

The central offices of state, regional, and national facilities should be approached for listings. If, as is usually the case, there are no such listings for educational purposes, request should be made to those in authority for the creation of a comprehensive registry or listing of available facilities. Political involvement, that is, school boards meeting with county supervisors as well as being involved with government agencies, can produce sites for school use. Many industrial complexes are now providing land for educational use. Imagination in the development of "improbable" sites (for example, streets, empty lots, playgrounds, and dumps) is another solution. School districts which have been successful in developing unique areas should share the key to their successes; a brief "how to do it" guideline would be helpful and could be distributed widely.

(3) NEED: TEACHER INVOLVEMENT

A program without proper supervision and instruction will be a loss from the start. The need to involve teachers, not only as instructors but also as planners, is most imperative.

Problems

Some teachers will consider extra activities, such as outdoor education, a drain on their private lives. More frequently, teachers may feel an insecurity or lack of confidence in their ability to instruct in what is often considered a science subject. This is because a significant number of teachers do not realize the comparative ease of discovery-teaching with environmental education vehicles. In-service programs rarely solve the problem because the instruction usually centers on the scientific approach. Teachers do not often receive an adequate explanation of the philosophy, methods, and objectives specific to their preparation and teaching situations.

Solutions

The first big step toward positive teacher involvement is administrative understanding and support for an adequate environmental teacher-education program. A well-organized program, reinforced by the expertise of consultants and specialists, will give teachers the added incentive and background necessary for implementing an environmental education experience. Positive attitudes are attained through clear and logical explanation of the values of the program. Goals are set that are reasonably high but not intimidating, and supplementary, student-motivational materials are used to alleviate teacher insecurities. The explanation of programs should demonstrate relevancy and a pragmatic association with learning activities. There should be an understanding that environmental education is not a frill and that using the environment as a reference is as necessary as using the school library. A valuable dialogue between teachers, administrators, and environmental specialists can be gained through environmental teach-in's such as this seminar series. The ultimate scheduling of the environmental program should consider the feelings of reluctant staff so that alienation factors will not ultimately destroy a total program. Many variations for faculty assignments have been considered, as for instance, exchanging classes during on-site visits with faculty who enjoy this type of experience and are more capable of implementing outdoor programs. Use of college students and high school seniors to augment teacher ranks has also solved assignment and coordination problems.

(4) NEED: ADMINISTRATION/LEADERSHIP

Since all-important coordination and articulation are functions of the administrator, informed instructional leadership is a necessity for initiating an environmental education program.

Problems

Those in a position to lead environmental education programs too often are lacking in a full understanding necessary to implement a comprehensive program. Traditional beliefs about in-class education can stifle the flexibility and spontaneity necessary for a successful experience with the environment. To some administrators, environmental education represents a departure from tradition which they are unwilling to risk. Administrative insecurities are sometimes underlined by ill-defined or inadequately communicated environmental objectives and philosophy. Most important, administrative concern is often divided among many other recently defined priorities for special education, such as drugs, sex education, and ethnic studies.

Solutions

The school district's sociological makeup often dictates the priorities of its education programs. Teachers and parents aware of the necessity for environmental education might embark on a public relations campaign to "sell" the program to the community and the school board. Present measuring and evaluation devices should be applied and adapted so as to demonstrate the necessity and adequacy of environmental education to meet the local desired goals. As in the solutions for teacher involvement, environmental philosophy and objectives can be clarified in such seminars as those in this series.

(5) NEED: ENVIRONMENTAL INFORMATIONAL RESOURCES AND MATERIALS

Most new programs suffer from a lack of adequate background information and the foundation of past trials and errors. So it is with environmental education. There is a great need for integrated resources and experienced consultants.

Problems

Both instructional and reference materials are at a premium and often what little there is lacks cohesion and often seems contradictory. It is often difficult to fit the fragmented existing materials into the school's curriculum. This can be complicated by special interests of the agencies which provide materials. Outside environmental experts have little knowledge of the problems of school operation and bring about coordination difficulties.

Solutions

Materials from the various agencies, collated and evaluated for the teacher, should be a function of an instructional department at the district level. This will help insure materials which will be coordinated with subject-matter areas found in the traditional school program. This instructional department should compile an adequate index of materials which can readily be used for environmental education. If none fit the district's needs, the available materials can often serve as guidelines for the creation of an individualized set of materials for the district. Problems with outside resource personnel can be solved through orientation. Especially when dealing with the on-site program, school and site personnel should meet and discuss mutual objectives so that no clash will occur on the actual experience.

SUMMARY

The degree of difference from one seminar to another was more in the realm of emphasis than in disregard for any aspects of environmental education. For example, the emphasis in the San Francisco Bay area conference was on logistics—how to establish the environmental education program, the facilities, and the financial arrangements. In the Chicago area the theme focused more generally on the background of environmental education, its needs, and the availability of facilities for teaching it. In Boston there was more emphasis on the availability of curriculum materials and the development of programs for teaching environmental education. The above observations were subjectively noted and these observations do not mean to imply that there was an exclusion of other discussed topics at each of the seminars.

In general, seminar speakers, panelists, and participants indicated three major areas for concentration of effort: politics or interactions in the educational community, the economic community, and the social community.

The political relationships of school personnel to conservation groups, to community planners and internally within the school faculty should be resolved so that constructive relationships exist.

To the economic community, additional educational programs often mean additional taxes. Also economically, many producers are wary of consumer-education biases generated in terms of environmental concepts. Often the local industrialist fears a role as the villain in an environmentally oriented program. Local polluters must be considered only in terms of rational assessment of environmental problems.

Socially, many groups of culturally different people are wary about programs that take students away from home. They hesitate to relinquish parental control. An active parent-education program is a necessity to demonstrate the benefits of the on-site experiences.

Finally, pressure must be applied in the field of politics in its strictest sense. If environmental/ecological education is to become an important factor in the schools of our nation, the interest of legislators should focus on the problems of bringing adequate resources to our schools for relevant environmental education. ∎

"Many more people are waking up to the environmental crisis we are facing, and finally are understanding some of the concepts and causes conservation educators have been pleading for years."

THE ENVIRONMENTAL EDUCATION BANNER

Wilson B. Clark

THE GOAL of environmental education is to bring home to every citizen, so that he knows it deep in his heart and bones, the simple facts that he is absolutely dependent on his environment, that he is affected by his environment, and that he affects his environment. These self-evident truths are obviously neither self-evident to nor considered truths by many people, judging by their actions. For if they were considered both self-evident and true we would not have 2,100 communities in the U.S. today still dumping raw sewage into streams, nor Lake Erie giving its last gasp, nor some 140 million tons of air pollutants spewed into our atmosphere each year, nor the small dollar payroll of an industry like a paper mill in Missoula, Montana, being allowed to outweigh the considerations of the health, comfort, and indeed economics of thousands of people. The examples of idiotic, even criminal irresponsibility to the environment are endless. To try to cure this idiocy, this blindness, this irresponsibility is the reason for all the recent concern about environmental education, and the past as well as continuing concern about conservation education.

We've come to the point where today the banner of environmental education is the rallying point for hundreds of newly awakened people. It's a new quest, a new crusade, they say. And yet, it's not really new. What's happening is merely that many more people are waking up to the environmental crisis we indeed are facing, and finally are understanding some of the concepts and causes conservation educators have been pleading for years.

If we go back to read of the early days of conservation and of conservation education in this nation, we can find all of the ingredients of today's environmental education. True, they perhaps were not tied together as well, but what is Aldo Leopold's philosophy of "harmony between man and the land" but an early, clear, succinct statement of modern concepts of human ecology. The old saw that "conservation means wise use of natural resources" seemed to never quite do the job, for it was so subject to value judgements of what constituted wise use. And indeed, the very word conservation unfortunately did not then- and even today does not — convey to many people anything more than saving things. Certainly the widely used "Conservation Pledge," recited by thousands of school children, has reinforced this "saving" concept, and has done little to foster the needed wider meaning of conservation.

From this narrow interpretation has stemmed many problems. It has caused fierce and bitter polarization, between the avid savers on one side and the overt exploiters on the other. And even within those organizations and agencies ostensibly devoted to conservation the broad concepts of conservation have been splintered, fractionated, shattered

Dr. Clark is Chairman, Division of Science and Mathematics, Eastern Montana College, and President of the Conservation Education Association. This article is based on his address to the Governor's Environmental Education Conference, Boise, Idaho, March 28, 1969.

into many pieces—with each agency or organization clutching its little interpretation to its bosom as the one true gospel. Witness the fights that have gone on between the Bureau of Reclamation and the Forest Service, or the Forest Service and the Park Service, or the Soil Conservation Service and the Extension Service. Witness the "holier than thou" attitude of many private conservation organizations, each waving its own flag and never realizing that its goals and philosophy are but a tiny piece of the whole picture. The internecine warfare between conservation organizations has been one of the major obstacles to genuine conservation progress. But happily that situation seems to be diminishing, and the totally inadequate "wise use" definition of conservation is being replaced.

A step forward in definition was that which stated: "Conservation involves the making of intelligent choices among the competitive uses of resources." This definition recognized that many resource-use decisions are irreversible and preclude other decisions. For instance, once our Class I irrigated valley lands of the western states are under the concrete or asphalt of the interstate-highway system— at the cost of 40 acres per mile—we cannot again use that valuable agricultural land for crops. It is gone as irrevocably as if it had been swept away by severe erosion. How intelligent are the decisions made by the engineers and road-building officials, very few of whom have any broad concepts of resource interrelationships and relative values of competitive uses of resources?

In the last few years the long-existing and broad conservation philosophy has finally been articulated, by Dr. Matt Brennan, for instance, in a definition that embodies a truly broad view. It states:

"Conservation consists in the recognition by man of his interdependence with his environment and with life everywhere, and the development of a culture which maintains that relationship through policies and practice necessary to secure the future of an environment fit for life and fit for living."

This statement is definitive, all-inclusive, and succinct. It gives a yardstick by which to measure resource-use or development techniques. It states clearly that we must view our total environment rather than the small pieces, as in the past. It clarifies the objective of resource management as being the creation not of mere dollars—which has too long been the objective—but as being the creation of an environment which gives us <u>what</u> we need to live and also which gives us a <u>livable</u> place.

Brennan's definition does the job admirably, for defining conservation, or conservation education, or the now popular term environmental education.

For years and years the broad conservation message has been broadcast. Some people who should know better say that conservation education failed, through faulty planning, or poor educational techniques. Their answer seems to be to kick conservation education under the rug and raise the flag of environmental education. But in my book conservation education did not fail to the extent claimed; rather, it

fell on infertile, unresponsive ground. Perhaps like spreading manure on land to make things grow, we had to get our destructiveness so evident and the manure of our civilization so widespread before the seeds of conservation education could really take hold.

And so to me the terms conservation education and environmental education are and always have been synonymous. The latter term is now in vogue. It's all right with me. I care not one bit what handle we give to the concept. I do care how we go about the job, for environmental education is just as amorphous a term as is conservation education, and is subject to just as many different interpretations.

The major concepts of environmental education are few in number but all-inclusive in content. They have been stated in many places and in many forms, but in my opinion one of the clearest presentations of the three major concepts is in the recently published <u>Teachers' Curriculum Guide to Conservation Education</u>, the result of the Pinchot Institute's South Carolina project. These three fundamental concepts are as follows:

1. Living things are interdependent with one another and with their environment.

2. All organisms (or populations of organisms) are the product of their heredity and environment.

3. All organisms and environments are in constant change.

These three concepts lie at the heart of environmental education. All aspects of an environmental education program need to be weighed as to their contribution towards building understanding of these major concepts. But environmental educators—as they like to call themselves—will be making a serious mistake if they think this is a brand new educational area. A major part of the previously produced material, curriculum guides, handbooks, or workshop outlines that have been the products and tools of conservation education are applicable to the field of environmental education.

The techniques of conservation education—or environmental education if you prefer—embrace many classroom projects, studies, and activities; they include school ground experiments and explorations; and they often involve outdoor education activities in park or camp situations. But each phase of any such program needs to help the person build an attitude of understanding and responsibility—personal, individual responsibility—towards the total environment. Each phase must help him see that man—every single person—is part of the environment.

Some good environmental education programs are going on now. Many fine conservation education programs have gone on for years. The real key to success in these efforts is <u>not</u> the money, <u>not</u> the grants, <u>not</u> the beautiful published materials, <u>not</u> the fancy camp facilities, <u>not</u> the specially-built laboratory facilities. The key is the attitude of educational administrators and officials. If they consider conservation education important, it can be (and in many areas has been) incorporated significantly into school curricula without major trouble or expense. The attitude is indeed the key.

Today education in general is suffering from a disease—the disease of judging the worth of a program by the size of the grant of money obtained for it. The major question often asked is "how large a grant can be obtained"; rather than "what can be done to solve the educational problem." There are quite a number of Title III ESEA (Elementary and Secondary Education Act) programs in conservation or environmental education headed by individuals talented in writing grant proposals but having little background or experience in the field. I actually had one person write me to the effect that he had obtained a $300,000 grant, and he needed ideas of how to use this.

And then today we find some organizations and agencies who with much fanfare inaugurate a NEW PROGRAM, yet are largely ignorant of the fact it isn't new, and also are inexperienced in dealing with the subject as applies to school curricula.

To make real progress in conservation or environmental education we need to have our schools and school officials and administrators responsive to the rising public understanding of the environmental crisis. We need to have our college administrators and teachers get their heads out of their narrow little specialties and realize that educational compartmentalization is no longer tenable. We need to have our technical training institutions critically examine their objectives and curricula. Nothing in their training programs gives their students any basis for broad ecological understanding.

Why do we find ourselves in this sad state of educational affairs? Why have we come so far so blindly?

First and foremost, I believe we are in this fix because of several myths—myths supported by and perpetuated by not only our educational system but by most every aspect of our society and culture. In particular, we believe in the myth of endless abundance of resources; we believe in the myth of the infallability of science (also called the "Science is a Sacred Cow" dogma); and we believe in the myth of the environment having an insatiable capacity to absorb punishment and abuse.

The belief in these myths in turn seems to me to be the result of several things.

First—our economic philosophy, traditions, and history all lead us down the rosy path. For instance, we worship the Gross National Product, and overlook many of the elements of the human condition which GNP cannot measure. We praise bigness and growth, irrespective of the nature of the growth or of the often destructive, stupid, or near-criminal violation of the environment involved in achieving the bigness. Our measure of success is the dollar, and only the dollar.

In The Conservation Attitude, Luna Leopold points out that just as many religions tend to obscure their ethical goals with rituals, temples, and prayer-sticks, so in resource management and manipulation we lose sight of the ultimate goal being the meeting of the material and spiritual needs of humans. We genuflect to large dams; we give thanks for a lovely body of water by gleefully counting (and reporting to the Chamber of Commerce) the number of powerboats using and fouling it; and we make burnt offerings (by means of the internal combustion engine) while exclaiming over the beauties of the Grand Canyon. We observe the rituals and have the trappings of conservation, but we've lost sight of the fundamental ethical concepts.

A second cause of our belief in these myths is perhaps due to the imbalance we've developed in our educational system. Most people today are merely trained, not educated. If you find a really educated man, you'll usually also find that probably his condition was acquired after he finished his formal "education." In the main, the scientists and engineers, lawyers and doctors, educators and astronauts are but highly trained and narrowly educated individuals. They lack perception, knowledge, or often even much curiosity about things outside of their own special ruts.

Microscopic views are the order of the day, but we forget that the bigger the magnification, the smaller the field of vision. Look at the nature of many beginning biology courses today—even those which are terminal or general-education courses for non-science students—in which a student might end with the ability to draw the DNA molecule, but won't have much idea of how biological systems interact.

That the narrowness and often self-defeating or circular education of professional people vastly hinders broad resource management has been pointed out many times by many people. The delusion we all suffer from is that because we are perhaps competent in one line, we presume to pass ourselves off as competent in others—and I most certainly include myself in this castigation. Value judgements often bear no relationship to the degree of "expertise" possessed by an individual. Nowhere is this delusion of omnipotence more dramatically or often more tragically illustrated than in the field of civil engineering, in which merely because the arts and technology of an engineer show him HOW to build a dam or a superhighway or an urban development, he presumes to also know WHERE to build it (irrespective of other possible competitive uses of that land), and he seldom considers WHETHER it should be built.

But more deeply significant than either the confining and horizon-shrinking nature of much professional education, or the deification of the dollar, in explaining our belief in those several myths, is the nature of several other aspects of our society. We forget, to paraphrase Dr. Norman Taylor, the "...land is neutral; it is the people that cause the problems."

There is something seriously wrong in our patterns of social thought, our processes of education, and our public sense of responsibility. A child today grows up and lives in such a synthetic, pre-packaged, Teflon-coated, Dacron-padded environment that he has little realization of the vastly intricate man-made and natural interdependencies of which he is the beneficiary. His knowledge of his own environment extends only to things within his ken, and most of these are taken for granted. His knowledge of the world outside his range of personal experience frequently is limited to the pap delivered by the idiot box, occasionally interrupted by worthwhile programs, and always subject to the vagaries of viewer ratings. In

so many instances neither the informal education occurring in a child's home nor the formal education
he receives in school gives him any sense of identification with the to-him-unfamiliar natural world,
which in the final analysis is the basis of his artificial world. Thus he grows up knowing some things
about his man-made environment, but ignorant of
the natural environment. He does not understand
his total environment.

Thus a child may grow up to become an engineer,
slick with a sliderule but frequently not realizing that
when water runs downhill, it moves soil. Or he graduates in law, and staunchly defends the right of a smelter
to denude many square miles of land—perhaps land that
is the watershed of a town. He may, if he is glib enough
of tongue, go into the real estate business, without
a thought to the suitablility of a particular soil for
a housing development. He'll of course always demand clear, clean water out of the tap, and vote
against a bond issue to build a sewage treatment plant.
Perhaps this child will become a vociferous hunter,
with an image of himself as a modern-day Dan'l Boone,
and he will loudly claim the God-given, red-blooded,
true-blue American right to have just as much freedom of movement and action as Boone had some two
centuries ago—before game biologists and bureau-
crats were invented. Of course, he'll have to take
along his refrigerator, and he'll complain if there is
not an outlet for his electric razor in the campground
washroom, while he lets his campfire set the woods
ablaze. This child may even turn into a school board
member who sees absolutely no connection between
the tax base which supports the schools, and the quality
of land and water management of the district.
Or, good grief, the man has become a college or
school administrator and has become so concerned
in juggling the curriculum demands of his faculty
(most of whom are rather narrow specialists) that
he takes no real leadership in seeing that environmental understanding is built, or a chance and challenge given for students to develop an ecological conscience.

Many more examples could be given of individuals
possessing fine formal and technical backgrounds,
yet who are but half-educated. They know their urban and metropolitan environments. They know their
professions and social positions. But these people
do not know their total environment—that all-encompassing environment of the man-made world plus
the natural world. They are blind to the fact that
the former depends absolutely on the latter.

Are there ways out of, or solutions to the environmental crisis? Many people believe so. While some
ask, ''Is mankind playing a game of environmental
Russian roulette?'', others state:

Man is not defenseless against the on-
slaught of modern technology. Knowledge
gained through research—and applied (with
wisdom)—can enable him to deal with the
great majority of environmental hazards.
But he is still a long way from adequate
understanding of the intricate web of life
which links plants, animals, and man.

Still others, such as Dr. Lynn White, explain
our past actions and arrogance as a species on the
deeply rooted concept in Christianity and Judaism

that God planned all of the world explicitly for man's
benefit and rule, and western man (or industrial man,
if you wish) has missed the real meaning of stewardship. White suggests that western religions must
revert to the teachings of St. Francis of Assisi to
understanding of the ''virtue of humility, not merely
for the individual but for man as a species''—if man
is to come to peaceful terms with his environment.

But can we afford to wait for a religious revival,
or even for biological or physical science to find
some more answers? I doubt it. We can, however,
mend our ways here and now. We can apply what
we know, as wisely as we can, now. We can start
taking the responsibility implicitly associated with
the freedom we have, but which too many people ignore. We can apply the scientific knowledge we have,
now, towards the solutions of environmental problems we have, now, and be willing to pay the costs
involved, now.

We know many answers, but refuse to apply them
or to bring to bear adequate social, educational, and
political pressures to cause them to be applied. To
do nothing about a situation is the easiest solution
but we must not forget that doing nothing still indicates that a value judgement has been made, and far
too many people have made this judgement. And we
must realize that the real costs of correcting environmental destruction will not decrease with time, and
that the problems won't go away if we close our eyes.

What's the answer? It's really very simple. We
must refocus our educational goals. No longer can
it be sufficient that our elementary schools merely
teach the 3 R's. No longer can it be enough for our
high schools to emphasize specializing at an early
age, or accelerating programs merely because educators have come to realize how much children can
learn. No longer can colleges and universities be
largely vocationally oriented. We've come to the
grim time in history when every citizen must have
a deep feeling of his own relationship to the total
environment. We've come to the time when it is essential that a social cost of doing business—any business—is the prevention of the degradation of the environment. We've come to the time when educational
officials must face the reality of the serious deficiency of our present educational system in largely
overlooking conservation education or environmental
education at every level of our formal educational
structure.

Some good programs are going on. Some teachers at every level do have the breadth and the attitude
to do the job of environmental education. Some few—
far too few—educational administrators and school
officials have seen the vital importance of incorporating environmental education into existing curriculum structures, and have encouraged teachers to
do so.

Everyone has a stake in this, in one way or another, whether you are a teacher, an educational
administrator, a representative of a federal or state
resource agency, a lawyer, a politician, or a busi-
nessman. Merely by being a person and a citizen
you have a deep responsibility to do all you can—in
large ways or small—to forward environmental education outside of as well as within the formal educational structure.

"The role of environmental education is ready for review."

TOWARD COURSE CONTENT IMPROVEMENT

Matthew J. Brennan

IF MAN is the only organism on earth which can consciously manipulate, control, destroy, or preserve his environment, then a knowledge of how he manipulates, controls, destroys, or preserves his environment, and equally important, a knowledge of the consequences of his actions in relation to his environment should be an essential element of man's understanding. It is not. Yet man, in common with all other living things, is the product of his heredity and his environment. The present environment is, and the future environment will be, largely determined by man. What man does, in turn, will be largely a consequence of his education.

It is a matter of fact that environmental education has not proven successful in aiding man to understand his environment. If this were not true, the quality of the environment would not be one of man's greatest concerns. Man must rely on his environment as it is and as he strives to conserve it.

Conservation is the recognition by man of his interdependence with his environment and with life everywhere, and the development of a culture which maintains that relationship through policies and practices necessary to secure the future of a sanative environment (2). As witnessed by public information today, the nature of man's environment is not completely known, and is particularly of questionable nature in the future.

Many educators readily admit that past and present activities in environmental education have been suspect in their effectiveness and efficiency for aiding man to maintain a sanative environment. Too often in the past decade, attempts at educational change have been exercised without a perspective of the role of education in society. The recent curricular organizations in science seem to be becoming suspect and seem to be losing acceptance in the educational enterprise.

The role of environmental education is ready for review. There exist today large numbers of examples of efforts in environmental education in America. These are evident in:

1. Published materials, of which there have been several thousand, most of dubious value to the educational enterprise, and generally not used (6). These publications are often conceived and developed without recognition of the problems faced by teachers in instruction of a given concept within the time given over to the particular study recommended, and its construction.

2. Teacher training programs (such as at the University of Michigan).

3. Model school environmental education programs, as currently operating in 20 locations in the nation, assisted by the Pinchot Institute for Conservation Studies.

4. State Department of Education conservation curriculum development projects, such as that in operation in South Carolina, which resulted in the publication of eight curriculum guides (3).

5. 103 ESEA Title III programs in conservation and environmental education.

These and other enterprises have possibly made some impact on what is considered environmental education. There are, however, several views which must be taken of the role of environmental education in America.

We need a study that will establish the role of education in the development of man's understanding of his environment. Such a study will establish relationships among man, environment, and education, as they were exercised in the past, are now, and will potentially be in the future. The need for such a

---

Dr. Brennan is Director, The Pinchot Institute for Conservation Studies, Milford, Pennsylvania.

study has an essential urgency as prescribed by the seemingly inefficient environmental education of the present, and the deteriorating quality of the environment. The American Association of School Administrators, N. E. A., has devoted two of its yearbooks to this urgency (4, 5). As stated in the foreword of Conservation-in the People's Hands (5), the A.A.S. A. said, "The manner in which this responsibility (conservation) is met depends in great measure upon a broadly conceived educational program that reaches all the people."

The recent White House Conference on Natural Beauty (1) emphasized the encompassing nature of the newer view of conservation as pervasive in t h e life of modern man. This newer mood and mode of conservation needs careful analysis and review. The development of curricular and instructional programs should not proceed without it.

REFERENCES

1. Beauty for America, (Washington, D. C. : Proceedings of the White House Conference on Natural Beauty, May 24-25, 1965).

2. Brandwein, Paul F., in Future Environments of North America, (New York: Natural History Press, 1966), p. 630.

3. Brennan, Matthew J. ed., People and Their Environment-Teacher's Curriculum Guides to Conservation Education, Grades 1-12, (Chicago: J. G. Ferguson Publishing Co. (Doubleday), 1969.)

4. Conservation Education in American Schools, (Washington, D. C. : American Association of School Administrators, 1951).

5. Conservation-in the People's Hands, (Washington, D. C. : American Association of School Administrators, 1964).

6. Johnson, Carl S., and Bambach, Charles A. , A Survey of Printed Materials for Conservation Education, (Columbus, Ohio: Cooperative Research Project No. 2213, The Ohio State University).

"Conservation is shifting from natural science theory to social science practice."

CONSERVATION IN TRANSITION

Ruben L. Parson

TO GEOGRAPHERS in general, and to resource geographers in particular, Outdoor Education is neither new nor startling. Geographers of my vintage have been preoccupied with the outdoor approach since they began their professional training, and, hopefully, throughout their professional careers. As students, some 30 years ago, their ears fairly vibrated to such tunes as "natural environment," "environmental determinism," "regional composites," "natural-cultural relationships," "place attributes," "human response to natural conditions,"— in keys both major and minor, in tones both harmonious and discordant. They spoke glibly about natural controls and human adaptations. They summarized the natural earth phenomena inherent in a given area and interpreted human cultural attainment in relation to those phenomena. There were those who spoke and wrote geography under the label "human ecology."

Then came a "reformation" that greatly discounted environmental determinism in geographic thought; whilst, at the very same time human ecology became a discipline quite independent of geography. Ideas once compatible have now become discordant: geographers disdain their old-fashioned determinism as something almost profane; human ecologists, meanwhile, venerate the idea of human conformance to nature as a basic precept. The younger discipline, human ecology, innocently promulgates profundities long since discredited by the older discipline, geography, which fostered them initially. Communication is obviously lacking!

I have used this oblique approach for a purpose: before I end this short epistle I shall caution my friends, the Outdoor Educators, about certain trends in their philosophy that may require modification.

Certainly geographers would applaud Outdoor Education such as I have observed. Field study of natural environmental attributes, and particularly of the interaction of atmosphere, hydrosphere, lithosphere and biosphere must ever be fundamental to Physical Geography. And, when we relate these facts and concepts to man and his culture, we have the scope of Geography in general. All kinds of nature study contribute to a foundation on which to build geographic knowledge; the unique virtue of Outdoor Education (as I envision it) is that it integrates the components, and thus lays a more complete foundation. As a Geographer I salute the Outdoor Educator!

As a Resource Geographer I am less enthusiastic, because I fear that Outdoor Educators may be going out on a limb soon to be sawed off. I am referring here to their bold venture into the realm of Resource Management. Here I fear they may be overextending themselves. I am aware that various and sundry have got astride Conservation as a convenient horse to ride; but I can also predict that some will fall off and be trod upon. Outdoor Education will be badly bruised unless it revises its precepts to accommodate Social Sciences as the prime movers of conservation. This done, it will have approached the central idea in Geography— the integration of environmental and cultural phenomena.

Why this admonition? Because Conservation is surely in transition. It is shifting from Natural Science theory to Social Science practice — a departure long overdue. It is changing alignment much as Pedology changed when it shifted from Geology to Agriculture. And unless the Outdoor Educator adjusts accordingly, he will be propounding the obsolete, much as the human ecologists who remains adamant about environmental determinism.

The abandon with which so-called "Outdoor Conservation Education" has been hitched onto elementary nature study reminds me of the spiritual, "Glory Road," made famous by Lawrence Tibbett several years ago. It seems that everyone got on the long horse, and he swept them all into the sky to glory — free of bridle and reins. We assume that the believers arrived safely without a driver.

Conservation (Resource Management) needs drivers--leadership; but such leadership is certainly not generated by elementary nature study, whatever the label it bears. Nor should nature study be warped to accommodate this superficial conservation "caper." Its special kind of nature study has given Outdoor Education the status and promise it now holds. Its prestige and usefulness might be better enhanced by refinement than by spreading and diluting.

Can it be that Outdoor Education, while still young and immature, has come to a philosophical crossroad?

Professor Parson is Chairman, Geography Department, St. Cloud State College, Minnesota. This article first appeared in the Fall, 1968, <u>Journal of Outdoor Education</u>, under another title.

Has it so completely accomplished its original purpose that it can now assume new objectives? Can it enlarge its scope without commensurate expansion of concept? Can it preserve its identity despite a vast expansion of compass, incorporating social sciences with the natural? Is its identity worth retaining? These are questions demanding answers—from educators and the public alike.

If one of my colleagues in Outdoor Education were to ask my opinion, I would without hesitation offer him these friendly suggestions: 1. Do not corrupt the integrated nature study for which Outdoor Education was conceived. 2. If you must embrace conservation, see that you also incorporate the social sciences—economics, demography, sociology, political science, etc. 3. Study and teach the natural attributes as you did before; then relate them to man's culture and his progressive development of resource management. 4. Finally, integrate the natural with the cultural. Analyze, describe, interpret, predict, and direct the course of events generated by natural resources and their manipulation. Now, if you can preside over this operation, you will be practicing geographic synthesis as an integral part of Outdoor Education. Personally, I believe you have a professional obligation to incorporate it and then to see that it is adequately accommodated.

"Producing a citizenry that is knowledgeable concerning the biophysical environment and its associated problems, aware of how to help solve these problems, and motivated to work toward their solution."

THE CONCEPT OF ENVIRONMENTAL EDUCATION

William B. Stapp, et. al.

WITHIN THE past 50 years, the United States has become a predominately urban nation, both in thought and in physical character. Large and middle-sized communities, many within complex urban regions, have evolved to where over 70 percent of this country's population resides on one and one-half percent of the nation's land surface. By 1980, e i g h t out of ten Americans will probably live in an urban environment. Consequently, the independent rural-oriented living that once characterized this country's social and political heritage is no longer a dominating influence in the lives of most Americans.

In rural surroundings, direct daily contact with the basic natural resources was prevalent, especially within man's immediate environment. As man b e-came progressively urbanized, his intimate association and interaction with natural resources diminished and, with it his awareness of his dependency on them. Yet, it is imperative that man, wherever he lives, comprehend that his welfare is dependent upon the proper management and use of t h e s e resources.

Man should also have an awareness and u n d e r-standing of his community and its associated problems. Our communities are being plagued with problems such as: lack of comprehensive environmental planning; indiscriminate use of pesticides; community blight; air and water pollution; traffic congestion; and the lack of institutional arrangements needed to cope effectively with environmental problems. While these problems are legitimate concerns of community governmental officials and planners, the responsi-bility for their solution rests, to a l a r g e extent, with citizens.

To an increasing extent citizens are being asked to make decisions that affect (directly and indirectly) their environment. Specifically, c i t i z e n s make these decisions as they cast v o t e s on community issues; as they elect representatives to policy-making bodies; as they directly act upon t h e environment itself. Citizens can be effective in influencing sound policy in other ways. They can ask informed questions, at the proper time, of the right people. They can serve on advisory and policy-making committees. They can support sound legislation directed at resolving environmental problems. To perform these tasks effectively, it is vital t h a t the citizenry be knowledgeable concerning their biophysical environment and associated problems, aware of how they can help solve these problems, and motivated to work toward effective solutions.

Most current programs in conservation education are oriented primarily to basic resources; they do not focus on community environment and its associated problems. Furthermore, few programs emphasize the role of the citizen in working, both individually and collectively, toward the solution of problems that affect our well being. There is a vital need for an educational approach that effectively e d u c a t e s man regarding his relationship to the total environment.

The Supreme Court decision regarding the one-man, one-vote concept, is enabling the increasing urban majority to acquire greater powers in decision-

The definition and major objectives of environmental education presented in this paper were developed in a graduate seminar in the Department of Resource Planning and Conservation, School of Natural Resources, The University of Michigan. The members of the seminar were: Mr. Dean Bennett, Mr. William Bryan, Jr., Mr. Jerome Fulton, Miss Jean Mac Gregor, Mr. Paul Nowak, Mr. James Swan, Mr. Robert Wall, and Professors Spenser Havlick and William B. Stapp.

making, makes it imperative that programs developed
for urbanites be designed with them in mind. It is
important to assist each individual, whether urbanite or ruralite, to obtain a fuller understanding of the
environment, problems that confront it, the interrelationship between the community and surrounding
land, and opportunities for the individual to be effective in working toward the solution of environmental
problems.

This new approach, designed to reach citizens
of all ages, is called "environmental education."
We define it in this way:

Environmental education is aimed at producing a
citizenry that is knowledgeable concerning the biophysical environment and its associated problems,
aware of how to help solve these problems, and motivated to work toward their solution.

The major objectives of environmental education
are to help individuals acquire:

1. A clear understanding that man is an inseparable part of a system, consisting of man, culture,
and the biophysical environment, and that man has
the ability to alter the interrelationships of this
system.

The principal feature of the philosophy of environmental education is that man is an integral part of
a system from which he cannot be separated. Specifically, this system consists of three components,
man, culture, and the biophysical environment. Culture, in this context, incorporates organizational
strategies, technological processes, and social arrangements (political, legal, managerial, educational, etc.) through which man interacts with the biophysical environment. The biophysical environment
designates both the natural and man-made components
of the environment.

The fundamental relationship between the integral
parts of the system is man's interaction   through
culture on the biophysical environment to produce
or obtain the goods and services that he needs.

Within the system, man has the ability either to
strengthen, weaken, or maintain the interrelationships between the system's major components. The
ultimate goal of environmental education is the development and maintenance of a high quality system
in which man interacts through culture on the biophysical environment to advance human welfare.

2. A broad understanding of the biophysical environment, both natural and man-made, and its
role in contemporary society.

The existence of any civilization is dependent upon man's use of natural resources. Resources are
defined as those parts of the biophysical environment
which are appraised by man as being immediately or
potentially useful to him.

A basic understanding of natural resources ideally
includes their characteristics, distribution, status,

interrelationships, and their present and potential
uses. Natural resources serve man in many ways,
whether in a relatively undisturbed condition or in
the highly altered utilitarian forms of the man-made
biophysical environment. A strong understanding of
how these resources are used requires knowledge
of the social, political, economic, technological
processes, institutional arrangements, and aesthetic considerations which govern their utilization.

The man-made components of the biophysical environment results from man's use of natural resources. An understanding of this aspect is also
essential: it should ideally include familiarity with
urban and rural design, including transportation systems, spatial patterns of development, and aesthetic
qualities which have a major impact on the functioning
of society. Fundamental to these understandings
should be the realization that the development of the
man-made environment should strive for a high quality system which improves human welfare in relation
to the natural environment.

3. A fundamental understanding of the biophysical
environmental problems confronting man, how these
problems can be solved, and the responsibility of
citizens and government to work toward their solution.

Biophysical environmental problems result from
the interactions between man, culture, and the
biophysical environment. Pollution, the inefficient
utilization and management of natural resources,
the indiscriminate use of pesticides, urban blight,
and transportation congestion are just a few biophysical environmental problems. These problems,
caused by a complex set of biological, physical, and
social factors, affect the total environmental system.

Citizens need to understand how to work toward
solutions of biophysical environmental problems
through laws, public policies, planning, resource
management, research, technological developments,
and institutional arrangements.

Citizens should realize that the responsibility
for solutions to these problems belongs to them and
the governments which represent them.

4. Attitudes of concern for the quality of the biophysical environment which will motivate citizens
to participate in biophysical environmental problem-
solving.

The word "attitude" used in this context implies
more than simply the knowledge of a body of factual
information. Instead, it implies a combination of
factual knowledge and motivating emotional concern
which result in a tendency to act. Further, it is
understood that clusters of attitudes about similar
environmental conditions will motivate individuals to
express their attitudes. Therefore, for environmental education to achieve its greatest impact, it
must: 1) provide factual information which will lead
to understanding of the total biophysical environment;
2) develop a concern for environmental quality which
will motivate citizens to work toward solutions to
biophysical environmental problems; and 3) inform
citizens as to how they can play an effective role in
achieving the goals derived from their attitudes.

"'Conservation' has lost its real significance. We need a new name, a larger base,

to accommodate the magnitude of the need."

TOWARD A CURRICULUM IN ENVIRONMENTAL EDUCATION

Douglas C. Covert

ECOLOGISTS, conservationists, educators, sociologists and economists are gradually coming to a full realization of the enormity of man's impact on his environment. Man's disruptive influence on biological ecology, his economic demands and his ability to engineer his surroundings are forcing upon us a gigantic sociological problem with which we are not prepared to cope--either technologically or philosophically. It is time for a new and vital educational approach to the ramifications of man's interaction with his environment.

There has been a small, but strong movement in this country toward the development and protection of what has been termed quality in our environment. The concepts of this movement have encompassed more than the biological and physical characteristics of the land--they have been extended to include, among others, the social, economic, cultural and esthetic factors. The aim has been stated in the broad terms of "conservation and development"of environmental quality. But, what is environmental quality? And who is to set the standards of quality control? And how are we to determine when today's standards of quality have become outmoded? In other words, Who is to be the judge of quality in our environment?

Our surroundings are a dynamic and finite continuum of natural forces. The human population is only one of those forces. Yet the human population has the capacity for the greatest impact. In any attempt to protect and develop quality in our environment, we must consider man's needs, his desires, and his characteristics, not from the standpoint of any individual or group, but as an interaction of the total population. Such a philosophical approach lies more within the realm of sociology than resource management, yet it is the resource managers and conservationists who have been most directly involved in this interaction and have been, consequently, the strongest advocates of environmental quality.

The efforts to promote a sense of responsibility in the American people toward their environment has come from those engaged in Conservation Education. Unfortunately, the word conservation has come to have a rather narrow meaning. In the minds of most it signifies special use of resources rather than the broader "wise use" concept. It has a rural connotation, and a relation to water and air pollution, vanishing wilderness and vanishing species, hunters and fishermen, Audubon Societies, and the National Geographic, and so on. Conservation has lost its real significance. We need a new name for a larger base to accommodate the magnitude of the need. It is time to abandon Conservation Education, as we know it, in favor of Environmental Education. This is not a radically disruptive alteration, but rather an adjustment to our changing needs. It is a broader outlook deriving from the interrelationships between resources and sociology. Conservation education must become more comprehensive in its content and in its effect on the total population.

Several decades of effort in conservation education have produced a didactic instructional pattern with emphasis on natural resources and their wise use. But, the present basis of relating academic study of natural science to a limited natural ecology without considering man's influence, and the restricted use of an "outdoor laboratory" is no longer adequate. The total environment of man and all the impinging factors of interaction are of far greater significance. The limited approach of the past and present rural orientation to resource use, and the outdoor biology - ecology laboratory as presently employed have a small meaning for today's needs.

Most efforts in conservation education place emphasis on a special aspect or orientation: on natural science ecology; on water pollution, air pollution, pesticides and so on; on careers related to natural resources and their use; on "a state of harmony between men and land." The urban citizen, on the

Mr. Covert is Programs Administrator, Educational Media, Inc., Detroit.

other hand, is just as concerned and more directly involved with conservation in his own environment— population shifts, traffic congestion and the decay of cities. These aspects of the total environment are just as important to man as forestry and agriculture. We can no longer be satisfied with the "outdoorsy" orientation of conservation education. We must face the changing nature of our population--the fact that, by 1980, eight out of ten Americans will be living in the cities, and that the pressure of leisure has and will continue to change the nature of our outdoor recreation. Today's effort must be directed at an adjustment of attitude if we are to implement our responsibility to people and to the natural systems of which we are a part. The goals must be broad: citizenship--an environmental awareness--a conservation conscience--a sound sociological philosophy. The result must be a reasonable and realistic attitude of the American people toward their environment.

The urgency is apparent and we must not let ourselves be discouraged by the false assumption that the task of conversion from the present method is enormous. Many subjects of the elementary and secondary school program have been and are being revised--mathematics, science, and social studies are obvious examples. With development and proof of these programs, implementation comes swiftly. It can be even easier and quicker to convert from today's conservation education to an expanded and vital program of Environmental Education. A favorable climate already exists. All that is missing is a specific and effective program and the tools for implementation.

How would an effective program in environmental education be implemented? By the development of an integrated, interdisciplinary and modular curriculum, flexible and adaptable to meet, primarily, the needs of urban children and adults, large city or small town, with the emphasis on the total environment. Such a program would have an inherent capacity for teacher modification to meet specific needs without destroying the validity of the total program. This program would be oriented primarily to the needs of the majority of our population but would also

well serve the rural student who is now feeling the impact of urban pressure and may well become a part of it.

With a developed and tested program, we have the opportunity for teacher training. Effective methods have already been used in other subject areas. In addition to training in colleges of education, teacher workshops and in-service training programs have proved themselves as efficient techniques for implementation. Continuing in-service programs aid teachers in acquiring competence. With valid and useful tools for both teacher training and classroom use, we can readily incorporate environmental education in existing curricula for an integrated total experience.

The present absence of an organized program of instruction has prevented the inclusion of the necessary environmental education in elementary and secondary school curricula. Therefore, it is proposed that an integrated, interdisciplinary, instructional program be developed in environmental education, designed to promote an environmental awareness and a sociological attitude.

The basic purposes of such a program are twofold: to provide information as a basis for intelligent action and a recognition of consequences; and to promote perception of the problems and ramifications of man's impact on his environment and the ability of man and the natural system to adjust to the consequences of the interaction.

Today's narrow approach to natural science ecology and to the economics of use of our natural resources can not begin to meet the need for intelligent recognition of consequences and consideration of alternatives. There is the utmost urgency to establish a national environmental awareness and a sound sociological attitude toward the total environment. We need a new cultural orientation to man's interdependence with his environment, a positive program to develop an attitude of responsibility, an academic commitment to an all-encompassing and vital curriculum in environmental education.

"Education must present conservation as realistic, practical, and farsighted public policy worthy of concern by an informed electorate."

VITALIZING NATURAL RESOURCES EDUCATION

Beverly H. Southern

THERE exists in the United States and in the world a grave and subtle conservation challenge— one that has implications for the prosperity and even survival of mankind. The challenge is that of an exploding population, a shrinking allotment of space per person, the inevitable conflict of apportioning available space, and how to make natural resources available to all while yet preserving environmental quality.

The challenge to education cannot be denied. According to former Secretary of the Interior Udall, "the concept of conservation cannot be isolated on little islands of awareness. It must become universally accepted as a familiar, taken-for-granted part of everyday life. Only thus can the 'golden days balance' we now enjoy be preserved"(4). In meeting this challenge, education must present conservation as realistic, practical, and farsighted public policy worthy of concern by an informed electorate. The approach must be broad-based and relevant to both rural and particularly urban societies. It must truly be environmental education— the study of man in relation to his environment.

Conservation education, or Natural Resources Education, as it is here conceived, is essentially education for attitudes. It would develop in the child a social conscience in respect to the environment. Social conscience implies particular attitudes toward environment. The attitudes and values determined to be the most desirable outcomes of Natural Resources Education are respect for, identification with, and responsibility toward the total environment. "Respect" may be expressed by the attitude that all living things have the right to exist. It might also take the form of a cautious approach when dealing with natural forces. "Responsibility" may be expressed in individual or collective terms and would probably appear in both forms. For the individual it means management of the resources with which he comes in contact. Collectively, it means exercising the vote to maintain, preserve, and create resources.

As more people become producers of services or deal with resources secondarily, fewer have the opportunity for meaningful contact with the land. A feeling of alienation, or lack of purpose may be the result. People must be reunited, must "identify" with the natural environment if they are to recognize its inherent value.

It is proposed herein that if the child acquires particular broad environmental understandings (knowledge) he will develop a social conscience (attitudes) that will affect his behavior (actions) toward the total environment.

Knowledge, respect, responsibility, identification, and action are not the automatic result of exposing children to a particular curriculum structure. Communication or meaning flowing between the education agent (e.g., teacher or community, through vicarious or direct experience) and the child is a critical factor in determining whether natural resources education takes place.

There appears to be little doubt that the responsibility for developing informed and aroused citizens who will take an active role in local, state, national, and international resource issues lies with the schools. It is also true that, in addition to transmitting the cultural heritage, "schools have come increasingly to accept such purposes as (a) helping citizens to become more fully aware of the problems of society and (b) studying those problems with the view of improving the conditions for living, and ways of living"(1). This point of view undoubtedly led the 1948 Yearbook Committee of the Association for Supervision and Curriculum Development to state that: "... the school is obligated to make the facts of resources known; to make the possible choices and consequences clear; and to guide individuals to establish sets of values which will balance immediate gain against future need and private riches against social good (2).

It is important, and may soon become critical, that Americans become apprised of resource problems and their remedies. It is even more important that they understand the requirements for quality environment. Man has accelerated environmental change to the extent that he has it in his power to take a course of action toward resources and populations which will force future human beings to live at a mere subsistence level, if they survive at all. The choice is his--"if each of us fails to help in building the kind of world that he wants to live in he may find too late that the 'brave new world' that someone else has created has no place in it for him" (3).

The demand for educational change to meet environmental change cannot be ignored; the charge for public education is clear.

REFERENCES

1. American Association of School Administrators, Conservation Education in American Schools, American Association of School Administrators, Washington, D.C., 1951, p. 62.
2. Association for Supervision and Curriculum Development of the National Education Association, Large Was Our Bounty: Natural Resources and the Schools, National Education Association, Washington, D.C., 1948, p. 7.
3. Dasmann, Raymond F., Environmental Conservation, John Wiley and Sons, Inc., New York, 1964, pp. 2-3.
4. United States Department of the Interior, Quest for Quality, United States Department of the Interior, Washington, D.C., 1965, p. 8.

Mrs. Southern is Director of the Natural Resources Education-Demonstration Center, Title III, ESEA, De Kalb County, Genoa, Illinois.

"Desperately needed is interdisciplinary research on the development of environmental education curricula and methodology."

A SYSTEMS APPROACH TOWARD ENVIRONMENTAL EDUCATION

J. Y. Wang

IN AN ARTICLE entitled "A Rational Approach to Clarification of Environmental Sciences" (3), the author has defined a total environmental science as "the horizontal science which considers all conceivable and/or measurable components affecting man as an individual and his society as a whole. These components may be broadly classified as the

Physical (energy, air, water, and land)
Biological (plant, animal, microbe, and man as a biological body)
Socioeconomic (society, politics, economics, and law)
Behavioral (conceptual and perceptual processes of man and animals as a result of physical, biological, and socioeconomic environments)

The interaction and interdependence of these components and factors thereof are basic and logistic considerations to all theories and practices of total environmental science."

According to the definition above, some basic concepts of total environmental science are in order:

1. a new science which is non-existent by itself, integrated through a group of interdisciplines emphasizing the interaction and interdependence of man and his environment;

2. an applied and interdisciplinary science rather than a basic and multidisciplinary one;

3. a problem-oriented science with its final goal as the establishment of problem-solving techniques;

4. a human-centered science and therefore human values in such senses as one's dignity, birth right, aesthetics, quality of life, and survival, are the most fundamental of all considerations.

Such factors as the motivation and change of attitudes of individuals and groups, as well as social ethics are therefore of paramount importance to total environmental science which strives to preserve and improve the overall life-supporting systems.

These concepts or criteria are universally applicable to logical subdivisions, namely: environmental research, education, and service in natural and man-made environments. Of these three, research, both basic and applied, contributes to a better understanding, interpretation, and integration of all factors in an environmental system, supplying this fundamental knowledge and information to environmental sciences. Education trains future research workers, teachers, practitioners, and citizenry. Service provides instrumentation for the communication of environmental information among decision-makers, scientists, professors, students, industrialists, businessmen, and citizens. This includes consultant services offered to the public on both technological and social issues. An environmental service administration may be considered as a clearinghouse and a data disseminating center as well.

This article will stress the development of a total environmental education system through the cooperation of interdisciplinary scientists and educators. It must be understood that although some environmental problems require immediate attention, it is not, of course, the function of an educational system to initiate action in solving the problems. Instead, however, the educational system should provide the student with adequate knowledge for alleviating such conditions.

ENVIRONMENTAL EDUCATION

Undoubtedly the complications of such an educational system are tremendous. For clarification, first of all, it will be necessary to classify a total environmental science with respect to the problem areas and the processes involved. These will be provided in Tables 1 and 2. Secondly, it will be essential to demonstrate the implementation of a total environmental education system. This is illustrated in the four-dimensional matrix shown in Figure 1. Obviously, this matrix can only serve as a frame of reference or a guideline for the future development

Dr. Wang is Director of the Environmental Sciences Institute, 125 South Seventh Street, San Jose, California.

TABLE 1

CLASSIFICATION OF PROBLEM AREAS ACCORDING TO ENVIRONMENTS

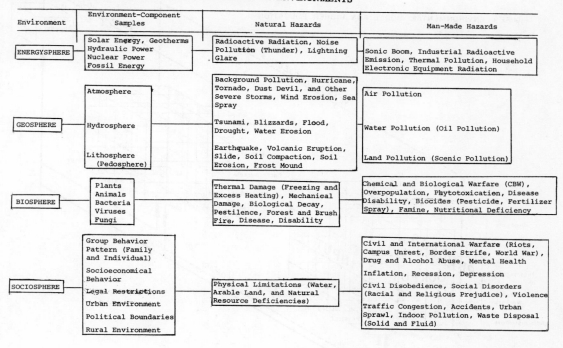

Environment	Environment-Component Samples	Natural Hazards	Man-Made Hazards
ENERGYSPHERE	Solar Energy, Geotherms, Hydraulic Power, Nuclear Power, Fossil Energy	Radioactive Radiation, Noise Pollution (Thunder), Lightning Glare	Sonic Boom, Industrial Radioactive Emission, Thermal Pollution, Household Electronic Equipment Radiation
GEOSPHERE	Atmosphere	Background Pollution, Hurricane, Tornado, Dust Devil, and Other Severe Storms, Wind Erosion, Sea Spray	Air Pollution
	Hydrosphere	Tsunami, Blizzards, Flood, Drought, Water Erosion	Water Pollution (Oil Pollution)
	Lithosphere (Pedosphere)	Earthquake, Volcanic Eruption, Slide, Soil Compaction, Soil Erosion, Frost Mound	Land Pollution (Scenic Pollution)
BIOSPHERE	Plants, Animals, Bacteria, Viruses, Fungi	Thermal Damage (Freezing and Excess Heating), Mechanical Damage, Biological Decay, Pestilence, Forest and Brush Fire, Disease, Disability	Chemical and Biological Warfare (CBW), Overpopulation, Phytotoxication, Disease Disability, Biocides (Pesticide, Fertilizer Spray), Famine, Nutritional Deficiency
SOCIOSPHERE	Group Behavior Pattern (Family and Individual), Socioeconomical Behavior, Legal Restrictions, Urban Environment, Political Boundaries, Rural Environment	Physical Limitations (Water, Arable Land, and Natural Resource Deficiencies)	Civil and International Warfare (Riots, Campus Unrest, Border Strife, World War), Drug and Alcohol Abuse, Mental Health; Inflation, Recession, Depression; Civil Disobedience, Social Disorders (Racial and Religious Prejudice), Violence; Traffic Congestion, Accidents, Urban Sprawl, Indoor Pollution, Waste Disposal (Solid and Fluid)

TABLE 2

EXAMPLES OF ENVIRONMENTAL IMBALANCES

Environment	Natural Hazards	Man-Made Hazards
ENERGYSPHERE:	-Excess electromagnetic waves (Thunder, lightning glare, magnetic disturbance) -Crustal forces imbalance (Earthquake) -Fluid pressure imbalance (Volcanic eruption)	-Shock (accoustic) waves (Noise pollution) -Excess industrial heating on water (Thermal pollution) -Radioactive pollution
GEOSPHERE:	-Atmospheric pressure imbalance (severe storm) -Seismic seawaves (Tsunami) -Precipitation exceeds evapotranspiration, runoff and percolation to the extreme (Flood) -Evaporation exceeds precipitation to the extreme (Drought)	-Excess airborne chemicals (Air pollution) -Excess chemical and biological materials (water pollution) -Excess oil in water (Oil pollution) -Excess fertilizer and waste deposits (Land pollution) -Irrigation salt deposition (Farm land pollution)
BIOSPHERE:	-Heat deficiency (Freezing damage to biosphere) -Excess heat (Foehn) -Lightning ignition (Forest and brush fire) -Pestilence (Vegetation damage and destruction and epidemics)	-High birth rate, low mortality rate, and insufficient occupant space (Famine and urban sprawl) -Imbalance of nature (Extinction of species) -Excess biocides (Health hazard) -Drug and vaccine accidents
SOCIOSPHERE:	-Physical limitations of earth (Shortage of land, water, and other resources)	-Overpopulation, racial strife, herd behavior (Warfare) -Excess vehicles (Congestion, accidents, and air pollution) -Urbanization (Alienation and social disorders) -Poverty (Unemployment, hunger, and social disorders)

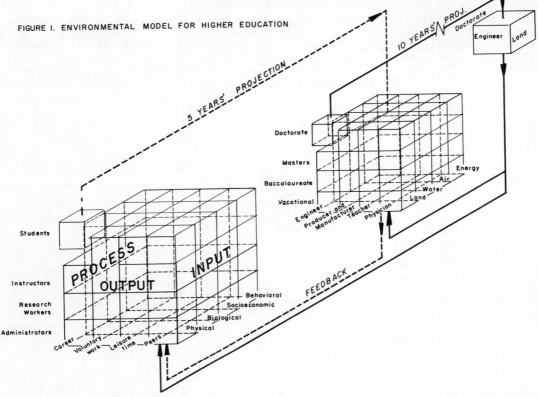

FIGURE I. ENVIRONMENTAL MODEL FOR HIGHER EDUCATION

of such an education system. Owing to its greater complexity, this system will require years of research and experience (service) for its initial establishment. As the concepts and understanding of man and his environment are constantly revised and re-evaluated, so too must the educational system adapt to these changes accordingly.

As shown in Table 1, the problem areas, both natural and man-made, are classified in accordance with the four major types of human environment: physical (geosphere and energy), biological (biosphere and energy), sociological (sociosphere and energy) and energy (energy sphere and the other three types of environment). Imbalances of nature and/or urban society are the sources of environmental problems. Needless to say, of course, under certain conditions those "natural hazards" listed in Table 1 may be beneficial, such as a brush fire in a Sequoia forest which may facilitate regeneration. Once an environmental problem arises, however, it may well produce a series of related problems in a chain-reaction manner.

Overpopulation in a city causes "urban sprawl" which is an environmental problem. As overpopulation persists, urban crime, pollution, traffic congestion, and the like follow. When overpopulation spreads over a large geographical or political region, it inevitably results in famine, infirmity, disease, and death. An imbalance of energy may cause such environmental problems as thermal, noise, and radioactive pollution. The classification of the human

environment according to both natural and man-made processes related to these problem areas is illustrated in Table 2.

In any educational system, an information input of human environment components (physical, biological, socioeconomic, and behavioral) is processed and transformed into useful form through the educational components (administrators, research workers, instructors, and students). It must be noted that the input is integrated environmental information, or environmental curriculum. The term "curriculum" here designates more than merely an outline of a course or a textbook per se; it encompasses a constant flow of up-dated research findings, field performance, and laboratory experiments. An output which represents all major activities of the individual may include career, voluntary work, leisure time, and peer group activities. The output itself may be divided into two groups: career- and non-career-oriented activities. The latter may be further divided into an infinite number of activities, depending upon the scope of the individual. Hence, the output activities shown in Figure 1 merely represent an arbitrary illustration.

This educational system may be conveniently described by the 3-dimensional matrix for higher education which is illustrated in Figure 1. The input (or subject matter) enters the matrix on one side of the educational system cube element, and processing (or decision-making) enters on the other side of the cube. The output, which may only be determined by close cooperation, may be measured through individual reports, subjective evaluations, and objective surveys. It is obvious that an integrated procedure exists among the four components of each of the first two matrices. The result of the interrelationships among the components of the first matrix is the integrated knowledge or information of the input. The cooperation and interaction among administrators, research workers, instructors, and students are the products of the process.

Variations are to be expected from the output owing to individual differences in interest, age, mentality, social sect, religion, etc. This 3-dimensional matrix cube element, which may be considered as a model, should be treated further with a TIME factor, or the fourth dimension. Since the human environment is subject to change, the projection of short- or long-term effects for the three-dimensional matrix must be considered. While a short term may be designated as 3 to 5 years, a long term may range from 10 to 30 years. Of course, these figures depend solely upon the problem to be solved and are flexible. The question is—does the present model meet future requirements? A projection must therefore be accompanied by a "feedback" process which will eventually change the original model. The broad and general procedures have been considered thus far; however, details must be worked out to fulfill requirements of the "real world" situation. The latter will undoubtedly involve race, religion, social ethics, regional problems, and many other complicated factors.

The 5-years' projection will generate a new model in which the expansions of the first two matrices are self-explanatory. The expansion of the third matrix, on the other hand, may require additional elaboration:

Career	Type
Engineer	Designing of instruments or equipment (hardware or software) for environmental data acquisition
Producer and Manufacturer	Production of goods for the betterment of the environment
Teacher	Teaching of environmental courses at any educational level (including citizenry)
Physician	Medical researcher concerned with effects of environmental pollution on humans

The above listing of careers, merely an illustration, is far from sufficient. Obviously, it can be expanded into many other areas.

REVOLUTIONARY APPROACH

The present higher educational system has been inherited with its more or less artificial boundaries between one discipline and another; whereas in the natural and social environment such boundaries are irrelevant or non-existent. In order to avoid these boundary restrictions revolutionary steps must be taken by all who are concerned and/or involved in environmental education. The following steps are recommended:

1. The concepts or criteria mentioned above must be agreed upon by those concerned with the environment.

2. The procedures, as described in our 4-dimensional matrix, must be followed in order to render environmental education workable as well as effective.

3. Regarding environmental educational institutions, the Office of Science and Technology (2) has issued two significant recommendations: "(a) substantial or complete control of faculty reward structure and (b) freedom to be innovative in introducing course material, educational programs, work study programs, and curriculum requirements for degrees." These arose from the growing frustrations of environmental scientists over lack of funding and short-lived programs.

4. The preparation of course material involving new textbooks should be specified for general as well as technical courses. A highly technical course such as cybernetics, for example, when applied to environmental sciences, should be offered to graduate students in the areas of bioengineering and operational analysis. A general environmental sciences course offered to high school students should stress overall environmental problems in a qualitative manner which is informative and comprehensive, yet nontechnical.

5. Evaluation of the environmental education system should be made in sequences of input-process-feedback-output. Here the input refers to the background education and mental capabilities of the student. The process involves the teaching methods, learning environment, audio-visual aid techniques, and the like. The feedback system designates the responses of subjects (e.g. students or community audiences) to the designed process(es). Henceforth, continual modification of the original design will be possible. The output will be the contribution and performance of graduates.

6. Finally, environmental research and service should be implemented alongside the overall educational programs in order to innovate the system. In fact, any improvement in educational systems requires both basic and applied research in environmental science. On the other hand, service of any kind will offer practical experience and better communication to the educators and students alike. It will narrow the gaps among all groups.

Traditionally courses offered in conservation education, natural resources education, outdoor education, ecology, agriculture, environmental health, and the like have emphasized specific phases of the environmental problems area. Although tremendous achievements have been made, many improvements are being suggested (1, 2). With the exception of environmental health, almost all of the courses offered are restricted to the rural areas. It is estimated, however, that by 1980, about 80 percent of the population of the United States will be concentrated in urban areas.

Schoenfeld (1) has contrasted yesterday's conservation education with today's environmental education. His listings may be reclassified and modified as follows:

CATEGORIES		CONTRASTS	
	past		present
Goals	Classical education on all levels	Citizen education in addition	
	Unilateral solutions	Open-ended options	
	Elementary education	Adult education	
Methods of Approach	Biophysical sciences	Social studies	
	Evangelical	Ecological	
	Gospel of efficiency	Quest for quality	
	Printed media	All media	
	Hunch	Research	
	Business as usual	Sense of urgency	
Regional Coverage	Local	Global	
	Rural	Urban	
	Terrestrial	Universal	
Disciplinary Boundaries	Artificial	Natural	
	Multidisciplinary	Interdisciplinary	
	Compartmentalized	Comprehensive	
	Parochial interest	Broader awareness	
Solutions	Appended rationales	Indigenous concern	
	Resource-centered	Man-centered	

In conclusion, research on the development of a total environmental education system is desperately needed. Establishing curricula for all levels of environmental education is the first task of this research. Its degree of success depends upon the willingness and closeness of cooperation among interdisciplinary scientists.

FOOTNOTE

1. The author wishes to acknowledge the assistance and critical review of Dr. Harvey I. Scudder of Cal-State College, Hayward, California, Dr. Fred Gordon and Miss Patricia Fenton, freelance environmental education experts. Thanks also are extended to Mr. Ralph Miner, Director, Institute of World Ecology of Monterey, California for his advice in the preparation of this article.

REFERENCES

1. Schoenfeld, C., "What's New About Environmental Education?" Environmental Education, 1:(1) 1-4, Fall 1969.

2. Steinhart, J.S.; Cherniak, Stacie, "The Universities and Environmental Quality (Commitment to Problem-focused Education)," Office of Science and Technology, U.S. Government Printing Office, Washington D.C. 20402, 1969, 71 pp.

3. Wang, J.Y., "An Approach Toward A Rational Clarification of Environmental Sciences," Proceedings on Man and His Environment: Interaction and Interdependence, Environmental Sciences Institute, San Jose, California, 1969, pp. 147-166.

4. Wang, J.Y.; Scudder, H.I., A Proposed Western Center for Environmental Education, Environmental Sciences Institute, San Jose, California, 1969, 14 pp. ∎

We must adopt self-imposed restraints.

A NEW ETHIC OF RESPONSIBILITY

J. George Harrar

ENVIRONMENTAL damage has been going on for years, but it is only recently that a general concern and a growing awareness that we are face to face with an ecological crisis have come about. Most of us now recognize the need for immediate measures to arrest the palpable threat to the quality of life, and realize that there is no single-formula solution to the problem. Numerous individuals and groups in both public and private life are currently attempting, in their own ways in their own specialized fields, to cope with, or at least to push back to some degree, the impending crisis. Municipal authorities, scientists, doctors, technicians, state and federal legislators, city planners, university faculties and students, philanthropists, and corporations are increasingly involved in finding ways to prevent the further impairment of our environment, to slow down its rate of deterioration, or to repair the damage done thus far.

T h e problem has, of course, reached its most serious proportions in the developed nations where industrialization and technology a r e highly advanced. Nevertheless, the crisis is beginning to assume global dimensions and is becoming a concern of the developing nations as well. It threatens islands as well as continents, rural as well as urban populations, t h e high seas as well as the coastal waters, the tropics as well as the tundras, the Volga as well as the Hudson, and the Caspian Sea as well as Lake Erie. Moreover, we are coming to realize that what is done to the environment in one place today is likely to affect it also in other places and at other times.

At this critical juncture, when we are finally coming to realize the hazards and dangers of our situation, it would be well for man to question the validity of his attitudes toward nature and to consider seriously the desirability and wisdom of formulating a new ethic for dealing with his natural environment, an ethic which would transcend most of the values we have traditionally held concerning our world. The Bible tells us that God gave man dominion over all the earth and o v e r every living creature on it. Man has misinterpreted this injunction as a license to exploit rather than as a conferral of responsibility. In the last analysis, man does indeed have dominion over all the earth, but this

puts him under grave obligations. Morally no society has the right to over-utilize the world's resources for its own contemporary and selfish interests. Man must understand biological systems and conduct his affairs in such ways as to improve the quality of life rather than to degrade it through wanton exploitation.

It is admirable and public-spirited to b e deeply committed to the well-being of the present generation, and hopefully this attitude will grow and continue. It is even more commendable for men living today t o become increasingly concerned about the future of their children and their children's children i n the face of a worsening environment. But the new ethic of ecological responsibility must extend far beyond even this highly humanitarian concern. It must embody the highest responsibility of all—the ultimate responsibility for the total natural environment, the biosphere, and life itself—not human life only, but all life, in its varied and diverse forms.

The first principle of the new ethic would be that man must control his own fertility. Whether we are concerned primarily with the present population of the world, with future generations, with man's survival as a species, or with preserving the stability of the entire biosphere, it is absolutely imperative that the human birth rate be curtailed. Man's superior intelligence and his belief in the intrinsic worth of each human being do not entitle him to assume that the natural environment should be dedicated to the production and maintenance of the human race. Instead, it is incumbent on man, as the only species capable of making moral decisions t o move toward a zero rate of increase.

The new ethic would also reject the premise that technology alone can provide answers to all or most of our environmental problems. It is true that technology has been a major and constructive force in the development of our society, and is using its inventiveness today to provide new methods of cleaning up after itself, of controlling pollution at its source, and of reusing the residuals being produced by our present industrial system. But technology does have its limitations. Advanced technology has a tendency to create

J. George Harrar is president of the Rockefeller Foundation. This statement is the preamble to its 1970 Report.

a need for even more technology and often merely substitutes one kind of pollution for another.

It is easy to blame technology for many of our environmental ills, but it must be remembered that technological advances are often in direct response to public demand. The entire society has the responsibility of recognizing what we are doing to our environment and of making individual and collective efforts to reverse the negative effects of certain forms of technology. We are prone to overvalue the production of nonessential material goods which rapidly become obsolescent and are eventually consigned to the already tremendous body of accumulated waste that is piling up around us. We must, of necessity, adopt self-imposed restraints by which the individual voluntarily refrains from contributing further to our ecological imbalance and is ever conscious of the need to live. Conserve and not destroy. Only when increasing numbers of individuals, groups, and communities recognize and accept their responsibilities and take organized action can improvement occur. Today, in this country, we have more than 200 million people, all contributing in some measure to the degradation of their environment. When these individuals can be persuaded to embrace the new ethic, to become "conservers" in the best sense of the word, a major victory will have been won.

The third principle of the ethic of responsiblity for the environment is that we, in the more advanced nations at least, should put considerably less emphasis on that form of economic growth that simply multiplies production and consumption of material goods. We dwell in a finite world where many changes and processes are irreversible. Our resources are not limitless, and when those that are non-renewable are consumed or transformed, they can never be replenished. Our present resources should be carefully husbanded and conserved. With stabilized populations, more attention and resources could and should be devoted to services and to those areas of life that enrich the quality of human existence: cultural activities, the arts, literature, intellectual and scientific pursuits, aesthetic improvements, and human relationships.

A final basic principle is that man should consider the equilibrium of the natural environment before initiating any actions that would disturb existing ecosystems. Modern technology, urban expansion, and rapid industrialization have drastically altered the ecological balance in many localities, extinguishing certain plant and animal species. Complex genetic material, once destroyed, cannot be recreated in a laboratory. Not only will the natural environment be altered and impoverished; it will become a much less varied, interesting, and desirable place for man to live. ∎

What should a person know about environmental management in order to function as an effective citizen?

FUNDAMENTAL CONCEPTS FOR ENVIRONMENTAL MANAGEMENT EDUCATION (K-16)

Robert E. Roth

THE QUESTION: "What should our citizens know about environmental management?" is prereqisite to developing meaningful environmental educational programs and curricula for children a n d adults. Regardless of t h e educational procedures adopted relative to environmental management education there are several needs that must be fulfilled for an ef - fective program: 1. The concepts important to an understanding of environmental management must be identified. 2. Identified concepts must be coordinated with existing school courses, and 3. Concept grade placement must be determined. The concern of this report is the identification of the important environmental management concepts that relate to scientific, social, humanistic, a n d technological disciplines. The process of identifying the conceptual content appropriate to the study of environmental management may thus begin by asking a variety of scholars:"What should a person know about environmental management education in order to function as an effective citizen?" In this procedure it is assumed that scholars from environmental-management related disciplines have informed and essentially agreeing opinions as to what concepts in and of environmental management should be included in the education of citizens. The recognized need and assumptions served as t h e bases for this study.

THE PROBLEM AND ITS SIGNIFICANCE

The Problem. To develop a taxonomy of conceptual objectives related to environmental management education for use in planning programs of instruction (K-16).

Subproblem. To determine whether biases exist as follows: (1) among scholars in representative disciplines relative to the conceptual objectives of environmental management education, and (2) among scholars residing in selected ecological regions relative to the conceptual objectives of environmental management education.

Significance of the Study. The present investigation is an attempt to provide a structure of important ideas which may be helpful to educators at all school levels in developing meaningful programs of environmental management education. A focus on envrionmental management that is different from the traditional agrarian approach is needed; one which will bring man, the physical and cultural environments, and their interrelationships into a different structural organization for instruction and understanding.

This investigation is important because:

1. It will provide a list of conceptual objectives important to understanding environmental management. This kind of information is essential before a new instructional program can be developed.

2. It will provide some information concerning biases of experts from 40 professional areas and several ecological regions regarding judgments relative to the importance of certain environmental concepts.

3. It will provide an organized structure of the important environmental management concepts as a suggested base for instructional purposes. This and other follow-up studies may help answer such questions as: "How, in what environment(s), and at what grade level(s) should the various environmental management concepts be taught?"

Definition of Terms. The terms "environmental management education," "environmental education," "conservation education," "outdoor education," and "resource (or resource-use) education" are often used interchangeably and are confused. For purposes of this study the term "environmental management of education" is defined as being the process of developing a citizenry that is:
1. knowledgeable of the interrelated biophysical and sociocultural environments of which man is a part;
2. aware of the associated environmental problems and management alternatives of use in solving these problems; and
3. motivated to work toward the maintenance and further development of diverse environments that are optimum for living (modified after Stapp, and others (5)).

"Optimum environment"—Potter (4) "one which... induces each individual to develop continually from birth to death as a result of systematic challenges by physical and mental tasks which elicit normal adaptive responses within his rapidly increasing and eventually declining capabilities."

"Sociocultural environment"—social systems within which individuals and groups with different cultures participate and interact.

"Culture"—Goodenough (3) "...the shared products of human learning."

Dr. Roth is Assistant Professor of Conservation and Outdoor Education, School of Natural Resources, The Ohio State University. A complete version of his doctoral study can be obtained from the Research and Development Center for Cognitive Learning, The University of Wisconsin, Madison.

"Biophysical environment"—the biological and physical aspects of environment with which man interacts and from which he obtains life supporting sustenance and natural resources.

"Management"—the intentional and rational manipulation of objects or events to achieve a predetermined end, goal, or objective.

Procedure. This study utilized survey techniques involving both written instruments and personal interviews to obtain and validate concepts appropriate for environmental management education. The population surveyed consisted of scholars in disciplines related to environmental management who were associated with The University of Wisconsin (UW) and other selected universities in the United States. In order to economize on time and effort, the project of concept selection was initiated by first utilizing UW scholars. The derived list of concepts was then submitted to a National Panel of Scholars (NPS) consisting of the same professional areas as those responding in the Wisconsin phase. The concepts included in the final taxonomy were those agreed upon by 90 percent of the scholars responding.

Selection of Populations to be Surveyed.
1. "Wisconsin Panel of Scholars" (WPS). The WPS included about 80 practitioners and/or educators from 40 disciplinary areas including the sciences, humanities, and social studies who met the following criteria: a. interested, or actively engaged in conservation and or environmental management education; b. located at the UW; and c. likely to participate in the study.

2. "National Panel of Scholars" (NPS). A NPS of 699 environmental management educators and practitioners corresponding by professional area to those in the Wisconsin phase of the study were selected who met the following criteria: a. generally committed to the area of this study by professional activity and interest; and b. willing to devote 2 hours to completing the survey instrument.

To assure breadth of coverage in the United States, two universities located in each of 12 of Transeau's Major Vegetation Zones (6) were selected (Tundra, Boreal Forest, Pacific Forest, Rocky Mountain Forest, Hemlock-Hardwood Forest, Grassland, Chaparral, Northern Desert, Deciduous Forest, Southeast Evergreen Forest, Sonoran and Chihuahuan Desert, Tropical Rain Forest). Twenty-seven universities were selected from those listed as having membership in the Association of University Summer Sessions and/or the National Association of College and University Summer Sessions which met the criteria of being large universities and having extensive graduate programs. The director of summer sessions (ss) from each of the selected universities was contacted and asked to provide the names of 40 individuals corresponding to the 40 academic areas selected in the WPS. The ss director was believed to be the one who was likely to know of the professional interests and activities of many of the faculty members within his institution. The total sample consisted of about 700 individuals.

CONCEPT LISTS

1. Initial List. By reviewing the relevant literature in each of the eight major areas traditionally considered to be conservation (1. wildlife management; 2. plant ecology; 3. water management; 4. soils; 5. political

science; 6. economics; and also 7. sociology and 8. cultural anthropology), 89 major concepts were collected and formed into a list. The list was presented to the panel at UW.

2. Establishing Concept Credibility. The initial list of 89 concepts was sent to the the WPS with a letter indicating the nature of their desired participation. They were asked to accept or rewrite the concepts listed and to make additions wherever necessary. Each WPS was contacted so that an interview at a mutually convenient time could be scheduled when the completed survey instrument was received by the investigator. During the personal interview with the investigator each scholar was requested to respond to the question: "What should a student know about environmental management?" A standard form of questioning was used, and all relevant comments made by the panel members were recorded by the interviewer.

3. Revised-Concept List No. 2. A revised list of 157 concepts based on results of the mail survey and interviews with the WPS and a cover letter were developed and sent to all respondents participating in the initial survey. The revised list was reformulated into an instrument utilizing a modified Blanchet scale technique (2). The scale included four acceptable choices in descending order of importance and one unacceptable choice [Essential (+5), High Desirable (+4), Desirable (+3), Satisfactory (+2), Unacceptable (-5)]. This procedure eliminated the necessity of marking each item twice by providing an indication of acceptability and degree of essentiality for each concept with one response thus reducing the total time required of each respondent. In addition respondents were invited to react to the credibility of items.

4. Revised-Concept List No. 3. A third list of 128 concepts was prepared based on the responses received from the WPS and reformulated again utilizing the Blanchet scale technique. The revised list was sent to the 699-member NPS with a cover letter explaining the nature of their desired participation for evaluation in terms of credibility and degree of acceptability.

Schedule of Operations. Phase (1): Instrument No. 1 was sent to the WPS and within 2 weeks an oral interview was scheduled with each panelist at which time the completed instrument was obtained.

Phase (2): Instrument No. 2 was developed based on the written and oral comments received, and the revised instrument was sent to all respondents participating in Phase (1). One probe letter was sent to all respondents not complying with the suggested termination date.

Phase (3): Instrument No. 3 was revised based on the written comments obtained in Phase (2) and sent to the NPS. Up to three probe letters were sent to those respondents who failed to reply within the time limits established by the investigator. The letters were spaced about 3 weeks apart thereby allowing about 2 months for acceptable responses.

TREATMENT OF DATA

1. Wisconsin Phase. The written comments and additions made by the WPS on Concept List No. 1 were recorded for use in revising the initial list.

Data obtained from the WPS's reactions to List No. 2 (Blanchet scale) were tabulated using the RAVE (Reciprocal Averages Program, Baker, (1)), and the frequencies of response for each of five categories were determined. A 75 percent level of total acceptability was established as a criterion to exempt a concept from further revision or exclusion.

2. <u>National Phase.</u> Data from the NPS reactions to List No. 3 were tabulated using the RAVE (Baker, 1), and frequencies for each of five categories of response were determined. A 90 percent level of acceptability was established as requisite for concepts included in the final list. Therefore, any concept receiving 10 percent or more unacceptable responses was eliminated and reasons for its exclusion were analyzed.

3. <u>Forming the Topical List.</u> Concepts receiving a 90 percent or greater level of acceptability were ranked in descending order of importance based on a weighted item-mean score derived by using the following formula:

$$\frac{5n_1 + 4n_2 + 3n_3 + 2n_4 - 5n_5}{\Sigma n_i} = \text{Weighted Item-Mean Score}$$

Using this formula the maximum score was 5.0. Concepts were arranged and rearranged in lists based on the similarity of content until a topical outline became evident. The content and the weighted item-mean scores were used to determine the relative position of each concept within each topic in the taxonomic list. It was assumed that the panels of scholars represented the interdisciplinary area of environmental management education and that their judgments of the relative importance of each concept was a true measure of its importance.

4. <u>Subproblem 1.</u> The possible relevance of academic discipline of respondents as a basis for concept rejection was tested by reviewing the academic affiliation of those individuals who rejected the concept. A determination of academic discipline biases was made by analyzing the frequencies of "unacceptable" markings and the written comments made about each item excluded.

5. <u>Subproblem 2.</u> The possible relevance of ecological region of respondents as a basis for concept rejection was tested by reviewing regional association of those individuals who rejected concepts. A determination of regional biases was made by the same method used in Subproblem 1.

RESULTS (In three parts)

The National Panel. The NPS initially selected consisted of 699 scholars representing 40 scholarly disciplines in 24 universities from 12 ecological zones in the U. S., however, useable responses were received from only 350 (50.07 percent) of the scholars chosen. There were four or more responses from each of the 24 universities (see Table 1); however, no institution had 100 percent responses. The discrepancy between the total number responding (350, 50.07 percent) is accounted for by those not completing questionnaires who usually indicated their reason(s) as "no time," or "beyond my professional competence and/or interest."

The distribution of the competencies of the panel members (see Table 2) includes the 40 professional areas selected and a minimum of three scholars from each. Although the number of respondents varies from one professional area to another it is assumed that the unequal number of respondents does not affect the results of the investigation.

The Taxonomic List. The 111 concepts that met the criterion "acceptable by 90 percent of the panel members responding," are classified by topics in Table 4. Note also, from Table r, that although the concepts

met the criterion, all were not rated at equal levels of essentiality; the weighted item-mean scores vary from 4.85 to 2.54. Concept No. 1 has implications for the majority of topics that follow and therefore has been placed singly at the top of the list. Topics and number of concepts that were used in classifying each concept are: Environmental Management (16); Management Techniques (8); Economics (18); Environmental Problems (3); Environmental Ecology (8); Adaptation and Evolution (9); Natural Resources (18); Sociocultural Environment (10); Culture (4); Politics (5); The Family (1); The Individual (6); and Psychological Aspects (4). The classification of concepts used here is not considered exhaustive nor is it suggested as the only possible organization of topics and concepts.

TABLE 1

RESPONSE BY UNIVERSITY TO MAILED SURVEY

University Number	Total Mailed	Total Respondents	Completed Instruments
1	31	28	25
2	29	23	13
3	38	26	23
4	31	19	11
5	30	15	12
6	27	15	6
7	36	11	4
8	30	26	21
9	33	20	14
10	34	24	19
11	36	25	17
12	28	23	21
13	12	8	7
14	30	28	26
15	23	17	11
16	26	13	10
17	27	13	8
18	19	11	7
19	35	19	13
20	32	19	16
21	38	24	20
22	20	10	6
23	35	27	22
24	29	19	18
Totals	669(100%)	463(66.23%)	350(50.07%)

Subproblem Analysis. Examination of "unacceptable" concepts and frequency of rejection of each concept (see Table 5) reveals little to help understand the cause of rejection. Observable, however, is the fact that only one concept (No. 65) was rejected by 27 percent, whereas the other 16 concepts were rejected by only 18 percent or fewer judges.

1. A speculated cause of rejection of a given concept was that scholars in a given professional area may, because of orientation, not assess a high value to it. When rejected concepts are tabulated according to professional area of respondents, there is little evidence to support this speculation. Examination of Concepts 15, 18, 24, 43, 100, 111, and 112 provides no clear evidence of any pattern. While analyses of the tabulations of the remaining ten concepts reveals very little pattern, a slight indication might be suggested. Four concepts were rejected by 45.5-60 percent of the respondents of a given professional area as follows:

TABLE 2

RESPONDENTS BY PROFESSIONAL AREA

Professional Area	Respondents
1. Agriculture (General)	5
2. Agriculture Economics	5
3. Art (Fine Arts)	11
4. Botany (Plant Ecology)	14
5. Chemistry	14
6. Civil Engineering (Sanitation Engineering)	13
7. Commerce (Business)	6
8. Community Leadership (Extension Education)	8
9. Computer Sciences	6
10. Economics	10
11. Education	18
12. Environmental Design	4
13. Food Science	13
14. Genetics	7
15. Geography	13
16. Geology (Mining Engineering)	11
17. Guidance and Counseling	7
18. Hydrology (Water Resources)	5
19. Journalism	6
20. Landscape Architecture	9
21. Mass Communications	7
22. Medical Education	7
23. Meterology	5
24. Music	7
25. Natural Resources Conservation	10
26. Oncology (Biochemistry)	7
27. Parks and Recreation Management	4
28. Pharmacology	4
29. Physics	12
30. Political Science	10
31. Public Health	7
32. Recreation Education	13
33. Rural Sociology	3
34. Social Work	7
35. Sociology	12
36. Soils (Agronomy, Soil and Water Conservation)	9
37. Theater Production	10
38. Urban and Regional Planning	8
39. Veterinary Science	7
40. Wildlife Ecology (Wildlife Management, Zoology)	16
TOTAL	350

Concept 21–eight of 16, Wildlife Ecology (50 percent); Concept 25–three of six, Commerce (50 percent); Concept 77–six of ten, Political Science (60 percent); Concept 94–five of 11, Geology (45.5 percent). Three concepts rejected by 40-60 percent of two groups of respondents are as follows: Concept 45–four of ten, Political Science (40 percent), and three of seven, Guidance and Counseling (42.9 percent); Concept 46–six of ten, Political Science (60 percent), and three of

seven, Social Work (42.9 percent); and Concept 65–five of ten, Natural Resource Conservation (50 percent), and four of eight, Urban and Regional Planning (50 percent). One concept was rejected by about 40 percent of the respondents representing three professional areas as follows: Concept 55–three of seven, Oncology (42.9 percent), four of ten, Political Science (40 percent), and five of 12, Sociology (41.7 percent). Two concepts were rejected by 40-50 percent of the respondents from five professional areas as follows: Concept 53–two of five, Agriculture (40 percent), six of 14, Botany (42.9 percent), two of five, Hydrology (40 percent), four of ten, Natural Resources Conservation (40 percent), three of seven, Social Work (42.4 percent); and Concept 54–four of seven, Medical Education (57.1 percent); five of ten, Natural Resources Conservation (50 percent), three of seven, Music (42.9 percent), three of seven, Oncology (42.9 percent), four of ten, Political Science (40 percent). However, since the preceeding is based on fewer than 20 percent of the respondents on the NPS, it would seem that any indication of bias of respondents affiliated with a given professional area would be tenuous at best.

2. Another speculated cause of rejection of a concept was that scholars in a given ecological region might, because of a regional orientation, not assess high value to the concept. Analysis of rejected concepts by ecological regions reveals little to support this. While no clear pattern of response is in evidence, there appears to be a very slight indication that respondents representing the Hemlock-Hardwood Forest region might have a tendency to reject more and respondents representing the Northern Desert region might have a tendency to reject fewer concepts.

3. A third cause speculated as a basis for rejection of a concept was the possibility of multiple interpretations or vagueness of meaning (see Table 5) and some

TABLE 3

RESPONDENTS BY ECOLOGICAL ZONE*

1. Tundra	13
2. Boreal Forest	21
3. Pacific Forest	30
4. Rocky Mountain Forest	33
5. Hemlock-Hardwood Forest	52
6. Grassland	75
7. Chaparral	11
8. Northern Desert	33
9. Deciduous Forest	24
10. Southeast Evergreen Forest	32
11. Sonoran and Chihuahuan Desert	29
12. Tropical Rain Forest	7
TOTAL	350

* From E. N. Transeau (1948).

TABLE 4

TAXONOMIC LIST OF CONCEPTS FOR ENVIRONMENTAL MANAGEMENT EDUCATION ORGANIZED ACCORDING TO TOPICS ON THE BASIS OF WEIGHTED ITEM-MEAN SCORE

Concept No. *	Concept	Weighted Item-Mean Score
1.	(1) Living things are interdependent with one another and their environment. 315 Essential 17 Highly Desirable 14 Desirable 2 Satisfactory 0 Unacceptable	4.85

ENVIRONMENTAL MANAGEMENT

2.	(4) Man has been a factor affecting plant and animal succession and environmental processes. 246 Essential 66 Highly Desirable 28 Desirable 8 Satisfactory 0 Unacceptable	4.58
3.	(78) The management of natural resources to meet the needs of successive generations demands long-range planning. 236 Essential 65 Highly Desirable 24 Desirable 11 Satisfactory 5 Unacceptable	4.42
4.	(56) Environmental management involves the application of knowledge from many different disciplines. 186 Essential 82 Highly Desirable 48 Desirable 23 Satisfactory 0 Unacceptable	4.27
5.	(62) Modern man affects the structure of his environment. 175 Essential 84 Highly Desirable 53 Desirable 20 Satisfactory 6 Unacceptable	4.08
6.	(127) Esthetic resources and recreational facilities of economic and noneconomic value are becoming increasingly important in leisure-time activities. 156 Essential 100 Highly Desirable 52 Desirable 25 Satisfactory 3 Unacceptable	4.08
7.	(87) Man has ability to manipulate and change the environment. 161 Essential 87 Highly Desirable 54 Desirable 28 Satisfactory 5 Unacceptable	4.01
8.	(86) A knowledge of the social, physical, and biological sciences and humanities are important for environmental understanding 164 Essential 96 Highly Desirable 47 Desirable 21 Satisfactory 9 Unacceptable	3.98
9.	(60) Social and technological changes alter the interrelationships, importance and uses for natural resources. 124 Essential 114 Highly Desirable 76 Desirable 22 Satisfactory 3 Unacceptable	3.93
10.	(102) There are certain risks taken, and limitations experienced, when manipulating the natural environment. 133 Essential 98 Highly Desirable 67 Desirable 37 Satisfactory 2 Unacceptable	3.92
11.	(63) Resource depletion can be slowed by the development and adoption of alternatives. 134 Essential 105 Highly Desirable 65 Desirable 24 Satisfactory 8 Unacceptable	3.84
12.	(97) Environmental management has effects on individuals and social institutions. 114 Essential 88 Highly Desirable 84 Desirable 45 Satisfactory 3 Unacceptable	3.74
13.	(68) Man's need for food, fiber, and minerals increases as populations expand and levels of consumption rise. 139 Essential 68 Highly Desirable 83 Desirable 39 Satisfactory 10 Unacceptable	3.67
14.	(73) Conflicts emerge between private land use rights and the maintenance of environmental quality for the general public. 122 Essential 93 Highly Desirable 76 Desirable 30 Satisfactory 11 Unacceptable	3.65
15.	(93) A cultural and time lag exists between the development of knowledge in science and technology and application of that knowledge to resource and environmental problems. 97 Essential 90 Highly Desirable 90 Desirable 47 Satisfactory 11 Unacceptable	3.44
16.	(90) Management is the result of technical and scientific knowledge being applied in a rational direction to achieve a particular objective 60 Essential 84 Highly Desirable 91 Desirable 56 Satisfactory 34 Unacceptable	2.62
17.	(91) The management of natural resources is culture bound. 50 Essential 66 Highly Desirable 98 Desirable 68 Satisfactory 31 Unacceptable	2.52

MANAGEMENT TECHNIQUES

18.	(69) Increased population mobility is changing the nature of the demands upon some resources. 101 Essential 96 Desirable 90 Desirable 39 Satisfactory 7 Unacceptable	3.61
19.	(96) Options available to future generations must not be foreclosed. 154 Essential 86 Highly Desirable 53 Desirable 16 Satisfactory 26 Unacceptable	3.51
20.	(113) A variety of institutional structures are involved in planning and managing the environment. 80 Essential 81 Highly Desirable 102 Desirable 64 Satisfactory 2 Unacceptable	3.49
21.	(47) Hunting regulations are useful in maintaining and restoring populations as well as in distributing the game harvest. 92 Essential 84 Highly Desirable 87 Desirable 61 Satisfactory 8 Unacceptable	3.43
22.	(71) Multiple use is a practice in which a given land area functions in two or more compatible ways. 91 Essential 104 Highly Desirable 78 Desirable 46 Satisfactory 13 Unacceptable	3.41
23.	(42) Management of habitat is considered to be an effective technique of wildlife management when the desire is to increase numbers of particular populations. 79 Essential 100 Highly Desirable 94 Desirable 41 Satisfactory 13 Unacceptable	3.35

24. (122) Architecture can be one of the positively persuasive influences in developing a congenial environment.
    <u>74</u> Essential <u>95</u> Highly Desirable <u>85</u> Desirable <u>71</u> Satisfactory <u>10</u> Unacceptable   3. 27
25. (72) Zoning is a practice in which land uses are prescribed based upon value judgments regarding the needs of society.
    <u>72</u> Essential <u>89</u> Highly Desirable <u>101</u> Desirable <u>54</u> Satisfactory <u>14</u> Unacceptable   3. 20

ECONOMICS

26. (84) Ready transportation, growing interest, money surpluses, and increased leisure time combine to create heavy pressures on existing recreation facilities and demands for new ones.   3. 96
    <u>159</u> Essential <u>83</u> Highly Desirable <u>65</u> Desirable <u>26</u> Satisfactory <u>6</u> Unacceptable
27. (128) Outdoor recreation is an increasingly important part of our culture and our economy.   3. 93
    <u>138</u> Essential <u>93</u> Highly Desirable <u>71</u> Desirable <u>32</u> Satisfactory <u>3</u> Unacceptable
28. (28) The economy of a region depends on the utilization of its natural, human, and cultural resources and technologies over time.   3. 79
    <u>147</u> Essential <u>96</u> Highly Desirable <u>65</u> Desirable <u>22</u> Satisfactory <u>12</u> Unacceptable
29. (82) Economic efficiency does not always result in conservation of a natural resource.   3. 79
    <u>157</u> Essential <u>88</u> Highly Desirable <u>47</u> Desirable <u>36</u> Satisfactory <u>12</u> Unacceptable
30. (61) The distribution or location of resources in relation to population, technological and economic factors are critical to problems of resource conservation and use.   3. 73
    <u>125</u> Essential <u>87</u> Highly Desirable <u>88</u> Desirable <u>33</u> Satisfactory <u>7</u> Unacceptable
31. (58) The political and economic strength of a country is in part, dependent upon its access to domestic and foreign resources and international relationships.   3. 67
    <u>116</u> Essential <u>96</u> Highly Desirable <u>75</u> Desirable <u>40</u> Satisfactory <u>8</u> Unacceptable
32. (66) Conservation policy is determined by the interaction of science and technology; social and political factors; and aesthetic, ethical, and economic considerations.   3. 61
    <u>127</u> Essential <u>92</u> Highly Desirable <u>78</u> Desirable <u>28</u> Satisfactory <u>14</u> Unacceptable
33. (83) Conventional benefit-cost analyses do not always result in sound conservation decisions.   3. 54
    <u>123</u> Essential <u>94</u> Highly Desirable <u>62</u> Desirable <u>39</u> Satisfactory <u>15</u> Unacceptable
34. (85) A sound natural resource policy is dependent upon a flexible political system, pragmatically appraising and reappraising policies and programs in terms of their effect upon the public interest and in light of scientific knowledge about the natural resources.   3. 53
    <u>126</u> Essential <u>89</u> Highly Desirable <u>65</u> Desirable <u>37</u> Satisfactory <u>16</u> Unacceptable
35. (75) Consumption practices are constantly being expanded by our ability to produce and create wants and market, which affects the rate of resource use.   3. 45
    <u>90</u> Essential <u>103</u> Highly Desirable <u>80</u> Desirable <u>47</u> Satisfactory <u>11</u> Unacceptable
36. (81) Individuals tend to select short term economic gains, often at the expense of greater long term environmental benefits.   3. 27
    <u>131</u> Essential <u>88</u> Highly Desirable <u>52</u> Desirable <u>42</u> Satisfactory <u>27</u> Unacceptable
37. (76) Increasing population and per capita use of resources have brought changed land to man or resource to population ratios.   3. 21
    <u>99</u> Essential <u>63</u> Highly Desirable <u>85</u> Desirable <u>57</u> Satisfactory <u>17</u> Unacceptable
38. (80) Goods and services are produced by the interaction of labor, capital, natural resources, and technology.   3. 18
    <u>82</u> Essential <u>67</u> Highly Desirable <u>85</u> Desirable <u>90</u> Satisfactory <u>10</u> Unacceptable
39. (105) Long range planning for the use and allocation of natural and human resources is continually evovling.   3. 17
    <u>95</u> Essential <u>87</u> Highly Desirable <u>82</u> Desirable <u>46</u> Satisfactory <u>22</u> Unacceptable
40. (74) Choices between needs (essentials) and wants or desires (nonessentials) are often in conflict.   3. 15
    <u>96</u> Essential <u>75</u> Highly Desirable <u>93</u> Desirable <u>49</u> Satisfactory <u>21</u> Unacceptable
41. (79) Raw materials and energy supplies are generally obtained from those resources and places where they are available at least cost, usually in short economic terms.   2. 96
    <u>69</u> Essential <u>80</u> Highly Desirable <u>94</u> Desirable <u>73</u> Satisfactory <u>20</u> Unacceptable
42. (64) Supply and demand, in relation to values held by society, determines what is a resource and its economic values.   2. 86
    <u>78</u> Essential <u>89</u> Highly Desirable <u>102</u> Desirable <u>36</u> Satisfactory <u>32</u> Unacceptable
43. (67) The more efficient use of some resources is the result of technical and marketing improvements.   2. 76
    <u>54</u> Essential <u>67</u> Highly Desirable <u>111</u> Desirable <u>69</u> Satisfactory <u>23</u> Unacceptable

ENVIRONMENTAL PROBLEMS

44. (9) Safe waste disposal, including the reduction of harmful and cumulative effects of various solids, liquids, gases, radio-active wastes, and heat, is important if the well being of man and the environment is to be preserved.
    <u>275</u> Essential <u>51</u> Highly Desirable <u>17</u> Desirable <u>2</u> Satisfactory <u>3</u> Unacceptable   4. 65
45. (8) Pollutants and contaminants are produced by natural and man-made processes.   4. 09
    <u>211</u> Essential <u>60</u> Highly Desirable <u>47</u> Desirable <u>13</u> Satisfactory <u>12</u> Unacceptable
46. (49) Increasing human populations, rising levels of living and the resultant demands for greater industrial and agricultural productivity promotes increasing environmental contamination.
    <u>204</u> Essential <u>71</u> Highly Desirable <u>22</u> Desirable <u>22</u> Satisfactory <u>15</u> Unacceptable   4. 01

ENVIRONMENTAL ECOLOGY

47. (2) Natural resources are interdependent and the use or misuse of one will affect others.   4.35
   245 Essential _64_ Highly Desirable _21_ Desirable _7_ Satisfactory _10_ Unacceptable

48. (20) In any environment, one component like: space, water, air, or food may become a limiting factor.   4.22
   191 Essential _89_ Highly Desirable _39_ Desirable _20_ Satisfactory _4_ Unacceptable

49. (22) Most resources are vulnerable to depletion in quantity, quality, or both.   4.17
   204 Essential _74_ Highly Desirable _36_ Desirable _23_ Satisfactory _7_ Unacceptable

50. (5) The interaction of environmental and biological factors determines the size and range of species and populations.   3.84
   147 Essential _94_ Highly Desirable _77_ Desirable _13_ Satisfactory _11_ Unacceptable

51. (29) Natural resources, water and minerals in particular, are unequally distributed with respect to land areas and political boundaries.   3.75
   144 Essential _72_ Highly Desirable _81_ Desirable _38_ Satisfactory _8_ Unacceptable

52. (26) The renewable resource base can be extended by reproduction, growth, and management.   3.75
   136 Essential 106 Highly Desirable _58_ Desirable _23_ Satisfactory _13_ Unacceptable

53. (57) Natural resources affect and are affected by the material welfare of a culture and directly or indirectly by philosophy, religion, government, and the arts.   3.58
   106 Essential _99_ Highly Desirable _72_ Desirable _47_ Satisfactory _9_ Unacceptable

54. (3) The natural environment is irreplaceable.   2.96
   185 Essential _50_ Highly Desirable _37_ Desirable _18_ Satisfactory _52_ Unacceptable

ADAPTATION AND EVOLUTION

55. (10) An organism is the product of its heredity and environment.   4.14
   188 Essential _67_ Highly Desirable _60_ Desirable _26_ Satisfactory _3_ Unacceptable

56. (12) Man is influenced by many of the same hereditary and environmental factors that affect other organisms and their populations.   3.80
   148 Essential _81_ Highly Desirable _74_ Desirable _35_ Satisfactory _8_ Unacceptable

57. (14) The rate of change in an environment may exceed the rate of organism adaptation.   3.76
   133 Essential 101 Highly Desirable _72_ Desirable _26_ Satisfactory _10_ Unacceptable

58. (16) Organisms and environments are in constant change.   3.56
   142 Essential _74_ Highly Desirable _75_ Desirable _37_ Satisfactory _16_ Unacceptable

59. (11) All living things, including man, are continually evolving.   3.49
   143 Essential _77_ Highly Desirable _68_ Desirable _40_ Satisfactory _19_ Unacceptable

60. (13) The form of life present depends upon the coincidence of the life needs and their availability in an environment.   3.25
   107 Essential _79_ Highly Desirable _83_ Desirable _43_ Satisfactory _21_ Unacceptable

61. (17) Biological systems are described as dynamic because the materials and energy involved are parts of continuous cycles; inorganic materials and energy become part of organic materials and are subsequently broken down into simpler substances and energy as a result of the operation of organic systems.   3.09
   108 Essential _66_ Highly Desirable _84_ Desirable _43_ Satisfactory _26_ Unacceptable

62. (40) Animal populations are renewable resources.   3.08
   _90_ Essential _84_ Highly Desirable _91_ Desirable _45_ Satisfactory _24_ Unacceptable

63. (19) Succession is the gradual and continuous replacement of one kind of plant or animal complex by another and is characterized by gradual changes in species composition.   3.03
   _68_ Essential _77_ Highly Desirable 103 Desirable _51_ Satisfactory _19_ Unacceptable

NATURAL RESOURCES

64. (37) Water supplies, both in quantity and quality are important to all levels of living.   4.39
   226 Essential _57_ Highly Desirable _40_ Desirable _13_ Satisfactory _3_ Unacceptable

65. (7) The earth and life on it are greatly affected by the atmosphere.   4.29
   213 Essential _62_ Highly Desirable _53_ Desirable _16_ Satisfactory _3_ Unacceptable

66. (35) Water is a reusable and transient resource, but the available quantity may be reduced or quality impaired.   4.17
   190 Essential _88_ Highly Desirable _34_ Desirable _22_ Satisfactory _6_ Unacceptable

67. (70) As populations increase competition for the use of water increases resulting in a need for establishing water use priorities.   4.13
   163 Essential 100 Highly Desirable _48_ Desirable _22_ Satisfactory _3_ Unacceptable

68. (36) The amount of precipitation that becomes available for use by man varies with topography, land use, and applied management practices.   3.52
   110 Essential _93_ Highly Desirable _81_ Desirable _41_ Satisfactory _12_ Unacceptable

(Minerals)

69. (31) Mineral conservation involves the utilization of all known methods of using the minerals of the earth's crust that will cause them to serve more people for a longer time.   3.27
   124 Essential _79_ Highly Desirable _78_ Desirable _35_ Satisfactory _25_ Unacceptable

70. (23) The nonrenewable resource base is considered finite.   3.27
   147 Essential _65_ Highly Desirable _61_ Desirable _27_ Satisfactory _34_ Unacceptable

71. (32) Soil is classified as a renewable resource, but, because it may take a few years to thousands of years to be "renewed," it is more practically termed a depletable resource.   2.94
   _95_ Essential _98_ Highly Desirable _57_ Desirable _59_ Satisfactory _31_ Unacceptable

72. (30) Minerals are nonrenewable resources   3. 87
    <u>106</u> Essential <u>66</u> Highly Desirable <u>80</u> Desirable <u>49</u> Satisfactory <u>34</u> Unacceptable

(Soil)

73. (33) Maintaining, improving, and in some cases restoring soil productivity is important to
    the welfare of people.   4. 25
    <u>179</u> Essential <u>101</u> Highly Desirable <u>46</u> Desirable <u>15</u> Satisfactory <u>2</u> Unacceptable

74. (27) Geological process is like erosion and deposition modify the landscape.   3. 61
    <u>122</u> Essential <u>62</u> Highly Desirable <u>98</u> Desirable <u>56</u> Satisfactory <u>5</u> Unacceptable

75. (34) Soil productivity can be maintained by utilizing known agronomic, mechanical,
    and chemical processes.   3. 51
    <u>111</u> Essential <u>96</u> Highly Desirable <u>83</u> Desirable <u>33</u> Satisfactory <u>14</u> Unacceptable

(Plants)

76. (39) Green plants are the ultimate sources of food, clothing, shelter, and energy in most societies.   3. 56
    <u>132</u> Essential <u>82</u> Highly Desirable <u>68</u> Desirable <u>39</u> Satisfactory <u>15</u> Unacceptable

77. (38) Plants are renewable resources.   3. 44
    <u>101</u> Essential <u>81</u> Highly Desirable <u>89</u> Desirable <u>55</u> Satisfactory <u>10</u> Unacceptable

78. (6) Energy is supplied to an ecosystem by the activities of green plants.   3. 36
    <u>127</u> Essential <u>69</u> Highly Desirable <u>66</u> Desirable <u>38</u> Satisfactory <u>21</u> Unacceptable

(Animals)

79. (48) Wildlife refuges, undisturbed natural areas, and preserves may be of value in
    protecting endangered species and perpetuating the gene pool.   3. 99
    <u>140</u> Essential <u>101</u> Highly Desirable <u>61</u> Desirable <u>33</u> Satisfactory <u>2</u> Unacceptable

80. (44) Wildlife populations are important economically, aesthetically, and biologically. 3. 69
    <u>129</u> Essential <u>93</u> Highly Desirable <u>74</u> Desirable <u>29</u> Satisfactory <u>11</u> Unacceptable

81. (41) Wildlife is considered to be a public resource.   3. 26
    <u>101</u> Essential <u>100</u> Highly Desirable <u>71</u> Desirable <u>40</u> Satisfactory <u>22</u> Unacceptable

THE SOCIO-CULTURAL ENVIRONMENT

82. (126) Man has responsibility to develop an appreciation of and respect for the rights of others.   4. 38
    <u>216</u> Essential <u>70</u> Highly Desirable <u>30</u> Desirable <u>20</u> Satisfactory <u>2</u> Unacceptable

83. (115) Individual citizens should be stimulated to become well informed about resource issues,
    problems, management procedures, and ecological principles.   4. 29
    <u>188</u> Essential <u>89</u> Highly Desirable <u>48</u> Desirable <u>15</u> Satisfactory <u>1</u> Unacceptable

84. (117) Conservation responsibilities should be shared by individuals, businesses and industries,
    special interest groups, and all levels of government and education.   4. 16
    <u>184</u> Essential <u>85</u> Highly Desirable <u>43</u> Desirable <u>17</u> Satisfactory <u>6</u> Unacceptable

85. (98) Man has moral responsibility for his environmental decisions.   3. 94
    <u>178</u> Essential <u>80</u> Highly Desirable <u>43</u> Desirable <u>24</u> Satisfactory <u>12</u> Unacceptable

86. (88) Knowledge of the social structures, institutions, and culture of a society must be
    brought to bear on environmental considerations.   3. 75
    <u>119</u> Essential <u>96</u> Highly Desirable <u>82</u> Desirable <u>24</u> Satisfactory <u>8</u> Unacceptable

87. (59) The relationships between man and the natural environment are mediated by his culture.   3. 65
    <u>94</u> Essential <u>97</u> Highly Desirable <u>101</u> Desirable <u>41</u> Satisfactory <u>3</u> Unacceptable

88. (104) Man is developing the technical and sociological knowledge needed to control population
    growth, modify environments, and alter resource use patterns.   3. 58
    <u>124</u> Essential <u>100</u> Highly Desirable <u>65</u> Desirable <u>33</u> Satisfactory <u>15</u> Unacceptable

89. (109) Social values and mores influence personal conservation behavior.   3. 34
    <u>86</u> Essential <u>104</u> Highly Desirable <u>85</u> Desirable <u>48</u> Satisfactory <u>14</u> Unacceptable

90. (108) Public opinion constitutes a control over the use of conservation practices.   3. 11
    <u>84</u> Essential <u>104</u> Highly Desirable <u>76</u> Desirable <u>48</u> Satisfactory <u>23</u> Unacceptable

91. (114) In a democracy, a basic theory is that increasing restrictions on resource allocation and
    use are imposed by the consent or insistence of the people.   2. 92
    <u>69</u> Essential <u>80</u> Highly Desirable <u>89</u> Desirable <u>68</u> Satisfactory <u>22</u> Unacceptable

CULTURE

92. (50) The culture of a group is its learned behavior in the form of customs, habits, attitudes,
    institutions, and lifeways that are transmitted to its progeny.   3. 49
    <u>116</u> Essential <u>82</u> Highly Desirable <u>70</u> Desirable <u>53</u> Satisfactory <u>12</u> Unacceptable

93. (51) Man has psychobiological and biosocial needs.   3. 27
    <u>111</u> Essential <u>68</u> Highly Desirable <u>68</u> Desirable <u>51</u> Satisfactory <u>19</u> Unacceptable

94. (95) Human resources include the physical and mental abilities with which man in endowed
    and the knowledge he has generated.   3. 26
    <u>102</u> Essential <u>75</u> Highly Desirable <u>94</u> Desirable <u>48</u> Satisfactory <u>18</u> Unacceptable

95. (106) Historically, cultures with high technological development have used more natural
    resources than those with lower levels of technological development.   2. 98
    <u>79</u> Essential <u>78</u> Highly Desirable <u>91</u> Desirable <u>57</u> Satisfactory <u>23</u> Unacceptable

POLITICS

96. (116) Individual citizens should be stimulated to become active in the political process.   3. 85
    <u>148</u> Essential <u>92</u> Highly Desirable <u>58</u> Desirable <u>34</u> Satisfactory <u>8</u> Unacceptable

97. (118) We have "legal" ownership of some resources like real estate and control over others during our lifetime, but ethically we are "stewards" rather than owners of the resource base.   3.75
   <u>159</u> Essential <u>81</u> Highly Desirable <u>49</u> Desirable <u>34</u> Satisfactory <u>14</u> Unacceptable

98. (92) Policies, including natural resource policies, came about as the result of interacting social processes: science and technology, government operations, private interests, and public attitudes.   3.51
   <u>110</u> Essential <u>92</u> Highly Desirable <u>74</u> Desirable <u>45</u> Satisfactory <u>12</u> Unacceptable

99. (110) Conservation policies are often the result of group action.   3.51
   <u>102</u> Essential <u>94</u> Highly Desirable <u>85</u> Desirable <u>46</u> Satisfactory <u>10</u> Unacceptable

100. (107) As populations increase and/or as resource supplies decrease, the freedom of the individual to use the resources as he wishes decreases irrespective of the form of government.   3.44
   <u>133</u> Essential <u>76</u> Highly Desirable <u>63</u> Desirable <u>37</u> Satisfactory <u>20</u> Unacceptable

THE FAMILY

101. (103) Family planning and the limiting of family size are important if overpopulation is to be avoided and a reasonable standard of living assured for successive generations.   3.88
   <u>200</u> Essential <u>70</u> Highly Desirable <u>29</u> Desirable <u>21</u> Satisfactory <u>19</u> Unacceptable

102. (123) The individual must develop his ability to perceive if he is to increase his awareness and develop environmental perspective.   3.63
   <u>117</u> Essential <u>75</u> Highly Desirable <u>85</u> Desirable <u>46</u> Satisfactory <u>7</u> Unacceptable

103. (89) Individuals perceive different self-roles depending upon their position in the social and environmental context.   2.99
   <u>66</u> Essential <u>73</u> Highly Desirable <u>92</u> Desirable <u>80</u> Satisfactory <u>16</u> Unacceptable

104. (101) Man has the capability of improving society through sociology, psychology, and science.   2.95
   <u>91</u> Essential <u>91</u> Highly Desirable <u>67</u> Desirable <u>57</u> Satisfactory <u>29</u> Unacceptable

105. (52) Man is a high animal form because of his ability to reason.   2.83
   <u>102</u> Essential <u>61</u> Highly Desirable <u>71</u> Desirable <u>67</u> Satisfactory <u>32</u> Unacceptable

106. (99) Man is continually developing an ethical base for making value judgments.   2.65
   <u>63</u> Essential <u>82</u> Highly Desirable <u>86</u> Desirable <u>58</u> Satisfactory <u>33</u> Unacceptable

107. (119) Man performs some tasks at a high physiological cost.   2.62
   <u>60</u> Essential <u>62</u> Highly Desirable <u>78</u> Desirable <u>84</u> Satisfactory <u>27</u> Unacceptable

PSYCHOLOGICAL ASPECTS

108. (125) Opportunities to experience and enjoy nature are psychologically rewarding to many and are important to mental health.   3.60
   <u>120</u> Essential <u>106</u> Highly Desirable <u>62</u> Desirable <u>36</u> Satisfactory <u>13</u> Unacceptable

109. (124) The need of man to turn inward for self renewal can be stimulated by his external esthetic experiences.   2.79
   <u>83</u> Essential <u>74</u> Highly Desirable <u>81</u> Desirable <u>58</u> Satisfactory <u>31</u> Unacceptable

110. (120) Resources have a psychological impact on people.   2.78
   <u>74</u> Essential <u>59</u> Highly Desirable <u>97</u> Desirable <u>67</u> Satisfactory <u>26</u> Unacceptable

111. (121) Emotional reactions can be elicited by exposure to physical objects and geometric forms.   2.54
   <u>55</u> Essential <u>55</u> Highly Desirable <u>88</u> Desirable <u>96</u> Satisfactory <u>27</u> Unacceptable

*Concept numbers correspond to enumeration used on the questionnaire.

possible causes for rejection on this basis follow:

Concept 15–culture is equated with biological diversity.

Concept 18–fails to clarify that energy transfer is a consequence of the metabolic efficiency of organisms involved.

Concept 21–does not adequately define the term "level."

Concept 24–an editorial error was responsible for the use of the term "substance" when the term "substitute" should have been used.

Concept 25–a contradiction exists between the phrase "rate of renewal" and the definition of the term "exhaustible."

Concept 43–individuals, population, and species are equated thus leading to confusion.

Concept 45–confusion exists in definition of the term "stockpiled."

Concept 46–confusion exists in definition of the term "stockpiled."

Concept 53–might be interpreted to be contradictory because of the usage assigned the terms "growth" and "constant."

Concept 54–confusion exists in definition of the terms "excessive" and "optimum."

Concept 55–definition of the terms "satisfactory" and "optimum" are obscure.

Concept 65–mineral resources are equated with the cultural pyramid.

Concept 77–production and benefits are equated.

Concept 94–contains a typographical error in that the terms "Man to" should have been used in place of the term "nor."

Concept 100–terminology used is poorly defined.

Concept 111–poor definition of terms leads to confusion.

Concept 112– the phrase "countervailing power structures" is not defined.

Comments in relation to the above concepts were often noted by the respondents indicating some of the above possible causes for rejection.

4. Rating of the concepts indicates an individual divergence of opinion and interpretation, but no clear

TABLE 5

CONCEPTS RATED AS "UNACCEPTABLE" BY 10 PERCENT OR MORE OF THE NATIONAL PANEL

Concept	Frequency	Percent
15. A diverse biological community or culture perpetuates diversity within the gene pool.	35	10.0
18. At each successively higher level of an energy pyramid, the organic mass is reduced due to metabolic and energy transfer losses occurring at each exchange.	35	10.0
21. The carrying capacity of an ecosystem is the level at which a population can be sustained at an acceptable level of nutrition.	37	10.6
24. The rate of use of a nonrenewable natural resource is dependent upon supply and demand, availability of substances, and technology.	35	10.0
25. The rate of renewal of an exhaustible natural resource is usually extremely slow.	46	13.1
43. A rapid turnover of individuals making up a population of most species exists whether or not the species are exploited.	47	13.4
45. Nonmigratory small game wildlife populations cannot be stockpiled; when hunting mortality replaces natural mortality—the resource is utilized.	53	15.1
46. Migratory wildlife populations can be stockpiled for short periods of time.	55	15.7
53. Man's biological life requirements for growth and development are relatively constant.	59	16.9
54. Reduction of environmental stresses from excessive to optimum levels results in a feeling of well being.	63	18.0
55. A satisfactory level of physical, psychological, and social health for man depends upon an optimum level of environmental stress.	58	16.6
65. Mineral resources form the base of the cultural pyramid.	93	26.6
77. An increase in input (capital, labor resources) will produce a proportionate increase in production or benefits up to a limit defined as the margin of diminishing returns.	47	13.4
94. Science does not cause nor become independent of the natural environment.	48	13.7
100. There are sensory prerequisites to the appreciation of the cultural heritage.	47	13.4
111. Government is the interaction of custom, rule, and law.	47	13.4
112. Decisions in society are made through the interaction of countervailing power structures.	36	10.3

bias is evident on the basis of either professional area or ecological region. It can therefore be suggested that the 111 acceptable concepts included in the taxonomic list are reasonably well agreed upon.

SUMMARY, IMPLICATIONS, RECOMMENDATIONS

Summary. Based upon the findings of this study it may be stated that:

1. Lists of concepts related to environmental management recommended for teaching in grades K-16 can be formed by utilizing practicing scholars from many disciplines.

2. Scholars representing 40 disciplines agree on the majority of concepts to be emphasized in environmental management education.

3. Academic bias does not appear to exist relative to concept preferences for inclusion in grades K-16.

4. Regional bias based upon ecological region does not appear to exist relative to concept preferences for inclusion in grades K-16.

5. The cause of the rejection of selected concepts appears to be due to communication failures.

Implications. 1. The concepts included in Table 4 may be used in curriculum planning for grades K-16.

2. The concepts included in Table 4 may be divided into subconcepts and related to indigenous educational conditions.

Recommendations. 1. A variety of methodologies should be used in teaching the concepts and subconcepts to assess the probabilities of success of each approach.

2. The concepts and subconcepts should be taught at a variety of grade levels and in a variety of ecological settings to determine if relationships exist between maturity and/or ecological settings and concept attainment.

3. The degree of essentiality of each concept in the Taxonomic List (Table 4) should be reevaluated periodically (e.g., every 5 years) to ensure that the concepts appropriate for environmental management education are pertinent.

REFERENCES

1. Baker, Frank, Test Analysis Package, Laboratory of Experimental Design, Department of Educational Psychology, The University of Wisconsin, Madison, Wisconsin, 1966.

2. Blanchet, Waldo E., "A Basis for the Selection of Course Content for Survey Courses in the Natural Sciences," unpublished PhD dissertation, University of Michigan, Ann Arbor, 1946.

3. Goodenough, Ward Hunt, Cooperation in Change: An Anthropological Approach to Community Development, John Wiley and Sons, Inc., New York, 1966.

4. Potter, Van R., "The Role of the Individual in Modern Society," in Robert B. Boyd (Ed.), Concepts of Productive Living, University Extension, Madison, Wisconsin, 1967.

5. Stapp, William B., and others, "The Concept of Environmental Education," Environmental Education, 1:30, 1969.

6. Transeau, E.N., "Vegetation Zones of North America," lecture, The Ohio State University, Columbus, 1948.

Fundamental concepts in action.

ENVIRONMENTAL EDUCATION: AN INTEGRATED APPROACH

David Archbald and Paul Gundlach

SEVERAL PAPERS in the Fall 1969 issue of this journal made two points abundantly clear. Environmental education must be both (1) pervasive and (2) integrated. Southern (4) states, "It is proposed herein that if the child acquires particular broad environmental understanding (knowledge) he will develop social conscience (attitudes) that will affect his behavior (actions) toward the total environment." Covert (2) asserts, "Therefore, it is proposed that an integrated, interdisciplinary, instructional program be developed in environmental education, designed to promote an environmental awareness and a sociological attitude."

Stapp (5) claims, "A strong understanding of how these resources are used requires knowledge of the social, political, economic, technological processes, institutional arrangements, and aesthetic considerations which govern their utilization."

These educators are precisely "on-target" as demonstrated by a word frequency count of Roth's (3) environmental educational concepts.[1] See Table 1.

Table 1 tells us loud and clear of the pervasive nature of the key concepts in environmental education. It is not simply contour plowing, white-tail deer management, the life cycle of plants, etc., traditionally known as conservation education, but the study of man and his total relationship to his environment, i. e., environmental education. A selection of key words from Table 1 indicating the diversity of disciplines that contribute to environmental education is visually presented in Figure 1.

It is manifest that educational curricula have not discussed man's relationship to his total environment in terms of energy flow, values, cultural, social, political, legal, and long range quality implications, i.e., in terms of Table 1 and Figure 1. This educational gap has resulted in a nation of socio-ecologic illiterates committing an unending series of ecological atrocities with little thought of long-term effect. Furthermore, this gap has contributed to an almost total lack of development of: (A) channels for intelligent environmental communication among society's

TABLE 1

FREQUENCY OF OCCURENCE OF KEY WORDS IN THE 112 MOST IMPORTANT OF ROTH'S (5) ENVIRONMENTAL EDUCATIONAL CONCEPTS

Frequency of occurence	Key Words
16 or more	Environment, Man, Populations, Resources, Use (Utilize)
11-15	Economic, Increase, Management, Natural Resources, Social, Technological
8-10	Conservation, Culture, Development, Individual, Knowledge, Life, Needs, Values
6-7	Affect, Change, Energy, Factors, Land, Natural (Nature), Processes, Produce (Productivity), Risks, Science, Water
5	Ability, Biological, Human, Levels, Long-Range, Minerals, Others, Plant, Policy, Political, Public, Quality, Society

present decisionmakers, and (B) sufficient pressure from the public for broad environmental action programs.

A second startling analysis of these key environmental concepts is that 44 of the 50 most important concepts, as ranked by the computer, can and should be introduced in the K-6 curriculum. The grade level determination was based upon the evaluation of 120 K-12 teachers. Obviously, however, these concepts once introduced must extend throughout the students' education.

To develop an integrated curriculum, the following steps are being pursued.

1. Key environmental concepts were graded by level: K-3, 4-6, 7-9, and 10-12.

2. Concepts were grouped by relationship, i. e., economic, culture, ecology, and management.

Dr. Archbald is Managing Director of The University of Wisconsin Arboretum and on the Executive Committee of the University of Wisconsin Center for Environmental Communications and Education Studies. Mr. Grundlach is Project Director of a Title III Elementary-Secondary Education Act Project in Conservation Education at Cooperative Educational Service Agency 12, Portage, Wisconsin.

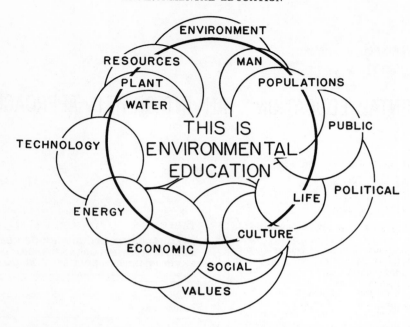

FIGURE   1. Key Words in Environmental Education Statistically Identified from the

112 Key Environmental Education Concepts   (See also Table 1.)

3. Teacher background and interpretive materials were developed for each concept.

4. A variety of student activities are being developed that are relevant and highly motivating and can be inductively taught.

5. The Quick-Key technique (1), a random access retrieval system will be used so the teacher can integrate the environmental curriculum into the existing school curriculum. That is, she will be able to identify in a few seconds, all the concepts and activities that relate to her subject and offer appropriate classroom and/or field activities at the level she teaches.

Preliminary field testing of the curriculum was conducted during the summer of 1969. This program was followed by a 2-week in-service program for 80 classroom teachers. The in-service program was designed to acquaint classroom teachers with the curriculum guide and familiarize them with the techniques of utilizing it during the 1969-70 school year. Based on their input, these 80 teachers are providing further refinement of the curriculum.

When materials are available, further details will be given in this journal.

FOOTNOTE

1. Roth's methodology, greatly simplified. He reviewed the literature for environmental concepts. Then he interviewed 80 University of Wisconsin scholars interested, or actively engaged in conservation and/or environmental

management education. They represented 40 disciplines including the sciences, humanities, and social studies. The concepts finally identified were then rated for relevancy to environmental education by a national panel of 699 scholars (50% response), corresponding to the same 40 disciplines as The University of Wisconsin scholars and representing 24 universities across the country. The results were computer analyzed which yielded a ranked order of 112 concepts from the most to the least important.

REFERENCES

1. Archbald, David, Quick-Key Guide to Trees (New York: Doubleday and Co., Inc. 1967).

2. Covert, Douglas C., "Toward A Curriculum in Environmental Education," Environmental Education, Vol. 1, No.1, (Fall 1969), p. 11.

3. Roth, Robert E., "Fundamental Concepts for Environmental Management Education (K-16), "Environmental Education, Vol. 1, No. 3 (Spring 1970), p. 65.

4. Southern, Beverly H., "Vitalizing Natural Resources Education," Environmental Education, Vol. 1, No. 1 (Fall 1969), p. 29.

5. Stapp, Wm. et al., "The Concept of Environmental Education," Environmental Education, Vol. 1, No. 1 (Fall 1969), p. 30.

WHAT'S NEW ABOUT ENVIRONMENTAL EDUCATION?

The Editor

Is there anything really new about <u>environmental education,</u> or is it simply conventional conservation education in a new bottle? Are we merely ''word-merchandising,'' or are we in fact creating new dimensions in ecological communications?

When these questions were put to a group of graduate students recently in The University of Wisconsin's Conservation Communications Program, the students were unanimous in the feeling that environmental education does indeed represent a significant new scale in the interpretation of man-land relationships. Asked then to define any changing concepts they perceive, the students developed a list of characteristics.

*   *   *   *   *   *   *

YESTERDAY   TODAY

Compartmentalized   Comprehensive

To a considerable degree, conservation education has been approached from single-resource orientations. ''We have had forest conservation, water conservation, soil conservation, wildlife conservation, and so on; what is more, each of these approaches has been institutionalized in various federal, state, and local instrumentalities of government or voluntary associations''(17). Environmental education tries to take a more encompassing view of man's environment. ''We are concerned with the total environment--its social, cultural, economic, and esthetic, as well as its physical and biological aspects. The development and management of this environment requires contributions by all the arts, sciences, and professions. The essential nature of environmental education looks toward research, teaching, and service arrangements that transcend traditional lines of endeavor and are concerned with the wholeness of the relationship between man and his surroundings'' (16). ''This need for an integrated approach to the problems of the human environment has become apparent to the various specialists in environmental management, and is being demanded from many quarters'' (7).

Parochial interests   Broader awareness

Yesterday's conservationist was generally satisfied with limited concerns. Today we increasingly sense, for example, the connection between overpopulation in India and drained duck marshes in the Dakotas. ''We are after the best possible living standard for every individual'' (1). ''Conservation is the recognition by man of his interdependence with his environment and with life everywhere'' (2). ''The conservationist was once involved mostly with the natural world and the rural scenes. Today conservation has necessarily become broader'' (6). ''Our concern must not be limited to stewardship of farmlands, or game management, or scouting skills. We must help the individual see himself as a part of a vast living ecosystem. Much of the customary conservation education and nature instruction has been narrowly concerned or directed to limited groups. Our concern should be to bring to all people the fullest realization of the life beyond self'' (14).

Local   Global

Put another way, environmental education does not stop at the boundaries of a state or the ocean edge. ''Resource problems are a national concern; at the local level they frequently are obscured and fragmented by provincial issues and politics'' (1). ''Today we know that the world we live in is one biosphere and, unless we take a global view of environmental problems, our chances for survival are slim'' (6). Witness, for example, ''The Unforeseen International Ecological Boomerang,'' in the February 1969 issue of <u>Natural History</u>. ''No man is an island, and no creature of any kind is independent of its habitat. Changes cannot take place in one part of the complex web of life without affecting the whole. Every proposed human change in the environment must be considered for its total effects. Ignorance of the long-term indirect consequences of human activities is the root of the contemporary crisis'' (13).

YESTERDAY   TODAY

Rural   Urban

Whereas yesterday's conservation was generally oriented to open-country people and problems, environmental education includes megalopolis in its circumference. "The attention of the conservationist was mainly directed toward the towns and cities where people were concentrated; now cities have become focal points of our concern for a threatened decline in the quality of human life" (7). "We can no longer be satisfied with the 'outdoorsy' orientation of conservation education; we must face the changing nature of our population" (3). "Our approach must be broad-based and relevant particularly to urban societies" (20). "The urban citizen is concerned with conservation in his own environment--population shifts, traffic congestion, and the decay of cities, and these aspects of the total environment are just as important to man as forestry or agriculture" (3).

Appended rationales   Indigenous concern

The first waves of conservation activities had to be linked for their support to regional economic development, depression pump-priming, or national defense. Today's concern for a sanative environment is salable on its own merits. "The frequent justification of conservation was in terms of patriotism, prosperity, national strength or greatness, democracy, and efficiency. But increasing numbers of Americans take the position that land health and beauty are desirable ends in themselves" (11).

Evangelical   Ecological

The emotional overtones of yesterday's conservation literature are giving way to a more profound approach. There is developing "a scientific discipline concerned with the relationship of humanity to the total environment" (1). "Environmental education presents conservation as a realistic, practical, and far-sighted public policy worthy of concern by an informed electorate" (20). "Environmental conservation is the effort to do something about problems that arise out of conflict between man's need and capacity to engineer his environment for economic use, and the need and capacity of natural systems to adjust to the consequences" (9).

Resource-centered   Man-centered

Yesterday's concern was often for the denizens of field and forest. Today the implications for human health are increasingly our touchstone. "Conservation means not only the protection and management of natural resources but also the maintenance of sanity in the human environment" (19). "A concern for keeping the world a fit place for people is the basis for conservation today" (7). "Environmental education deals comprehensively with both human resources and natural resources and their relationship to each other" (5). "It is possible, of course, to study the physical nature and the biological characteristics of the environment on an infra-human basis, but the emphasis in environmental education is on the study of man as he affects and is affected by his environment, for good or ill" (18). "The study of ecology leads conservation away from a preoccupation with resources per se and toward a consideration of man's fitness to the whole environment" (29).

Terrestrial   Universal

Oceans of water and air have joined the land as components of the biosphere in popular understanding. "It was possible 10 years ago for a text on conservation to give minor space to the problem of pollution of water and none to pollution of air. It is no longer possible" (6).

Biophysical sciences   Social studies

"Conservation is shifting from natural science theory to social science practice" (12). What is implied in environmental education is the broadest approach possible, going beyond the bounds of the typical science course. "As conservation becomes more man-environment oriented, it begins to occur more frequently in social studies curricula" (20). "Curricula must provide our people with an understanding of how man controls, transforms, uses wisely, preserves, or destroys his world, or how he is dependent upon it" (2). "The present basis of relating academic study of natural science to a limited natural ecology without considering man's influence is no longer adequate. The total environment of man and all the impinging factors of interaction are of far greater significance"(3).

Gospel of efficiency   Quest for quality

"The essence of yesterday's conservation was rational planning to provide efficient development of natural resources" (10). Today the basic issue in resource conservation is not quantity but quality. Conservation has become at least as much a matter of ethics and esthetics as economics (18). "Frequently a conservation issue reduces to the question of whether the nation, with all its well-known material abilities and appetites, also possesses an esthetic and spiritual sense" (10).

YESTERDAY   TODAY

The classic Governor's Conference of 1908 called for "conserving the resource foundations of our prosperity." Today's semantics, at least, are different: "Our conservation challenge today is one of quality--purity of surroundings, and opportunity to stretch, a chance for solitude, for quiet reflection" (21). "The ability to perceive beauty may, in the long run, prove man's salvation" (13).

Technical impetus   Public involvement

Where an association for the advancement of science may have energized conservation at the turn of the century, leagues of women voters carry it forward today. "Conservation did not arise from a broad popular outcry; conservation, above all, was a scientific movement. Conservation views did not arise from widely held assumptions and values. They came from a limited group of people with a particular set of goals who played a special role in society" (10). Today millions of Americans are expressing a deep concern about the management of their environment. As a Los Angeles business executive recently said, "I don't see how anybody can avoid getting on the conservation bandwagon."

Unilateral solutions   Open-ended options

Under environmental education we are taking a hard look at single-purpose practices with spill-over effects. "Unplanned consequences of man-induced change have coalesced to create an extra-ordinary crisis" (13). "Conservationists have often failed to offer valid alternatives to environmental destruction" (8). We are now concerned with "the development of open-ended solutions for environmental problems, rather than short-term approaches that may actually degrade the environment" (18). "In essence, we are coming to address ourselves to laying a basis for rational actions, to elucidating the choices in land and water use and relating them to general values and social objectives, to instilling in people a desire for construtive change, and to providing practical guidelines characterized by integrated approaches" (18).

Elementary education   Adult education

While interest in incorporating conservation lessons into school curricula has not abated, there is increasing attention to building adult awareness and action. We sense that the urgency of need will not be met through educational processes of normal pace and dispersion at the school level. "There is a special need for adult education programs in which new insights will be gained into the multidisciplinary character of resource problem-solving" (4).

Print media   All media

The audio-visual media are coming into their own as conveyors of the conservation messages. "An effective opportunity to reach larger segments of the public lies in media and television broadcasts. They are being used increasingly by public agencies as a more available and more attractive medium than the printed word for reaching a larger number of people more frequently" (5).

Hunch   Research

Conservation education and communications have been lacking in compelling theories of content and methodology. Classroom techniques and mass media approaches have all too frequently been combinations of hunch, old wives' tales, and soft soap. Now we are beginning to engage in deep-digging research that will inquire profoundly into public conservation attitudes and how they are formed, into unifying concepts fundamental to ecological understanding, into innovative pedagogy, into media avenues to the new conservation publics, and into effective themes and methods of public persuasion. "Various elements of the interpretive effort are now accepted areas of research in colleges and universities" (19). "Much research is needed to determine how best to improve the quantity and quality of the material presented" (5).

Business as usual   Sense of urgency

Twenty years ago conservation was characterized as "a sissy, with ruffled pantalettes, a May basket in her hand, and a yellow ribbon in her hair." Today a United Nations resolution addresses itself to the "environment crisis." "Man is the agent of this ecological crisis. Because of it he is at risk. Man indeed now holds his destiny in his own hands" (15). "We have a vital problem in communication. The message concerns the greatest challenge with which mankind has yet to deal" (1).

*   *   *   *   *   *   *

Some of these characteristics may be over-stated for effect. Some are more significant than others. Some might be deleted and others added. As a working outline, however, this list of old and new outlooks in conservation may serve to stimulate discussion and definition of the emerging content, clientele, and techniques of environmental education.

REFERENCES

1. Allen, Durward, "Needed: Citizen Conservation-ists," Environmental Education, Spring, 1970.

2. Brennan, Matthew J., "Toward a Course Content Improvement," Environmental Education, Fall, 1969, pp. 5-7.

3. Covert, Douglas, "Toward a Curriculum in En-vironmental Education," Environmental Edu-cation, Fall, 1969, pp. 11-12.

4. Dambach, Charles A., "Conservation through Adult Education," Environmental Education, Spring, 1970.

5. Dana, Samuel T., "Strengthening Environmental Education," Environmental Education, Fall, 1969, pp. 13-14.

6. Dasmann, Raymond F., "An Environment Fit for People: The New Meaning of Conservation," Environmental Education, Fall, 1969, pp. 15-16.

7. Dasmann, Raymond F., "Frontiers in Environ-mental Conservation," Environmental Educa-tion, Winter, 1969.

8. Hansen, Roger P., "How to Win Conservation Battles," Environmental Education, Spring, 1970.

9. Harrison, Gordon, "The Ecological View," Environmental Education, Fall, 1969, pp. 19-20.

10. Hays, Samuel P., Conservation and the Gospel of Efficiency (Cambridge, Massachusetts: Harvard University Press, 1959), p. 2.

11. Nash, Roderick, "The American and His En-vironment," Environmental Education, Winter, 1969.

12. Parson, Ruben L., "Conservation in Transition," Environmental Education, Fall, 1969, pp. 25-26

13. President's Council on Recreation and Natural Beauty, "A Report of the American Environment," Environmental Education, Fall, 1969, pp. 27-28.

14. Replinger, Mrs. J. Sanford, "The Preparation of the Interpretive Naturalist," Environmental Education, Spring, 1970.

15. Sargent, Frederick, "Informed Forces for En-vironmental Quality," Environmental Education, Spring, 1970.

16. Schoenfeld, Clarence A. "Environmental Edu-cation and the University," Educational Record, Summer 1968, pp. 309-310.

17. Schoenfeld, Clay, "Educating the Public in Nat-ural Resources," Journal of Soil and Water Con-servation, November-December, 1968, p. 31.

18. Schoenfeld, Clarence A., "The What and Why of Environmental Studies," Environmental Ed-ucation, Winter, 1969.

19. Shomon, Joseph J., "Interpretive Research," Environmental Education, Winter, 1969.

20. Southern, Beverly H., "Vitalizing Natural Re-sources Education," Environmental Education, Fall, 1969, p. 30.

21. Udall, Stewart, The Population Challenge, (Washington, D. C.: Conservation Yearbook No. 2, U. S. Department of Interior, 1966), p. 80.

III   *The Schools Encompass Environmental Education*

I N THE past, our schools have been asked to support a series of national goals—the melting pot, prosperity, depression pump-priming, national defense, the conquest of space, and so on. Today's mission is nothing less than human survival. To do something about environmental conservation, redevelopment,
and maintenance requires a sense of husbandry, a sense of responsibility on the part of every American citizen—
that man-land ethic or "ecological conscience" which Aldo Leopold bespoke. It is unthinking people who pollute
the environment; it is thinking people who can effect a "new conservation": to restore as well as to protect, to
bring beauty to the cities as well as to keep it in the countryside, to handle the waste products of technology as
well as the waste of natural resources, to halt the massive deterioration in the American environment.

We are talking then, about environmental education: a recognition by man of his interdependence with his
environment and all of life, and his responsibility for developing a culture which maintains that r e l a t i o n s h i p
through policies and practices necessary to secure the future of an environment fit for life and fit for living.

In the schools we are at the point where education in the physical sciences was 125 years ago, when scientists were debating whether a course in physics would be useful or whether it would be just as feasible to continue work in natural philosophy. We are at the point where a program in environmental management needs organization. Such a program should deal broadly with the development of a conservation literacy, aimed at contributing to a general knowledge of resource management science, t e c h n o l o g y, h i s t o r y, organization, and
philosophy, and to a basic understanding of current issues and problems calling for intelligent citizen decisions.
We are turning out too many engineers that are ecologically ignorant and esthetically insensitive, and too many
biologists that are sociologically and economically naive. Our major goal should be to help pupils develop broad
ideas and concepts useful in approaching resource problems. If anything, the program should emphasize that resource management issues are not simple and the answers not easy; yet, that in the absence of a concensus on
definitions and viewpoints, the educated man has a particular obligation to confront the problems involved w i t h
all the ecological facts and ethical considerations he can bring to bear.

It is clear that the content of environmental education is qualitatively different than the content of the older
conservation education. The confirming research was conducted by Dr. Robert Roth in his PhD thesis under the
supervision of Prof. Milton Pella of the University of Wisconsin School of Education. It is hard to overempha-
size the contribution of this research to meaningful environmental education. Greatly simplified, Roth's methodology was as follows: He reviewed the literature for environmental concepts. Then he interviewed eighty University of Wisconsin scholars interested or actively engaged i n conservation and/or environmental education.
They represented forty disciplines, including the sciences, humanities, and social studies. The concepts finally
identified then were rated for relevancy to environmental education by a national panel of 350 scholars c o r r e -
sponding to the same forty disciplines as the University scholars and representing twenty-four universities across
the country. The results were computer-analyzed, yielding a ranked order of 112 concepts, from the most to the
least important.

Upon further analysis of the 112 concepts, several things were especially revealing. First, a count of the
words most frequently used clearly showed the breadth, or interdisciplinary nature, demanded in environmental
management. Consider how broad a spectrum is covered by some of the most frequently used words in t h e s e
key concepts: environment, man, population, resources, economic, social, culture, individual, life, n e e d s, v a l u e s,
long-range, political, public, quality, and society. The point is clear. Environemental management is NOT simply
contour plowing, white-tail deer management, and life cycles of plants. That is, it is not the narrow focus traditionally
labeled conservation. Instead, environmental management is of the broadest scope in that it requires an understanding of man and his total relationship to his environment.

The second startling revelation from analysis of these key environmental concepts is t h a t forty-four of
the fifty most important concepts, as ranked by the computer, can and should be introduced i n the kindergarten
through sixth-grade curriculum. The grade level determination was based upon the evaluation of 120 kindergarten through twelfth-grade teachers. Obviously, however, these concepts once introduced must extend throughout
the student's education. It is manifest that educational curricula have not discussed man's relationship to his total environment in terms of energy flow, values, cultural, social, political, legal, and long-range quality implications. Nor have we provided any significant environmental instruction at the kindergarten through sixth-grade

level. These educational gaps have resulted in a nation of socio-ecologic illiterates committing an unending series of ecological atrocities with little thought of long-term effect. Furthermore, these gaps have contributed to an almost total lack of communication among society's present decision-makers, and insufficient pressure from the public for broad environmental action programs, says Dr. David Archbald.

Some of the more pertinent problems identified by William Stapp in the path of a successful national effort directed toward environmental education for youth through instructional programs (K-12) are a general lack of: (1) a coherent philosophy of environmental education among leaders in the field of conservation education; (2) teacher interest and background in environmental education; (3) school administrators dedicated to environmental educational programs for school systems; (4) existing programs that focus on environmental education; (5) well-conceived instructional material directed toward environmental education; (6) textbook orientation to environmental education; (7) individuals trained to serve as environmental educational consultants for school systems; (8) collegiate programs that provide adequate training in environmental education; (9) citizen concern in environmental education; (10) national, state, and local leadership in environmental education; (11) coordination among private and public conservation organizations; (12) a continuing information system directed toward environmental education.

Yet all is not black. We are beginning to make progress. This chapter presents clear evidence from around the country that our nation's schools are beginning to encompass environmental education policies and practices. ■

Environmental education programs and *opportunities through the U.S. Office of Education.*

NEW HORIZONS FOR ENVIRONMENTAL EDUCATION

Wilhelmina Hill and Roy C. White

AS MAN REACHES out into space, probes the depths of the ocean, and tries to renew the environment for living in its cities, environmental education is reaching for new dimensions. The improvement of the quality of man's surroundings, reduction of pollution, and accomodation to population increases and problems require studies in depth. A high priority is essential for educational programs that deal with new developments and problems related to man and the new technology.

Quality control of the environment is one of the basic needs of mankind. Preservation and enhancement of our natural resources go hand in hand with resource use developments that will benefit people. Survival on this planet is dependent upon man's willingness to cope with these problems.

Some of the most serious pollution problems with which we are now faced are in the areas of air pollution, noise, water pollution, and landscape desecration. Due to technology and population increases, some of these kinds of pollution are becoming extremely serious and difficult or impossible to control.

When 20th century man ventures into space, lands on the moon, or explores the ocean resources, he must cope with new environmental conditions and problems. Wherever people have clustered into urban centers, large or small, environmental problems have been encountered. And these people represent approximately three-fourths of the population in our country.

The new environmental education is resulting from the crucial needs and problems of man in relation to his environment. It is people centered and includes urban as well as rural areas. Natural resources—their uses, preservation, and enhancement—are considered in their relationship to people.

School children as well as adults require many opportunities to become aware of such natural resources as forests, lakes, or swamps. Outdoor education centers, such as the one at High Rock on Staten Island, New York, offer opportunities for children of New York City to visit a nature area with the guidance of naturalists. At such a center, inner city children often see many birds and animals other than the pigeons, starlings, and sparrows or even rats that inhabit their home nieghborhoods. One little girl reported, "this is the first time I've seen all the way around a horse." From first-hand knowledge and experience, children may gain not only knowledge but appreciation of their natural resources.

Responsibility for improvement of the environment and for attaining real action may often be learned effectively through actual experiences. Through participation in school ground and neighborhood conservation or beautification projects, children learn skills and develop interests in environmental improvement. Conservation then can become a way of life.

A striking illustration of pupil participation in conservation was carried out in the Shore and Marine Environmental Program at the Sandy Hook State Park in New Jersey. Among other activities, the children planted large numbers of used Christmas trees from New York City along the barrier beach. The trees were planted at such an angle as to catch sand and start the building of sand dunes. The project director, Richard Cole, reports that during a recent storm the part of the beach where the trees were planted withstood the wind and waves best.

Environmental pollution problems may be studied entirely through the use of textbook or lecture methods. Not so in the classes of Dr. Phyllis Busch of Project Spruce at Pine Planes, New York. When providing instruction about air pollution in inner city classrooms of mid-Hudson New York State, she takes the children into the streets and city squares. There they note the degree and types of air pollution, take samples on moist blotters or cloth, observe the sources of pollution, and consider ways in which it

Dr. Hill is Coordinator for Environmental Education, U. S. Office of Education. Dr. White is an Office of Education Fellow who was on leave from the University of Montana, Missoula, until last June 30.

The floating
laboratory ship
Fury II leaves
daily from
Newport Beach Harbor
on Balboa Island.

could be controlled or reduced. On rainy days the sampling may be made by similar methods on window sills. Every child has a role to play in these problem solving activities. In such discovery methods of learning, textbooks, reference books, magazines, films, television, and many other media are used as appropriate for the learners. The teacher's contributions are of value. However, the pupil is central, and the out-of-door resources, teachers, and communication media are the means to help him learn about the natural environment and his relationship to it.

Oceanography and marine science are meriting increased attention by students. The ocean world—its resources and its problems—is being probed as never before as a source of food, minerals, water, and energy. While students study the ocean, management problems related to uses and pollution are increasing.

Orange County children of California have been learning about the ocean's characteristics, resources, and pollution problems through an oceanography center at Santa Ana. The floating laboratory ship, Fury II, leaves Newport Beach harbor at Balboa Island daily with groups of 30 or 40 children and their teachers. The junior high school groups have 4-hour and the senior high 8-hour cruises. They divide into six or seven groups to study and record findings about plankton, water temperatures at various depths, sea birds, seals, types of pollution carried by the tides, and kinds of things netted from the ocean floor. Some of their findings are recorded and reported daily to science people in the area as valuable information.

A training project is being carried out on a vessel anchored in the Washington, D.C. area. Here 120 unemployed, disadvantaged young people are being given training to prepare them as oceanographic aides. This project is sponsored by the U.S. Office of Education under the Manpower Development and Training Act.

Approximately 15 oceanography and marine science centers have been funded through Title III of the Elementary and Secondary Education Act. They are helping many school systems develop new or improved education programs in this rapidly developing resource area from the oceans of the world.

In the bureau of Higher Education, fellowships have been and are being awarded in the support of graduate studies in Oceanography and Marine Science. Last year approximately 49 fellowships were awarded in this field.

As an outcome of the increased focus on environmental education, some curriculum guides have been produced or are in the process of development. The State departments of education of South Carolina, Louisiana, and Colorado are among those which have published such guides.

The ecological approach to environmental education is believed to hold considerable promise. Some progress in this direction has been made by an experimental planning project in the Arlington and Alexandria, Virginia public schools. Outstanding ecologists from the Smithsonian Institution and local universities have been working with the school people on this project.

Concept development is important in environmental as well as other curriculum areas. Various forms of generalized knowledge have greater significance and more likelihood of retention by the learner than factual knowledge only. These concepts and generalizations can be designed to run through the environmental curriculum as threads or strands in a more or less spiral order.

People concerned with various aspects of environmental education have been identifying and publishing basic concepts and understandings which could be useful in curriculum development. A special issue of the Grade Teacher on ecology contains one article that identifies four basic ecological concepts as well as other materials gleaned from outdoor education programs in Minnesota, Missouri, Idaho, and Connecticut. A fairly recent doctoral dissertation at the University of Montana (by one of the authors of this article) presents a comprehensive treatment of "conservation understandings associated with community resources."

In concept development, it is well to keep in mind

that one cannot teach concepts to people. Concepts develop within the individual as the result of his educational experiences.

Curriculum workers are as much concerned with human society and the quality of our environment as with the use of natural resources. As technology increases in sophistication, there is an apparent decrease in the quality of our environment. No longer can conservation education be concerned only with problems relevant to the proper use of natural resources. It must also become more concerned with social and health problems resulting from a rapidly increasing population and from an affluent society.

The educational community can, and must, provide action oriented programs of environmental education for young people. The students of today must become more cognizant of the consequences they will face tomorrow if the environment is allowed to become more polluted and the quality of the environment is allowed to deteriorate further.

Since all people are affected by their environment, it seems essential that all people become more aware of their environment and their relation with it. Therefore, environmental education does not lend itself only to a single subject, but may be incorporated into the total curriculum. It is important however that this incorporation into the total curriculum not place the teaching of environmental education in a subordinate position, as has sometimes happened in the past.

Many subject areas offer opportunities for the integration of environmental educational concepts. However, to accomplish this effectively, consideration must be given to another aspect of the educational spectrum, that is to teacher education.

At the present time many colleges and universities have courses related to environmental education available for teachers, or other students. Few of these institutions require or recommend that these courses be studied by prospective teachers. If we are to have young people educated about the relationship of man with his environment, we need classroom teachers who are somewhat knowledgeable about concepts of human ecology. To accomplish this goal, colleges and universities should accept the challenge of improving their curricula in environmental education. This could be done by providing expanded and improved programs in environmental education and requiring that some courses in this field be studied by all prospective teachers, along with expanded summer programs for experienced teachers.

Through the Education Professions Development Act, funds have been made available for proposals related to the education of teachers, including the area of conservation and evnironmental studies. Universities, states, and local school systems may apply for financial aid through this act. Fellowship programs, both at prospective and experienced teacher levels, provide an opportunity for full-time educational programs in a variety of fields, including those closely related to environmental education.

One Experienced Teacher Fellowship Program in Outdoor Education and Conservation was held in New Jersey. Currently a Prospective Teacher Fellowship Program in the same field, leading to a Master of Arts Degree, is being carried out through four cooperating institutions: Trenton State College, Glassboro State College, Montclair State College, and the New Jersey State School of Conservation.

The momentum thus far gained for contemporary environmental education cannot be increased only through curriculum development and teacher education. There is still another facet of the educational community that must be considered before a comprehensive environmental education program can become fully operational. The schools in a community usually reflect the educational philosophy of that community. If this is a valid assumption, we need to alert parents and other residents of a community about the urgent need for including environmental education in the school curriculum. School administrators, school governing bodies, and parents must support the environmental education program if it is to be effective. Unfortunately, community support for environmental education is sometimes lacking.

Many community resources can be incorporated into an environmental education program. Resources such as people, places, and things are available in all communities and if properly utilized can enhance the curriculum. Resource people residing in the school community may be available—and willing—to assist teachers and administrators with their environmental education program. Persons knowledgeable about conservation may be enlisted to serve as classroom visitors or assist with trips to natural areas. Thus, two kinds of community resources—people and field study sites—could be included in environmental programs.

Some outdoor education projects currently receive assistance from employees of state and national conservation agencies. These personnel may be employed by fish and game departments, state and national forests and parks, and public health agencies. College and university professors may also be available to assist with local environmental studies. Each community could identify available resource personnel for its geographic area.

Field study sites may be in a wide variety of areas, school grounds being the most accessible. Much study of the students' environment can be undertaken on the local school grounds and surrounding neighborhood. These areas, where available, should be used as extensively as possible.

In many environmental education programs, field study sites, whether large or small, are selected away from the school. Some schools take their students to national parks and forests, while others go to local parks, lakes, or vacant lots within the community. The students may stay at these field study sites for a few hours to a full week, or longer. Seasonal changes in the environment are observed by students in some programs as sites are visited several times in a school year.

Some programs involve the students during several weeks of the summer. The Summer Ecology Program at Deer Lodge, Montana, provides the opportunity for Powell County High School students to study ecology for 4 weeks in the out-of-doors. The students in the summer outdoor education program

←   Student activities at "Land Between the Lakes."

at Cedar Rapids, Iowa, have continuing classroom activities during the following school year.

Some programs furnish children the opportunity to live in an outdoor area for several continuous days. Such experiences are provided for students near Golden Pond, Kentucky, at "Land Between the Lakes." Other students from Marshfield, Wisconsin; Alberton, Montana; and North Bend, Washington, also live at outdoor camps for several days at a time.

Other environmental education programs limit the field experiences for children to short visits to outdoor sites, or to several visits to the same area during the school term. This type of program can be observed at Media, Pennsylvania; Newark, Delaware; and Missoula, Montana.

The variety of outdoor education programs reflects the philosophies of the communities and indicates the resources available within communities. It is encouraging to observe that many schools are providing diverse opportunities for their students to gain experiences related to their environment. It is also obvious that many schools are utilizing resources within the community to enhance their environmental education programs.

The U.S. Office of Education provides a wide variety of services and administers fiscal aid assigned to it through federal aid legislation. A good many of these programs are available for environmental education. Some have been used for developing a substantial number of conservation/environmental projects. The resources of others are just beginning to be applied to this rapidly developing field.

Title I, of the Elementary and Secondary Education Act is the Nation's largest Federal aid-to-education program. Each year since 1965-66 more than $1 billion has gone to serve underachievers from low-income families. More than 16,000 of the Nation's school districts participate.

Because of Title I, ESEA, many children who have never before had an opportunity to walk in a forest or see wildlife in its natural habitat are now having these experiences. Dozens of camping facilities are operating all year round, serving children from low-income families from the impoverished areas of the inner cities. Hundreds more operate during the summertime. There are nature and conservation camps, day camps, sleep-away camps, laboratories and science camps operating throughout the country with the support of Title I, ESEA.

In addition, during warm weather, some classes are also held outdoors—in places like Tiffin and Springfield, Ohio; Memphis, Tennessee; and Garrett, Maryland.

The outdoor camping programs are, generally, operated by local school districts—from Los Angeles and Seattle, to Detroit and New York City. In addition to the camps there are mobile science laboratories through which students are exposed to those areas of science which can be most directly related to their environment—marine biology, astronomy, and earth science. A typical project of this type serves the island, Martha's Vineyard.

Title III, ESEA, which funds innovative center projects, has made possible the funding of approximately 110 outdoor education projects. These have included such varied projects as the Oceanographic Education Center at Falmouth, Massachusetts; Suffolk Environmental Biology Center, Port Jefferson, New York; the Conservation and Environmental Science Center for Southern New Jersey at Browns Mills; the Program of Outdoor Education for southern Idaho (office at American Falls), the Napa Experimental Forest education center in California; an ecological oriented conservation project at Missoula, Montana, which includes habitat improvement; and Project Introspection, dealing with the cultural, historical, and natural resources of the Virgin Islands.

Over a period of 3 years, Title I of the Higher Education Act has provided funds for over 150 programs in areas of environmental education, including planning, beautification, land use, and conservation. These grants are available for community services and continuing education projects through designated State agencies and are to utilize the resources of colleges and universities to help solve problems relating to the quality of the environment.

Other Office of Education programs which have environmental education aspects or opportunities include:

Elementary and Secondary Education Act, Titles II, V, and VIII

Bureau of Research (especially Small Projects of the Regional Research Program)

Health, Physical Education, and Recreation program (Bureau of Elementary and Secondary Education)

Manpower Development and Training Act

Office of Construction Services ∎

"Conservation education in California: A progress report."

TOWARD AN ENVIRONMENTAL ETHIC

Rudolph J. H. Schafer

A FAVORED technique for encouraging a horse or mule to greater efforts is to dangle a juicy carrot before him just out of reach of his ever-advancing jaws. The current situation in conservation education in California might well be described by using this homely illustration. We have made, and are making, many significant advances but at the same time, our environmental problems are increasing at such a rate that much of what we accomplish may soon be negated.

Even though we recognize that no matter how hard we run, that carrot will probably always be just out of reach, we can take some satisfaction in out accomplishments to date as we redouble our efforts toward bringing about the day when all people will recognize their personal responsibility for caring for our environment and its resources and will be willing and able to take the action necessary to preserve and enhance them.

Perhaps the most important reason for the progress we have made to date in California is the growing interest and concern on the part of the general public in environmental problems and the role education must play in solving them. Organizations such as California Tomorrow, the Sierra Club, California Conservation Council, Audubon Society, California Parent Teachers Association as well as resource oriented federal and state agencies and responsible elements of the business community have been largely responsible for this growing public awareness and concern.

It might well be said that the modern age in conservation education in California began officially in March of 1966 with the State Senate Joint Education and Natural Resources Committee hearings on the subject "A Program of Conservation Education for the Department of Education." Prior to this time, conservation was a permissive subject in the schools of the State and minimal leadership and assistance was supplied to local school districts by the Department of Education and the California Resources Agency. Hugo Fisher, former administrator of the Resources Agency, had as far back as 1963, urged the Department of Education to take a more active role of leadership in the conservation education field, but for lack of funds and personnel, this was not done. The only legal requirement for conservation instruction in the schools was that "Conservation, Bird, and Arbor Day" was to be observed each year with appropriate educational activities.

Despite this official lack of interest, some good programs were under way in several local school districts throughout the State. San Diego City and County Schools, for example, established a resident outdoor school in 1948 enabling most of their sixth graders to participate in a week-long environmental education program. Long Beach City and Los Angeles City established similar programs and many districts made an effort to include some conservation instruction in the fourth-grade-California studies unit. The overall picture, however, was not too encouraging.

At the 1966 Senate hearings the status of conservation education in California was studies in detail, and it was determined that, despite the few bright spots noted, the statewide situation was far from satisfactory. A program of improvement with more effective statewide leadership by the Department of Education was recommended.

As an outgrowth of the Senate hearings, a planning conference was held at Asiolomar Conference Center near Monterey, California, July 9-11, 1966. Staff personnel from the Senate Committees, legislators, educators, conservationists, and industry representatives were invited. Plans and programs designed to improve and encourage conservation education in the Golden State were discussed, and a report containing basic recommendations was issued.

In May, 1967, the State Board of Education activated an advisory committee consisting of representatives of industry, government, education, and private conservation agencies to study in detail the problems identified by the Senate Committee and the Asilomar Conference and to make specific recommendations for solving them. In its Charge to the Committee, the State Board of Education requested that these specific areas, among others, be studied in detail:

1. Teacher training both at the undergraduate and inservice levels.
2. Cooperation with governmental, industrial, and private organizations in providing worthwhile printed materials, films, field trips, and other resources for teacher and student use.
3. The conservation content of State adopted texts.
4. The role of the State Department of Education and the Resources Agency in Conservation Education.
5. The possibility of establishing pilot conservation education programs at various locations in the State.

On July 5, 1967, Dr. Max Rafferty, State Superintendent of Public Instruction and Mr. Norman Livermore, Jr., Administrator of the State Resources Agency issued a joint statement of conservation education. In this statement Mr. Livermore and Dr. Rafferty agreed to pool the resources of their respective organizations under the leadership of the Department of Education in an effort to provide the best possible program of conservation for the public schools of California.

In October, 1967, Rudolph J.H. Schafer, at the time, Conservation Education Specialist with the Los Angeles City Schools, was appointed project coordinator to work full time with the Conservation Education Advisory Committee and to serve as Conservation Education Consultant to the State Department of Education. Mr. Schafer assumed his duties in Sacramento on January 2, 1968. Funds for committee operations and staff personnel were supplied by a federal grant under the terms of the Elementary and Secondary Education Act, Title V.

Mr. Schafer is Consultant in Conservation Education to the California State Department of Education.

Up to this point, conservation instruction was permitted in the schools but not required except on one day of the year—Conservation, Bird and Arbor Day. All this was changed in May of 1968 when the Governor signed Senate Bill 1 (Miller) into law which overhauled the entire State school curriculum structure. Included in this legislation was a requirement that adopted courses of study must provide for instruction in "... protection and conservation of resources" at appropriate grade levels and subject areas grades 1-12 and that "... man's relation to his human and natural environment" shall be part of the social sciences program.

Shortly thereafter, Senate Bill 206 (Moscone and Marks) was also signed by the Governor establishing a conservation education service in the Department of Education and authorizing planning grants to local districts to develop new conservation and outdoor education programs. No funds were provided for these purposes but the conservation education service duties were assigned to Mr. Schafer as a part of the Title V project.

As may be expected, the new conservation education requirement stimulated quite a bit of activity on the local level. Many new programs and projects were started and this trend continues to date. As a result of this increased activity, the demand for assistance from the Department of Education and the various resource management agencies in California increased dramatically. There appears to be no slowdown in sight in the demand for such services.

In September of 1969, the Conservation Education Advisory Committee presented their recommendations together with completed reports and studies to the California State Board of Education. Among their major recommendations:

1. California today stands at an environmental crossroads. Although much of the Golden State has been irreparably damaged or destroyed through past greed, neglect, and ignorance, much of value remains. The future lies in the hands of present and future generations. Children must be helped through an effective conservation education program, to acquire the skills, knowledge, and attitudes necessary to the development of an acceptable environmental ethic if we expect to continue living here in any degree of health and comfort. The Committee considers the encouragement and development of such educational programs to be deserving of the highest priority.

2. The State Board of Education and the State Department of Education should, with financial assistance from the legislature, assume the strong role of leadership in the field of conservation education required by law. A State supported consultant position with an adequate operating budget is considered a minimum. A close working relationship with county school offices, local school districts, industry, governmental agencies, and private conservation agencies should be established and maintained to provide the Department with the support and assitance it will need in this leadership role.

3. Financial assistance and leadership is also needed from the legislature to enable local districts to develop facilities, plan, and operate effective conservation education programs. The legislature has authorized the Department of Education to make planning grants to local districts to develop conservation education programs (Education Code 6011. 5) but has not provided funds for the purpose.

4. Recognizing that conservation is a social regarding the common environment, local school programs must be planned to emphasize the economic, political, and sociological aspects of conservation as well as the ecological and technological.

5. A frameword showing how conservation instruction may be integrated in the curriculum in many subject areas and grade levels should be produced by the State Department of Education to assist local districts in planning programs suited to local needs.

6. Efforts must be made to convince classroom teachers that they are the key to a successful conservation education program. Strong efforts at the preservice and inservice training levels must be made to provide teachers with the background knowledge and specific teaching skills necessary to assume this role of leadership.

7. Adequate materials are essential to an effective program. The State Curriculum Commission is urged to insist upon a strong emphasis on conservation when appropriate in all textbooks adopted for school use. The State Department is urged to expand and keep current the bibliography of free and inexpensive conservation education materials and the list of films and filmstrips begun as a part of the Committee study. These studies should be made readily available to county offices and the collected materials should be available for study at various locations throughout the State.

8. The resident outdoor education program is recognized as a most effective method of helping children develop an awareness of their interrelationship with their environment. The Committee urges the legislature, state and federal resource agencies, and the Department of Education to cooperate in making this experience available to all students at least once during their school career.

9. A great reservoir of potential assistance in the form of publications, field trips, and technical assistance is available to the schools from governmental agencies, industry, and private conservation groups. A close working relationship between these groups and educators at state, county, and local levels is essential.

At this point in time, fall 1969, it is still too early to determine what effect the Advisory Committee report will have on the Board of Education, the legisture, the schools of California, or the general public. What the future holds is by no means certain. The consultant position in the Department of Education is funded through fiscal 1969-70 under ESEA Title V. What happens after that is by no means clear. A bill in the legislature to provide $125,000 to operate the service and to make limited planning grants to local school districts died in committee during the 1969 session. Local programs may suffer as a result of a shortage of funds. The governmental agencies, private conservation agencies, and the business community are also caught in the financial crunch when expanded services and increased materials are called for. Clearly adequate financial support in many areas is needed if California is to continue the progress made in conservation education over the past few years. To slip back now when we have come so far would be indeed tragic.

Victor Hugo once said, "Nothing in this world is so powerful as an idea whose time has come." Has the time arrived for conservation education in California? Will the means be found to continue the progress made thus far? In the months to come we shall have our answer.

Teaching about people and their environment.

THE CONCEPTUAL FIELD TRIP

Matthew J. Brennan

SINCE EDUCATORS first directed their attention to the idea of helping children develop concepts rather than filling their minds with facts, the "concepts" approach has found general acceptance. Textbooks, elementary science projects, and more recently a series of teachers' curriculum guides for conservation education, have been developed under the South Carolina Curriculum Improvement Project using the same concepts.[1] Even so, in the field, teachers still stuff their pupils with facts. Some interpretive naturalists in the park and forest programs for the public also go in for the "whole load approach." A teacher, forester, or park naturalist may take a group out into the field and proceed to tell the children numerous facts he has learned during his formal education and work experience, in a period of 1 hour or less.

At some resident outdoor education programs, the children get the "whole load" on a different area of science every day (sometimes two a day). On a trip through a national park or forest, the child or visitor may be exposed to all about the geology, soils, plants, animals, and the type of conservation which the managing agency practices on the area. The result is that children in school and summer tourists are environmentally illiterate—they have no concepts of environment and particularly their own interdependence with the environment. If the conceptual approach is acceptable for textbooks, teachers' guides, and media materials, why not try it for teaching and learning in the field—in the natural science laboratory? A "conceptual field trip," can be used effectively, lasting 5 to 10 minutes, offering a child acquaintance with a single concept of the environment. In this way, rather than the "whole load" the teacher can present a sequentially planned series of field experiences which will lead to development of several concepts of environment.

In an analysis of the "whole load" presentation of several foresters, explaining the reasons for block cutting of Douglas fir, black walnut, or cherry, why not prepare a list of the concepts they briefly mention: germination on mineral soil, response to sunlight, tolerance to shade, effects of crowding, and thinning. These concepts can be better developed in a planned elementary science sequence, than through a unit taught a day or longer.

For example, at The Pinchot Institute, many interesting field trips are taken with children at all levels. With kindergartners, the Institute has had great success with a 10-minute trip to see three trees. One is big and tall and straight, the forester's dream tree. The second is a hemlock that blew down in a storm several years ago. Its roots are still intact and the tip has turned up toward the sun. (Or is it away from the pull of gravity?) The third tree was bent over when another fell on it in a storm. Three of its side branches are now growing upright.

At the kindergarten level, we are told that children cannot develop a concept of plant response to sunlight. That is generally done in third grade (or is it fourth?) by putting a box over a geranium plant in the classroom window. Nevertheless, when the 5-year-olds are asked what they have learned from seeing these trees, several in the class will invariably say, "All of the trees are trying to get up to the sun."

The other concepts necessary to an understanding of forestry can be developed just as easily as the child progresses through elementary school science. Last May, a different kind of "conceptual field trip" was tried with students from an Oregon school. As it began, the children were asked to look for two things: (1) evidence of change (concept: living things and the environment are in constant change); and (2) evidence that one living thing is dependent on another—that living things are dependent on one another, or interdependent. (Concept: living things are interdependent with their environment and each other.)

The directions for the 10-minute field trip were simple: "In the next 10 minutes, find as many examples as you can of change and dependence." The children regrouped after 10 minutes. They were loaded down with dead leaves, flowers, and seeds. The students saw all kinds of changes, and discussed how these were caused. They decided that changes in living things were:

- 1. natural (species) —buds ⁺ flowers ⁺

The author, a consulting editor of this journal, is Editor of <u>People and Their Environment</u> and a special consultant to the U.S. Office of Education. This paper first appeared in the March 1970 issue of <u>Science and Children</u>.

seeds → dead remains;

- 2. natural (caused by other living things)—chewed, sucked, mined leaves;

- 3. physical—storm, erosion, flood, time;

- 4. chemical—pH, mineral deficiency, salt spray;

- 5. man-caused (In another hour the children might have decided that man-made changes are also natural. Is not man a natural animal?)

The children further decided that changes are going on all the time. Living things change, environments change, sixth graders change, constantly.

Concepts of dependence and interdependence are just as quickly developed through this type of experience. In the very short time spent on the field trip, the children are beginning to develop the third major concept of environment—living things are the product of their heredity and their environment. This concept also applies to populations of organisms. What would happen if an animal ate all the leaves of a tree? If man killed all grouse? Why are two Sitka spruce trees different? Two daisies? Two sixth graders?

This type of field trip means a new role for the teacher—but it is an enjoyable one. All he has to do is direct his students to new experiences and help them explore unknown environments. Let them develop their own concepts of environment. Then every new experience they have in the environment in the future will reinforce their concept or cause it to be modified. ■

"Bigger than all indoors."

ABOUT PROJECT "SPRUCE"

Phyllis S. Busch

THERE WAS an air of excitement among the children as they filed out of their fourth-grade classroom one clear spring day. When they were outside, they hurried over to the privet hedge that surrounded the playground and peered at it closely. Spaced out along the hedge were clear plastic bags which the children had tied firmly on some of the branches. Under the guidance of their teacher they had closed some bags over dead twigs and others over live ones in an experiment to learn whether moisture is given off by leaves. The children shook the bags and made notes about the amount of water in each bag. Some were only slightly moist; some contained quite a lot of water; but all the dead ones were dry.

On another day, this same class went for a walk in a nearby field. It was pleasant outside, but very windy. They were enjoying the outing, especially the feel of the breezes ruffling their hair. Their teacher hadn't told them what she had in mind, but finally she stopped them and asked from which direction the wind was blowing. There was a difference of opinion among the children. One boy pointed to the flag waving on the roof of the school; another suggested an opposite direction. Finally, the teacher reminded them of the dandelions that dotted the field. The blooms had gone to seed and the teacher suggested that the students each pick one of the "blowballs" and watch where the wind scattered the soft feathery seeds. Later in the day they checked the wind direction again to see whether it had changed. At the suggestion of their teacher each of them took a deep breath of fresh air before they returned to their classroom for a lively discussion about where winds blow from and where they blow to. The children also talked about the scents and particles that the air carries.

The next day they discussed air pollution, and went outside to observe pollutants in the making. Their teacher tied a clean square of cloth over her car exhaust, turned the ignition on, and let the motor run for 30 seconds. She removed the cloth and held it up for the children to inspect. In the center was a circle of black deposit which the cloth had trapped.

Another day the children learned about differences in textures by feeling things. They walked from tree to tree, feeling the various barks with their fingertips. They compared the rough texture of two Norway maples with that of a slender birch nearby. They made bark rubbings by placing a sheet of tracing paper over a section of bark and rubbing the side of a crayon across the paper. Each kind of tree produced its own distinctive pattern. Indoors, the children could readily distinguish the maple rubbing from that of the birch.

On a day when it appeared that the sparrows were chirping more actively than usual the teacher called this to the children's attention and they trooped outside. Each found a "listening spot" from which they could concentrate on the sounds around them. They agreed that they could hear the sparrows better, as well as other things, when they were really attentive to sound.

When it began to rain, the children listened to the different sounds as the rain splashed on the leaves and on the ground. Before they went indoors the teacher asked them how rain tastes. Mouths wide open, they collected a few drops. Some children looked surprised and they were all amused.

This class has become used to studying science-conservation both indoors and outdoors. Their excitement is reflected in the joy they show when they make their own discoveries, either in their classroom or in the open. They have learned to investigate their environment by using all their senses: sight, smell, taste, hearing, and touch.

Project S. P. R. U. C. E. , a federally sponsored program (Title III, E. S. E. A.) is introducing such science-conservation teaching approaches in elementary schools. S. P. R. U. C. E. stands for Science Project Related to Upgrading Conservation Education. The emphasis is on extending science-conservation investigations to the outdoor environment because the world is bigger than all indoors.

This article originally appeared in the January, 1969, issue of <u>Jack and Jill</u>.

"The key to preserving the human environment is the collective behavior

of individual citizens."

SCHOOLS AND THE ENVIRONMENT

Edward A. Ames

THERE IS a characteristic impulse in our society to turn to education to solve complex social problems. This impulse was exemplified by the flood of attempts at curriculum reform in science and math that followed the launching of Sputnik in 1957. The emergence of Russia's scientific eminence was seen as a threat to national security and the scramble was on. So it is that Congress, reflecting the public's concern over the deterioration of the physical environment, is now considering two bills which would support educational programs designed to protect the quality of the nation's environment. This congressional effort may well reinforce the efforts of those educators and laymen who have worked to develop programs in conservation, outdoor education, and the natural science for our schools during the last few years. While this source of potential support can only be welcomed, some hard questions should be raised by the expectation that our schools can achieve the social goals which are implicit in this challenge.

Senator Gaylord Nelson, in introducing the Environmental Quality Act in Congress, recognized that the problem of checking environmental deterioration is largely a behavioral one. He then made the following statement:

> Education, I believe, is the only proper way
> to influence values, attitudes, and basic as-
> sumptions in a democratic society. Behavior,
> in the long run, can best be changed through
> the process of education.

A number of questions ought to be asked about this statement. For instance, what kinds of behavioral changes are needed to halt environmental deterioration? Who is to prescribe them? How are they to be achieved through education? How are behavior and social values affected by our school systems? I suggest, that if we really examined these questions we would get some unexpected answers, that the assumptions on which much of our current environmental education are based are of questionable utility, and that we have not yet come to grips with the underlying basis of the environmental problems which face us.

The values which affect society's behavior toward the environment are fundamental, widely held, and deeply involved with our perceptions of the world around us. For instance, as a society we attach an almost mystical importance to the inevitability of progress and to the value of economic growth. So much so that we seldom examine these ideas, even though they are by no means shared by other people around the world or even by all segments of our own society. Progress, of course, is not inevitable, and growth, whether in human population or in gross national product, has finite limits. The fact that we continue to behave as though this were an infinite world even though we clearly know better, leads us to some pretty grim conclusions about the future of our society. While one may disagree with the doomsday prophets predicting ecological disaster in this century, the trend is clear enough. [1]

SCHOOLS AND VALUES

If our behavior toward the environment is indeed based on unexamined values and faulty assumptions, then it should be the business of education to examine these values and challenge the assumptions. While this idea sounds revolutionary, nothing less direct will stand a chance of being effective in changing social behavior. After all, our assumptions about the nature of the world and our role in it are widely held in society because they are constantly reinforced. The communications media, the behavior of our peers, and even our folk culture confirm our perceptions of the world. Examination of these perceptions must start with our schools since they also tend to reinforce whatever values are widely held by society at any given time. Indeed, they are one of the means by which we institutionalize our beliefs and transmit them to succeeding generations.

Much of this communication is done through implicit messages which are a part of the school environment and may or may not be contained in textbooks or other teaching materials. For instance, one of the most important messages from the point of view of environmental significance has to do with the child's

Mr. Ames is a program officer in the Office of Resources and Environment of the Ford Foundation. This paper was prepared for the American Nature Study Society, 27 December, 1969.

perception of his role in society and of his ability to affect his environment, either for better or for worse. This is a particularly critical question in urban poverty areas where the effectiveness of the individual is so much in question. We can assume that a teacher who comes from a different cultural background and lives in a different neighborhood will not share the same environmental perceptions and concerns as his children. If, at the same time, that teacher has a low estimation of the ability of his children to relate to the broader social community in coping with their problems, a message of futility and isolation comes through to those children all too clearly. Students in more privileged suburban schools may receive different messages but ones which also have unfavorable implications for their values and behavior in relation to their environment. I would guess that it is an unusual classroom in which students are encouraged by either practice or example to examine critically that which is bad in their environment or to question at all the assumptions and values which underlie environmental deterioration. In general, we do not seem to give children a very high estimation of their ability to effect change or even to do more than passively cope with the environmental insults which our society has prepared for them.

David Hawkins, an educator at the University of Colorado, often performs the simple test of examining bulletin boards and physical materials being used by pupils to determine what is happening in the classroom with regard to environmental education. It is rare that he finds any significant clues as to the nature of that specific physical and social environmental surrounding a school. While there may be a map or two, most of the material is generalized and representative of any area of the country. Usually such physical evidence is a good indicator of the teacher's approach, of the children's activities, and hence of the kinds of learning experiences that take place in that classroom. A self-contained classroom isolated from the surrounding community provides a sterile atmosphere for learning about environmental problems, whether one approaches them from the point of view of their social or physical basis. But perhaps more importantly, this kind of classroom environment may impart implicit messages about the relevance of environmental concerns, messages with obviously negative implications for the way in which those children will perceive their role in effecting environmental change.

If we are to change the behavior of children through formal education, which is precisely the challenge before us, we obviously must understand and change some rather basic aspects of the school environment. Furthermore, education will have to be organized around the goal of teaching children how to be effective agents for change so that they in turn may participate in the social processes which shape their communities and their lives. Environmental education, when viewed in these terms, becomes a fundamental part of the school experience.

Much of the quite extensive effort at environmental education which has been mounted in recent years has been at quite a different level. The main thrust has been to teach children about the natural environment through interpretation of the landscape and the processes which change it. But this ecological emphasis, important though it may be in its own right,

has been mounted from outside the school system and has seldom come to grips with the broader social issues which now concern us. Ecology as curriculum content is primarily useful in that it relates a great deal of diverse information about the environment and its processes. I do not question for a minute the importance of environmental learning in this sense, but in competition with other subjects it must remain a relatively distinct part of the curriculum and as such represents only a limited gain.

What is needed is a far more eclectic approach to education, an approach which would embrace many new kinds of learning experiences. These new experiences would be selected to involve students in the critical analysis of, among other things, the social values and interactions that underlie environmental degradation. A high priority would be placed on the processes of inquiry and problem solving but the focus would be outward into the community and on actual problems affecting the lives of the students.

RESEARCH BY STUDENTS

A good example of this kind of environmental education is the water pollution research problem at the Tilton School in New Hampshire. The students learn about the science and technology of pollution by doing research on the water quality in local streams and lakes In addition to learning a good deal of basic science they also produce data that are useful to the Federal Water Pollution Control Administration. But, rather than stopping at the academic boundary of their subject, the students then investigate relevant legislation on water quality, and finally pursue the economic and political consequences of the enforcement of that legislation. All of this is done using actual local problems as a case study. The behavioral objectives of the Tilton work have to do with the ability of the students to carry out a research program, produce acceptable data, and analyze actual environmental problems. I can only surmise that the implicit messages that are communicated to the students doing such work will have an important influence on their roles as individuals in society and with their responsibilities in relationship to their environment.

There are, of course, all sorts of barriers to initiating such open-ended work in the schools. The basic structure and organization of the classroom are often inimical to environmental education and teachers lack the training and experience to organize such programs. It is far easier to teach about the environment as a generalized subject with the support of textbooks and films than it is to conduct an open-ended inquiry into the specific problems of an actual community. It is also easier to relegate the entire responsibility for environmental education to specialists from outside the school system, perhaps at the end of a bus ride at a local nature center, than it is to embrace environmental education as a fundamental aspect of the overall curriculum.

COMMUNITY INVOLVEMENT

Changes in education are taking place, however, and there are trends developing which should make it easier to pursue environmental education in the classroom. For instance, in many urban areas there is a drive toward greater community involvement in the schools. This is more than a matter of control over the administration of the school, although that may be the prime motivation behind the movement. In fact, community education makes it possible to draw upon many kinds of community resources, both human and institutional, to support the educational program at the school. In Philadelphia at the Parkway School, and in Baltimore's Dunbar High School, programs are either being developed or are underway in which entire segments of the curriculum are conducted in agencies of the municipal government, in businesses, and in local cultural institutions such as zoos and museums. Efforts are being made to involve representatives from the community and from local colleges in classes taking place within the school itself. The potential for environmental education is obviously far greater under these conditions than it has been in the traditionally more restrictive school. But this potential remains to be fulfilled and the opportunities for environmental education may not be recognized as such even in the schools themselves.

While the examples I have cited above happen to be high schools, there are similar trends developing in elementary schools. Here the line of attack is to break down the traditional concept of the self-contained classroom which has always limited the kinds of learning experiences provided by the school. Team teaching, to the extent that it involves teachers with a variety of backgrounds working in close cooperation with each other, has cracked the classroom wall. Further inroads are being made by schools experimenting with open-structure or with the integrated day[2], an approach to education based on the works of John Dewey and Jean Piaget, but developed most fully in British primary schools. Here as in the high schools, we are dealing with a potential for imaginative programming which has not been widely recognized, particularly on this side of the Atlantic.

The significance of the integrated day for environmental education is profound indeed. It places an emphasis on an eclectic environmentalism based on the heavy use of materials found in the local environment ranging from building rubble to living plants and animals. It combines classrooms, breaking down the walls so that children can work together in teams on problems which interest them and at the same time provide valuable learning experiences. It disregards the traditional subject area boundaries and follows a unified approach to learning which much more closely approximates the child's actual perception of his environment. It drops the rigid schedule enforced by periodic bells and allows the use of blocks of time to pursue problems which could not even be tackled in a more traditional classroom. In fact, after seeing an integrated day in process, it is hard to imagine how effective environmental education could be pursued in the elementary school under any less open-structured conditions.

An integrated day affords an opportunity to achieve certain behavioral objectives through the kinds of learning experiences that it provides for children. Thus the excavation of a pile of building rubble treated as a neighborhood archaeological site might be

used to teach children a good deal about exploratory techniques and problem solving as well as about the history, climate, demography, and so forth, of their community. But, in addition, the fact that the teaching deals with the immediate environment and involves children in an open-ended exploration of those surroundings carries an implication for the children that their own environment and their individual perceptions of it really count. This kind of individualized, child-centered learning which deals with the immediate physical surroundings certainly develops different and presumably more positive attitudes, values, and behavior toward the environment than the traditional, more structured approaches. Furthermore, we can make the assumption that programs which involve students in attempts to solve actual environmental problems can engender a social commitment that may have a lasting effect on their behavior.

The more successful environmental programs have undoubtedly contributed to the willingness of the schools to open the classroom doors to new experiences. The great public concern over environmental degradation is now reinforcing that movement and the result may be the best chance yet for introducing behaviorally effective educational programs. To realize this opportunity, schools must make use of that particular environment perceived by their students. In effect they must teach <u>through</u> the environment using the community as a source of learning experiences rather than just <u>about</u> the environment as a generalized object of study. Furthermore, if schools are to affect the behavior of children in order to moderate society's impact on the environment they must lead students to explore the social interactions and the whole system of human values, concerns, and assumptions which underlie our behavior. After all, the physical limitations of natural systems are constant, and technology is only effective in alleviating the pressures we place on our environment when we use it to that purpose. The key to preserving the human environment is inescapably the collective behavior of individual citizens. In the final analysis, the success of environmental education will be measured in terms of its ability to change the behavior of society.

FOOTNOTES

1. For a particularly enlighting treatise on this subject see Garret Hardin's article, "The Tragedy of the Commons," in <u>Science</u>, Volume 162, December 13, 1968.

2. The term "integrated day" refers to a way of organizing the classroom without the formal constraints imposed by fixed-length classes dealing with specialized, academic disciplines. It also implies an inductive, individualized approach to learning. ∎

A key to more and better environmental education programs.

THE RESOURCE AGENCY SEMINAR
Richard S. Peterson

FOR A NUMBER of years emphasis has been placed on school programs in environmental education. The following is a description of an innovative procedure we have used to get teachers, supervisors, and resource agency personnel in Utah's local school districts involved in planning and implementing comprehensive environmental education programs in grades kindergarten through 12.

INTRODUCTION

Utah has a statewide committee that is responsible for environmental education in the public schools. The chairman of this committee is the science specialist in the Office of the State Superintendent of Public Instruction, and membership is drawn from the public resource agencies, i.e., Forest Service, Bureau of Land Management, Soil Conservation Service, National Parks Service, and the State Department of Fish and Game. Also, institutions of higher learning are represented. It should be reiterated that the committee's membership from education and from the resource agencies is comprised of personnel who, for the most part, have leadership responsibilities that extend statewide. This committee, discharging one of its major responsibilities, developed guidelines for a comprehensive environmental education program in grades kindergarten through 12. It was clear, however, that the work was only a "paper tiger" and would remain just that until "life" was breathed into it.

PROCEDURE

How does one take statewide guidelines and give them "life" in 40 local school districts? Looking back over 2 years of experience, we would say: "Naturally, you conduct a series of Resource Agency Seminars."

Here is how they work. Members of the statewide committee, referred to above, planned a 2-day seminar in which many facets of a comprehensive environmental education program were presented to approximately six educators from each of four local school districts. Also in attendance were representatives of the Forest Service, Bureau of Land Management, Soil Conservation Service, National Parks Service, and Fish and Game personnel who worked in the same geographical area that the four school districts encompassed. The number attending each seminar was approximately 50. This technique brought the educators and the local representatives of the resource agencies together and built bridges that supported future working relationships. In many instances, this was the first face-to-face meeting of the two groups.

At the end of the 2-day seminar, a call to action was given and the "multiplier effect" was employed. One of the educators from each of the four school districts was asked to serve as chairman of a local district environmental education committee and to be responsible for establishing a <u>continuing</u> program in that particular district.

In cooperation with the superintendent of the district, the chairman invited other educators (representing K-12 and all subject areas) from the district and resource agency personnel who work in that district, or in close proximity, to serve on the committee. Committee membership, as well as number, varied from district to district. In some instances, in addition to educators and agency personnel, a county or city commissioner serves on the committee, thus insuring the consideration of problems and concerns by policy-making bodies.

No attempt was made to prescribe a fixed program for each of the 40 school districts; rather, each was free to synthesize its own unique program in environmental education. Most district committees leaned heavily upon the statewide guidelines but wisely included other features which made the program more appropriate to a given group of students in a given locale.

SUMMARY
We believe the approach is most successful. Thirty-eight of the 40 school districts participated in one or more of the seminars and a majority of them have organized a local committee. To our knowledge, this attempt to establish environmental education programs in every local school district within a state is unique to Utah. Further, the utilization of the multiplier effect through the establishment of a local committee, very similar in structure and composition to the statewide committee, is, we believe, also unique to Utah.

The cooperative working alliance of educators and resource agency personnel is most effective. It is unlikely that all educators or all resource agency personnel are "down" at the same time. Therefore, such an organizational pattern offers several avenues of stimulation, rather than a single one, and it leads to a more comprehensive program because more people are involved in a program which is really <u>theirs</u>. Things which previously had been thought impossible are now being done in environmental education programs in Utah, and the vision is constantly expanding.

Through this approach the efforts of the state group have been multiplied many times over. In short the opportunity for Utah pupils to become involved in thoughtfully planned environmental education programs has been significantly increased through the use of Resource Agency Seminars. The paper tiger has come to life!

Mr. Peterson is a Specialist in Science Education with the Utah State Board of Education.

THE ENVIRONMENT AND MAN

Robert E. Roth

A SHORT time ago a youngster from a metropolitan school, whom I shall call Billy, visited a nature center with his sixth grade class. Billy was understandably excited about the visit and also a bit relieved to get out of the classroom. "Let's go see the owl, and over there is something to look through," said Billy to two of his companions.

Beginning a pell mell race toward the cage they heard a rather stern command. "Boys! Please! Get back in line, and remember you are to stay with the class." Billy thinks to himself, "This ain't going to be any fun. I can't go see the things I want to see, and I gotta stay in line and listen to some guy talk again, just like last year. But, gee, he's got a uniform on, and look at that swell shoulder patch!"

The children's teacher, Mrs. Schwartz, begins, "Children, this is Mr. Green, our naturalist for today. He is going to lead us on our nature walk, and point out some of the plants and animals we came to see, and help us learn something more about ecology. Remember, while we are here I want you to all act like ladies and gentlemen, and pay very close attention to what Mr. Green has to say."

When Billy first heard about the field trip he probably set his goal as having a good time because he likes freedom of movement. He is curious about things most of the time, and he eagerly looks forward to anything he can do at the nature center. In short, he wants participation and involvement. Billy is concerned with his immediate surroundings—short term gratifications. He will respond to some structure, and he exhibits good social control when directed in a positive way. Subconsciously Billy notes voice inflections that give indication of values, patterns are observed as certain concepts are reinforced, and of course, he is impressed by the uniform and readily identifies with the naturalist, perhaps because the role he plays is one to which Billy aspires.

The teacher had some reasons in mind for coming to the nature center which were different from Billy's. First was the search for a culminating activity that would tie together some of the loose ends of their ecology unit. It was based on the concept that "living things are interdependent with one another and the environment," so the nature center immediately came to mind, because that's where these things happen. In addition, Mrs. Schwartz hoped the children could then come in more intimate contact with a variety of plants and animals because two sub-categories of information were: "There are many kinds of plants," and "There are many kinds of animals." Perhaps she also had hopes that man's role in relation to the environment might be included, but this did not appear in the syllabus, so it wasn't verbalized in the unit lesson plan. Similarly, the man-land relationship idea had been heard by her from time to time in the mass media, but it was still an unclear concept. However, she did like wild flowers.

Mr. Green, being a sensitive and effective naturalist-science teacher, evolved a format for his group presentation that had considerable content and could be adapted to the interests of the various groups quite readily. He based his efforts on a concept of conservation that embraced a philosophy of living as well as land management practices. Other categories of information to be included were the traditional things that can be "better taught" in the outdoors such as geology, minerals, soils, water, plants, animals, and of course, the various interrelationships. A concern that Mr. Green and his associates had been studying was how to provide more direct involvement activities for the visitors. But this was his third group that morning, and many other immediate duties kept him from giving a lot of thought to the problem.

Another problem that has continually confronted environmental educators, and one which you undoubtedly recognize, is that of disparity in goals and objectives, and a concomitant lack of communication. Billy had his goals, the teacher had hers, and Mr. Green had his. All three individuals were at different levels of sophistication and approach, and as a result, a considerable challenge existed in determining whether or not any or all of these goals were attained. Note in particular the level at which the "Land-man Ethic" if we can call it that, existed in the minds of our three role players. Billy was not

---

Dr. Roth is Assistant Professor, School of Natural Resources, The Ohio State University.

at the verbal level but he might have had a fleeting glimmer of the idea of land ethic as the naturalist gave some voice inflection that communicated an emotional concern. Mrs. Schwartz knew about pollution problems, over-population, urban sprawl, and that mass media promoted anti-litter campaigns as a public service, but here again, a verbalized knowledge of an ecological consciousness was not evident. It can be inferred consequently, that for the school, the class, and Billy, the Land Ethic didn't really exist even though they were studying ecology.

What about Mr. Green? Just how adequate was his knowledge about the "Land Ethic?" In fact, how adequate is the Land Ethic as described and formed by its author, Aldo Leopold? Does it contain sufficient dimension to cover all of the kinds of concerns to which we apply it, or not? Does it hold the possibility of conveying meaning to a boy like Billy who lives on the eighteenth floor of a high-rise apartment building in an urban renewal development? Can Mrs. Schwartz interpret enough from the statements about the "Land Ethic" already in print to be able to incorporate it as part of her verbalized lesson objectives, not to mention her way of life? These are becoming crucial questions in interpretation of the land ethic, which need careful thought and consideration from all of us. In short, what should a student know about environmental management?

THE ROLE OF EDUCATION

The schools have long attempted to translate pieces of our cultural heritage into teachable concepts, and have found that the related educational objectives exist at three basic levels—cognitive, affective, and psychomotor. The cognitive area is concerned with recall and recognition of knowledge and the development of intellectual abilities and skills. The clearest definitions also occur in this domain. Affectivity centers on values, judgments, appreciations, and emotions. The associated learning experiences that are appropriate for this area are not at all clear. Psychomotor or motor skills as an area of study is just beginning to be scrutinized. Education has developed approaches to teaching that are based on the needs, interests, and abilities of the children and on the knowledge, comprehension, and application levels of concepts from the cognitive domains. Knowledge represents the specifics in terminology; comprehension the understanding of what is being communicated; the application level represents the ability to apply abstraction without prompting and with no mode of solution being specified. Before the land ethic attitudes can be built, it seems probable that the ideas will have to be formulated in the cognitive, or verbal level. Emotionalism, or affectivity per se, will not do the job in the present state of the art. All of our past experience with failures in conservation education clearly indicate this. The only effective programs have been those that began in the knowledge area and then proceeded to blend with the emotional.

A second problem is that of an experience on the land. The idea of direct citizen involvement with the land was at least partly developed under the influence of Dewey's progressive education movement. Dewey's observation that we learn by experience and discovery from the environment in which we live made sense to Leopold, and was incorporated into his

thinking. This idea still appears to be valid and our land laboratories, school forests, school gardens and resident outdoor education programs have been some approaches used in addition to traditional science laboratory programs.

The area being confronted today is of course that of the environment of man in its total form, its social, cultural, economic, esthetic, biological, and physical aspects. To seek an optimum total environment requites an understanding both of human needs and the needs of a healthy environment, natural and man influenced. Leopold knew this and was trying to show us the way. His sudden and unfortunate death emanating from a cabin fire left us without the originator of the ethical idea. We have been groping ever since. But with the enormous complexity of problems facing us today in our environment we must get on with the search and see what can be done to draw closer to the philosophy Leopold saw so clearly.

ENVIRONMENTAL MANAGEMENT DEFINED

The terms "environmental management education," "environmental education," "conservation education," "outdoor education," and "resource (or resource-use) education" are often used interchangeably and hence confused. Environmental management education is the process of developing a citizenry that is:

1. Knowledgeable of the interrelated biophysical and sociocultural environments of which man is a part;

2. Aware of the associated environmental problems and management alternatives of use in solving these problems; and

3. Motivated to work toward the maintenance and further development of diverse environments that are optimum for living.

Note the fact that I suggest we recognize both the biophysical and the sociocultural environments. The definition suggested here also is an attempt to change the emphasis of man and his environment to that of the environment and man. In the past we have relied on the environmental pyramid depicted by Odum and others that progressed from the abiotic to the biotic and concluded with man on top. I am suggesting that the pressure of living, our increasing population, our finite resource supplies, and the cycle of the production of goods and waste, has altered that form of simplistic relationship. Man is reduced from the role of "dominant" or "master" in the Judeo-Christian ethical sense to a lower state of existence. He is part of the environment. A crude model of this idea might be as follows:

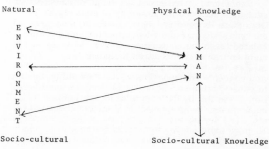

Building on this conceptualization and definition it becomes obvious that we must ask again: "What should our citizens know about environmental management?"

APPROACHES FOR ENVIRONMENTAL MANAGEMENT EDUCATION

There have been several approaches recently to the preceding question. Historically there have been other attempts. The former approaches did not produce any long lasting conservation education programs and it remains to be seen if the newer thrusts will be any more successful.

Visher attempted to determine those conservation principles and concepts desirable for use in the secondary schools. An original list was developed by analyzing 15 conservation textbooks, nine books for general reading, two special conservation-issue journals, one reprint series, five publications of professional material for teachers, and four doctoral dissertations. The list produced was submitted to 11 specialists in conservation for refinement and critical analysis. The refined list was then submitted to five nationally recognized leaders familiar with instruction at the secondary level. The result of the study was a list of 477 concepts that included the following areas and number of concepts per area: soil—85; water—56; forests—55; grasslands—20; minerals—57; wildlife—51; recreation—37; human resources—38; and general—78. This attempt resulted in a considerable expansion of both the number and quality of concepts appropriate for conservation education.

While developing a framework of "descriptive and predictive generalizations" pertaining to the field of conservation, Yambert surveyed and analyzed existing studies of generalizations related to conservation at the elementary and secondary levels. A broad range of professional literature in conservation and allied fields was included. Twelve generalizations were selected as being inclusive and/or representative of their group and others were formulated to compliment the previously selected 12. It was suggested that the generalizations developed could serve as a basic framework adaptable to many situations in conservation education with application to other areas as well. With a basic structure so developed, Yambert suggested that other concepts and principles could be appended. His investigation represents a first attempt to develop a different framework of generalizations of conservation for use in developing an expanded and less agrarian focused conservation orientation.

Hanselman investigated the scope of conservation education afforded the majority of students at The Ohio State University. Specifically he measured the current status of interdepartmental conservation-related teachings presented through the large enrollment courses. Procedures included: (1) a literature review to develop a list of important conservation concepts and concerns which "should be included in conservation education"; (2) revision and correction of the list by 24 leading conservationists, e.g., economists, geographers, ecologists, agronomers, etc.; (3) development of two survey instruments, an 18-page topic survey to determine the scope, and a 2-page opinion questionnaire to be used along with informal interviews with each of 54 cooperating professors. A list of 108 conservation related topics was developed covering 15 areas of conservation such as: economic, ecological, sociocultural, etc. After analyzing the results by card sort and hand tabulation it was concluded that professors showed a keen interest in conservation education and indicated concern for improving it. Also concluded was the idea that conservation education received by most students in attendance was spotty and inadequate. Hanselman's investigation provides a basis for developing an effective conservation education program through interdepartmental approaches in that both the concepts developed and the apparent interdepartmental concern and interest in conservation education could be combined to implement a refocused approach to conservation education.

White sought ". . . to determine some important conservation understandings that might be desirable for conservation education in grades 4 through 12," and ". . . to identify some community resources which could assist in the teaching of these conservation understandings." Related literature was examined and a list of understandings was developed and organized into nine resource areas for evaluation by people knowledgeable in each of the areas. Each resource area was rated by 30 people classified as being teachers in elementary or secondary schools, colleges, or as professional conservationists and interested resource personnel. Using a 5, 4, 3, 2, 1 rating scale, a mean score of at least 3.0 was used as the criteria for acceptance of the item. Of the 274 understandings evaluated: (1) 271 met the criteria; (2) all were associated with community resources in the geographic area in which the study was conducted; (3) 103 of the understandings were judged as appropriate for field study, and (4) 168 were appropriate for teaching in the classrooms. A marked individual difference in opinion on the majority of understandings was observed among professional conservationists and college teachers. It was also concluded that since 172 understandings were scored in the range from 1-5, conservation understandings more acceptable to conservationists were needed.

NEW APPROACHES

Presently there are several new approaches being attempted to develop concepts that are appropriate for environmental education. One of the more extensive was conducted by Brennan and the South Carolina Department of Education in 1968. A statewide workshop was held whereby about 80 teachers participated under the direction of Mr. Albert H. H. Dorsey to develop and write lessons based on about a dozen "conceptual schemes." Each lesson is composed of a concept, a purpose of the lesson, ways of introducing, developing, and extending the concept. Various instructional materials are suggested also. The topics are designed to be integrated with existing curricula through science, social studies, home economics, and biology, and in elementary, junior high, and high school grade levels.

The most common criticism is in the selection of exemplary teaching activities, and the assumptions that: (1) adequate reference materials are available; (2) in-service teachers are able to integrate conservation concepts with their existing curricula; and (3) that the teachers will integrate the suggested points of view. The activities w e r e developed i n South Carolina and consequently have been designed for use with local examples. Similarly, many teachers do not have either the interest or ability to integrate some of the rather complex concepts with their curricula. Rather it would seem that every ecological zone or region of the country will need to "grow their own" environmental education programs.

A second program is that entitled the National Environmental Education Development (NEED) program designed by Dr. Mario M. Menesini for the National Park Service. The major goal as indicated by Menesini is: "to foster an a p p r e c i a t i v e and critical awareness of their environment, particularly an understanding of the interactions of natural and social processes as illustrated in national park areas. Its aim also is to increase their will and capacity to improve the environment."

The NEED systems a n d interpretive materials for teaching are being developed at the University of California, Davis Campus, under the direction of Dr. Mario Menesini. Though they are presently being field tested at selected Park Service areas and outdoor schools throughout the nation, the programs are sufficiently flexible for adaptation to a wide variety of sites.

Basic to the NEED program is the premise that environmental awareness requires not only classroom work, but experience out-of-doors. Further, the outdoors experiences should be related to all subjects in the curriculum: to art, literature, and history, as well as the natural sciences. Materials are being created for pre-site (classroom), on-site (environmental school), and post-site follow-up.

The first phase of the NEED program emphasizes the appreciative level in an encounter w i t h natural phenomena at an environmental school site which will emphasize academic, aesthetic, and skill relationships with the natural order. This developmental phase will focus on a fifth to sixth grade level.

The second phase for the intermediate (grades 7, 8, 9) levels of the program, will emphasize man's positive and negative utilization of his natural r e - sources, a n d h i s efforts to rectify a self-imposed contaminated environment through technological applications.

In the third phase (grades 10, 11, 12) the necessity of environmental ethics, centered on attitudes of the individual, will be developed, integrating the disciplines of political science, economics, and sociology.

There is little information available at present that can be further evaluated. However, the Pilot Environmental E d u c a t i o n Program in Yarmouth, Maine being developed by Bennett is an attempt to focus on the concept of "Community." At the elementary level the program will focus on developing attitudes toward the theme environment—its physical elements and its environmental problems. The theme environments are selected to provide a means of expanding the scope and complexity of understandings. At the kindergarten-grade 1 level, the selected theme environment is the school; grades 2 and 3, the neighborhood; grades 4 and 5, the community;

and grade 6, the region. Each a n d every teacher plays an important role in maintaining the sequence of educational development. Without a year by year continuity in the educational process, the program will be weakened.

Briefly, the program at each grade level will consist of: (1) 20 to 30 minute classroom presentation by the coordinator relating to the school environment and providing an orientation for a field t r i p; (2) a field trip in the outdoors around the theme environment with the students led in small groups by the coordinator, teachers, and volunteer members of the community; and (3) follow-u p investigative, planning, and conservation action activities with assistance being given by the coordinator when and where needed.

Prior to the initiation of the program at your grade level, the coordinator will meet with the teacher and the field trip volunteer leaders t o further acquaint them with the program, go over the field trip in detail in the theme environment, set up schedules, and answer any questions. To prepare for this meeting, a teacher's guide has been prepared to give you detailed information about the operation of the program at your grade level. It is designed to assist in preparing your class for the presentation, field trip, and follow-up conservation activities.

During the program the learner will be guided to discover problems by interacting with the environment through an orientation presentation, field trip, and follow-up conservation activities. These three teaching "tools" will be directed at encouraging the student to become aware of how we use our environment to satisfy our needs. He will be led first to observe the things he likes and uses and then to discover or identify those things which he doesn't like o r which interfere with the capability of the environment to meet his needs (p h y s i c a l environmental problems). Problems will involve both natural and man-made physical elements of the environment. Finally, the student will be given the opportunity to investigate a problem further and actually do something to help resolve it.

Again, little evaluation has been accomplished to date. The pattern has worked under the guidance of Stapp, however, in the Ann Arbor, Michigan, public schools. There too the level of concept attainment remains to be determined.

Most of the preceeding environmental education programs have been initiated on the assumption that the concepts to be acquired by the students are known. I am unable to make that assumption because of the twist in definition to which I alluded earlier in this presentation. Because of the different ways of viewing things in the environmental context, it is necessary to again ask: "What should we know about environmental management?"

A project in which I was engaged from June 1967 to May 1969 was an attempt to develop a taxonomy of conceptual objectives for use in planning programs of instruction related to environmental management education (K-16). Coincidental to that, some indication of whether or not biases existed within selected disciplines representing several ecological zones throughout the U. S. was also given.

Survey techniques to obtain and validate concepts appropriate for environmental management education involved written questionnaires and personal interviews. The population consisted of scholars in disciplines related to environmental management who were associated with the University of Wisconsin and other selected universities throughout the U. S. A list of 128 concepts developed with the cooperation of the Wisconsin Panel of Scholars was submitted to the National Panel consisting of 699 scholars representing 40 academic disciplines in 24 universities from 12 ecological zones in the U. S.

Usable responses were received from 350 (50.07 percent) of the Scholars on the National Panel. There were 111 concepts that met the criterion of being accepted by 90 percent of the respondents. The acceptable concepts were organized into a taxonomic list according to topic on the basis of weighted item mean score. Thirteen topics served in classifying the concepts: Environmental Management, Management Techniques, Economics, Environmental Problems, Environmental Ecology, Adaptation and Evolution, Natural Resources, The Sociocultural Environment, Culture, Politics, The Family, The Individual, and Psychological Aspects. The classification of concepts used is not considered exhaustive but is suggested as one possible organization of topics and concepts.

Examination of the 17 "unacceptable" concepts and the frequency of rejection of each on the basis of response by professional area or ecological region provides little evidence to support any speculation of the existence of possible bias. One concept was rejected by as many as 27 percent of the judges while the remaining 16 concepts were rejected by 18 percent or fewer of the judges. The rating of the concepts does indicate an individual divergence of opinion and interpretation, but no clear bias is evident on the basis of either professional area or ecological vagueness of the concepts.

Scholars from the 40 professional areas and 12 ecological regions of the United States agree on the majority of concepts to be emphasized in environmental management education. Knowledge of the concepts contained in the taxonomic list of environmental management is appropriate for use in public schools throughout the United States. It is suggested further that the organization of topics used represents a more useful and appropriate structure of concepts for environmental management education than the agrarian focused conservation concepts and organizations presently existing in many public schools.

Gundlach and Archbald have initiated several attempts based on the formulation of the taxonomic list. Gundlach has had a summer pilot project conducted by teachers in the Portage, Wisconsin, area developing lesson plans and trying out activities based on these concepts. Similarly, Archbald is developing a "computerized key" of ecological examples to provide meaning for a variety of these concepts also. In addition, the Columbus, Ohio, public schools are in the design stage of a broad-based environmental and outdoor education program that will be based upon these concepts.

It can be suggested that each situation will demand the application of these concepts in its own unique way. The concepts must be adapted to the local situation and no amount of effort in developing a national curriculum in environment will have much applicability at a local level. Each teacher and naturalist will have to "grow their own" teaching activities that fit the environmental example and the personality of the teacher. So, hop to it! But, keep in mind this observation: "You have to be in the middle, because you can't stay on top very long." The ecological pyramid has been upset. ∎

The role of the private sector in curriculum and materials development.

AN ENVIRONMENTAL APPROACH TO MARINE SCIENCE K-12

Alan Rabinowitz

CURRICULUM development in the natural sciences has taken great strides in the past 10 years. Consideration was given first to the learner—as it should have been—but not to the "factors" outside and related to the learning process. Specifically, these "factors" include such things as teacher training and preparation in the subject area, availability of supplies and materials, environmental factors, and a climate conducive to student experimentation within the school per se and the community.

Ideally, a cooperative effort between private industry and the school system would create a well-coordinated team approach toward developing a meaningful science curriculum. Furthermore, those "factors" heretofore neglected by most curriculum projects would be given proper attention and consideration.

Oceanography Unlimited Inc., Lodi, New Jersey, serves the educational community in a rather unique way. In addition to manufacturing materials and supplies relating to environmental and marine science studies, its staff of consultants works with schools and school systems in curriculum development for the marine sciences. In this way, teachers, supervisors, and professional scientists can share thoughts and ideas and prepare a structure for curriculum design.

The educational division of Oceanography Unlimited is staffed by educators from all levels as well as professional marine scientists. The primary functions of the division are to prepare curriculum materials and coordinated teaching aids for the environmental and marine sciences. An example of such a cooperative effort in curriculum planning is the development of an environmental oceanography and marine science program for grades K-12 with the Fairfield Public Schools, Fairfield, Connecticut. Dr. Bette J. Del Giorno, formerly professor of science education at the University of Hartford and presently science consultant for the Fairfield Public Schools, has created a unique curriculum design called ReTAL: The Research Team Approach to Learning—A Structure For Open-endedness. ReTAL is an inductive or discovery approach to science study. The author and Dr. Del Giorno are preparing a K-12 environmental marine science curriculum based upon ReTAL.

The author is a licensed principal and a former science department chairman; as one of the educational consultants for Oceanography Unlimited, he brings his industrial as well as educational experience to share with the Fairfield school system. Together, he and Dr. Del Giorno are preparing the basic structures for the curriculum design:

I. Projects, Programs, Sub-programs, and Courses
II. Units
III. Lessons

The complete resources of Oceanography Unlimited will be made available to Dr. Del Giorno and her staff so that the final project can be practically and successfully implemented. The purposes of the cooperative venture between Oceanography Unlimited and Dr. Del Giorno are fourfold:

1. to promote teacher involvement in curriculum development through the ReTAL-based curriculum project;

The author is Executive Vice President and Coordinator of Curriculum Development, Oceanography Unlimited, Inc., Lodi, New Jersey.

1. A Secchi Disc and Fdrel Scale are Used to Study Light Penetration and Water Color.

2. Seining Provides the Opportunity to Collect Local Flora and Fauna.

3. On the Beach Students Reveal What They Have Collected in the Seine; Fish and Shrimp are Most Abundant.

4. This Plankton Tow Will Provide Approximately 30 Different Species of Marine Plankters.

2. to provide a teacher training tool and re-source package for immediate use upon completion of the curriculum project;

3. to make available to teachers and pupils, a K-12 curriculum in environmental oceanography and marine science;

4. to bridge the communications gap between industry and the schools and to permit teachers and scientists to work together on curriculum projects.

Dr. Del Giorno has selected the Pequot Elementary School in Southport as the pilot school for the curriculum project. Conveniently situated on Long Island Sound, Pequot School will provide outdoor laboratory experiences as well as classroom activities related to ecology, oceanography, and conservation for its teachers and students. The sequentially developed and logically integrated curriculum design will provide for continuity throughout the program with constant emphasis on ecological relationships and environmental awareness.

Marine Science is the study of the sea and includes the biological, chemical, physical, geological, and meteorological aspects of the total acquatic environment. The concepts of the ecosystem, limiting factors, ecological indicators, habitats, and applied ecology are included as part of the curriculum design.

Through independent work and experimentation, students will get first-hand experience with in-field testing procedures as well as develop competencies in study and research activities. Teachers will become acquainted with the most modern materials and equipment needed to study the marine environment and will develop "localized" curriculum packages for their schools using Pequot School as a model. In this way, they may involve their students in the study of limnology and fresh water biology where many of the activities and concepts from marine science are identical.

The private sector has a definite place in curriculum and product development. The expertise of the school community and the private sector can be shared for mutual benefit. Each has an important role to play and an investment in education. The preparation of our future leaders in the field of the natural sciences as well as the advances we as a country will make in basic research, are contingent upon the educational training received by our students. It is imperative therefore, that our curriculum designs not only meet the needs, interests, and abilities of our students but also provide them with meaningful and challenging content. Our stake in the future of our youngsters is too high, and our interest is too sincere, to overlook the significance of this cooperative relationship. Oceanography Unlimited has this premise as its basic philosophy and hopes other companies will follow its lead in working closely with the schools to provide the best possible curriculum and materials that can be developed. ∎

Sixth-graders examine their environment.

CHANGE TOWARD BETTER ECOLOGICAL STUDIES

Richard L. Delnickas and Edward G. Smith

WATER... air... trees... soil... so what? How could we make man's environmental problems meaningful to our sixth-grade suburbanites who assigned so little importance to the things which sustain our existence?

One day as we discussed previous attempts at teaching conservation and examined our resources, we came to several decisions: We would team to better utilize our time, talents, and techniques. Students' attitudes toward natural resources would have to change. Traditional textbook-film approaches wouldn't affect attitudes, so we would try field experiences coordinated with the latest technology. And we would seek help from the community media center and EPIC, the federally funded Educational Project to Implement Conservation.

Beefed up by four student interns, our team met several times with media specialists and project directors to plan selective learning experiences. To support our chosen objectives, we chose media to deliver a series of multisensory events. We listed hardware, teacher-prepared software, audio-equipped buses, and community resources. To get through to our television-oriented students, we would center our initial and followup environmental experiences around video tape.

"I know that place!" Our 15-minute video documentary on problem spots in our local area achieved the identification we wanted, and raised questions to introduce the concepts we were seeking to develop. "Where will we bury the trash after room runs out?" "What can we do for environment in our city?" "What is flood control?" These student questions provided directions and motivations for our study.

Small groups were formed to explore these subjects further through slides, newspaper articles, bulletin boards, reference books, and field equipment. To provide direct experiences, we planned to use some of the many community and regional resources available, such as Westfield State College, Springfield Water Works, Stanley Park, Harvard Forest and its Fisher Museum, Quabbin Reservoir, the Army Engineers. Project EPIC furnished the sound-equipped buses that became moving classrooms when we made field trips.

Because of their experience with local drought, the children already realized that the supply of water available to man is limited. To redirect pupil awareness to the problem, we replayed segments of our video tape and showed a film entitled Miracle Called Water, which was particularly relevant because it was about the neighboring city of Springfield. To focus attention on specific concepts, we developed transparencies and ditto masters.

The field experience revolved around the water system of Springfield. We visited Littlefield Dam, a pumping station, Cobble Mountain Reservoir, West Parish Filter Beds, and Provin Mountain storage tanks, with the students seeking information from experts as these places. By now class enthusiasm was high as the children wondered how we would attack the problem of forest resources. Video tape again became a major tool. Because of the emphasis on forest succession and economic significance of good forest practice, we chose the Harvard Forest and Fisher Museum, our camera recording significant information as the students experienced it firsthand.

On the 35-mile trip, we used the bus microphones to make commentaries on watersheds, wildlife management, and forest trimming practices. Children were asked to collect such data along the way as visible signs of air and water pollution, good and bad soil use, and potential recreation sites. Later comparative graphs were constructed to summarize their observations and reinforce the importance of keeping records.

Reading books and stories by Thornton Burgess provided direction for a study of native wildlife in its natural habitat, motivating a visit to his estate, now known as "Laughing Brook Nature Center." It was fascinating to see the children identifying various species and telling what they knew about them.

Subsequent trips were taken to other local nature areas. During a special trip to Mt. Tom Reservation, a public recreation and nature center, small groups investigated woodland use.

Our commitment to the conservation study plan was justified by the way our students attacked the projects in the culminating activities of the program. We built around a theme of communication to the community, utilizing posters, scrapbooks, bulletin boards, dioramas, displays of collections, and small group discussions. The climax was an open-house ceremony at our new Juniper Park School.

From a teacher's point of view, we felt that our program effectively focused students' attention on the pressing problems right at hand in our local environment. We found that the multisensory approach to teaching, highlighted by video tape and field experiences, was an effective vehicle for developing pupil interest, motivation, and understanding. ∎

The authors are sixth-grade teachers in Carew Street School, Springfield, Massachusetts. Their report was one of 25 winners in a recent Instructor magazine contest. (Reprinted from Instructor, February 1970).

ENVIRONMENTAL ENCOUNTERS

William B. Stapp

TODAY'S YOUTH in elementary and secondary schools will soon be assuming important roles as adult citizens in society. As citizens and voters, no matter what their occupations may be, they will be asked to make decisions that will affect not only the immediate environment in which they live, but also that of their country. To an increasing extent the votes they will cast and the choices they will make will be concerned with their environment. They will be asked to make social and economic decisions about recreation, transportation, beautification, water needs, and air and water pollution control. Since these issues affect the total environment in which we live, we must assist our young people (and adults) to acquire the experiences, knowledge, and concern necessary for making informed environmental decisions.

In our political system we depend upon the wisdom of individuals of the populace for making decisions. A major responsibility for assisting future citizens to obtain the knowledge and incentive necessary to make informed decisions has been delegated to school systems. Since environmental education is essential to our type of political system, it is important for the public to ask if school systems are effectively fulfilling their responsibility to society.

One of the most important challenges of education today is to develop an effective method of implementing environmental education into elementary and secondary school systems.

A STRATEGY OF CURRICULUM DEVELOPMENT

If individuals are to be prepared to make the kind of environmental decisions that our nation will face in the future, schools must embark on a comprehensive environmental education program that will span the curriculum—kindergarten through the twelfth grade—and link subject areas that relate most closely to the environment.

The information that follows reflects the author's 8 years of experience in serving as conservation consultant with the Ann Arbor Public School System; a graduate seminar[1] in environmental education, School of Natural Resources, The University of Michigan; and a comprehensive review of the literature. (See following Bibliography.)

BIBLIOGRAPHY

1. Atkin, Myron, "Behavioral Objectives in Curriculum Design: A Cautionary Note," Science Teacher, 35:27-30, May 1968.

2. Beauchamp, George, Curriculum Theory, 1965.

3. Bennett, Dean, Organization and Operation of the Yarmouth Maine Environmental Education Program, Yarmouth Public Schools, 1969, pp. 1-9.

4. Bruner, Jerome S., The Process of Education, Vintage Books, 1960.

5. Bruner, Jerome, Toward a Process of Instruction, W. W. Norton and Company, Inc. New York.

6. Bryan, William, "A Conceptual Plan for an Environmental Education Program," unpublished master's thesis, University of Michigan, Ann Arbor, 1967.

7. Cohen, Arthur R., Attitude Change and Social Influence, Basic Books, Inc. Publishers, New York, 1964.

8. Dewey, John, Experience and Education, Collier Books, New York.

9. Hess, Robert, "Political Attitudes in Children," Psychology Today, 2:(no. 8)24-28, January 1969.

10. Hess, Robert; Torney, Judith, The Development of Political Attitudes in Children, Aldine Publishing Co., Chicago, 1967.

11. Kretch; Critchfield; Ballachey, Individuals in Society, 1962.

12. Kelley, Earl, Education for What is Real, 1947.

13. Kelley, Earl, "The Place of Affective

Dr. Stapp is Associate Professor, Resource Planning and Conservation, School of Natural Resources, The University of Michigan, Ann Arbor.

Learning, " Educational Leadership, 22: 455-457, April 1965.

14. Lane, Robert E.; Sears, David, Public Opinion, Prentice-Hall, Inc., Englewood Cliffs, New Jersey, 1964.

15. Miller, H.; Smiley, H., Education in the Metropolis, The Free Press.

16. Montague, Earl; Butts, David P., "Behavioral Objectives, " Science Teacher, Vol. 35, March 1968.

17. Montague, Earl; Koran, John J., Jr., "Behavioral Objectives and Instructional Design: An Elaboration, " Science Teacher, Vol. 35, March 1969.

18. Neagley, Ross; Evans, Dean, Handbook for Effective Curriculum Development, 1967.

19. Ojemann, Ralph, "Should Educational Objectives be Stated in Behavioral Terms?" The Elementary School Journal, Vol. 68, February 1968.

20. Piaget, Jean; Inhelder, Barbel, The Psychology of the Child, Basic Books, Inc. Publishers, New York, 1969.

21. Rokeach, Milton, Beliefs, Attitudes, and Values, Jossez-Bass, 1968.

22. Science Research Associates, Youth Power, 1968.

23. Stapp, William B., et al., "The Concept of Environmental Education, " Environmental Education, 1:(no. 1) 30-31, 1969.

24. Stapp, William B., Integrating Conservation and Outdoor Education into the Curriculum (K-12).

25. Swan, James, "Response to Air Pollution: A Study of Attitudes and Coping Strategies of High School Youth, " Journal of Environment and Behavior, 1970.

26. Swan, James, "The Challenge of Environmental Education, " Phi Delta Kappa, 26-28, September 1969.

27. Taba, Hilda, Curriculum Development, Harcourt, Brace, and World, Inc. , New York, 1962.

28. Tyler, Ralph, Basic Principals of Curriculum and Instruction, 1950.

29. Vaiozey, John, Education in the Modern World, World University Library, Toronto, 1967.

30. White, Gilbert, "Formation and Role of Public Attitudes, " Environmental Quality in a Growing Economy, John Hopkins Press, 1966, pp. 105-127.

A school system (K-12) that is interested in developing an environmental education program might consider the following strategy:

Phase I: Identify the need for developing the program (page 36).

Phase II: Establish an environmental education committee to develop and implement the program and to facilitate communication (page 37).

Phase III: Establish the goal and sub-goals of the program (page 37).

Phase IV: Establish the objectives (in terms of behavioral predispositions) of the program (page 37).

Phase V: Review of the literature regarding theories of learning and instruction that apply to the formulation and implementation of the program(page 38).

Phase VI: Establish the curriculum organization of the program (page 38).

Phase VII: Establish the curriculum of the program (page 39).

Phase VIII: Establish a comprehensive in-service teacher education program (page 41).

Phase IX: Develop instruments to evaluate the effectiveness of the program (page 41).

Phase I: The Need for Developing an Environmental Education Program

Within the past 50 years, the United States has become a predominantly urban nation, both in thought and in physical character. Large and middle-sized communities, many within complex urban regions, have evolved to where over 70 percent of this country's population resides on 1 1/2 percent of the nation's land surface. By 1980, eight out of ten Americans will probably live in an urban environment. Consequently, the independent rural-oriented living that once characterized this country's social and political heritage is no longer a dominating influence in the lives of most Americans.

In rural surroundings, direct daily contact with the basic natural resources was prevalent, especially within man's immediate environment. As man became progressively urbanized, his intimate association and interaction with natural resources diminished, and with it his awareness of his dependency on them. Yet, it is imperative that man, wherever he lives, comprehend that his welfare is dependent upon the "proper" management and use of these resources.

Man should also have an awareness and understanding of his community and its associated problems. Our communities are being plagued with problems such as lack of comprehensive environmental planning, indiscriminate use of pesticides; community blight; air and water pollution, traffic congestion; and the lack of institutional arrangements needed to cope effectively with environmental problems. While these problems are legitimate concerns of community governmental officials and planners, the responsibility for their solution rests, to a large extent, with citizens.

To an increasing extent citizens are being asked to make decisions that affect (directly and indirectly) their environment. Specifically, citizens make these decisions as they cast votes on community issues; as they elect representatives to policy-making bodies; as they directly act upon the environment itself. Citizens can be effective in influencing sound policy in other ways. They can ask informed questions, at the proper time, of the right people. They can serve on advisory and policy-making committees. They can support sound legislation directed at resolving environmental problems. To perform these tasks effectively, it is vital that the citizenry be knowledgeable concerning their biophysical environment and associated problems, aware of how they can help solve these problems, and motivated to work toward effective solutions.

The Supreme Court decision regarding the one-man, one-vote concept, that has enabled the increasing urban majority to acquire greater powers in decision-making, makes it imperative that programs developed for urbanites be designed with them in mind. It is important to assist each individual, whether urbanite or ruralite, to obtain a fuller understanding of the environment, problems that confront it, the interrelationship between the community and surrounding land, and opportunities for the individual to be effective in working toward the solution of environmental problems.

Most current programs in conservation education are oriented primarily to basic resources; they do not focus on the community environment and its associated problems. Furthermore, few programs emphasize the role of the citizen in working, both individually and collectively, toward the solution of problems that affect our well being. There is a vital need for an educational approach that effectively educates man regarding his relationship to the total environment. (See Stapp's article "The Concept of Environmental Education," Environmental Education, Fall 1969.)

Phase II: Establish an Environmental Education Committee to Develop and Implement the Program and to Facilitate Communication

An essential component of most successful school programs is effective communication between the community and school system. The introduction of any new school program requires the involvement and preparation of the community, administration, teaching staff, and student. One reason many well-conceived programs have failed is because teachers and students were not involved in program development.

In developing an environmental education program, it is important that an environmental education committee[2] be formed to develop and implement the program and to facilitate communication between the community and the school system. The committee should consist of elementary teachers (representing each grade level), secondary teachers (representing each discipline), school administrators, community citizens, and students. The environmental education committee should report to the superintendent of schools (or to an individual or committee designated by the superintendent).

In developing an environmental education program for a school system, it is strongly recommended that an environmental education consultant position be created. The environmental education consultant[3] could provide the leadership and guidance essential to the success of any program. One of the major responsibilities of the environmental education consultant would be to assist in the development and implementation of the in-service teacher education program.

Some important duties of the environmental education committee (or committees) would be to:

. . . Assist in the development of the philosophy and structure of the program.

. . . Become familiar with existing instructional material relevant to environmental education.

. . . Identify community resources, both physical and human, to serve the program.

. . . Assist in the development and distribution of instructional material (such as environmental encounters).

. . . Provide a comprehensive in-service teacher education program.

. . . Train community citizens to serve the program.
. . . Assist in the development of school sites to serve the program.

. . . Administer the program.

. . . Make presentations to parent-teacher and other community organizations regarding the program.

. . . Evaluate the effectiveness of the program in achieving stated objectives.

Phase III: Establish the Goals [4] and Sub-Goals of the Environmental Education Program

Without a clear statement of goals, an environmental education program would become a series of unrelated experiences, focusing perhaps on limited program objectives. The goal (See Stapp, Environmental Education, Fall 1969.) of environmental education is to produce a citizenry that is knowledgeable concerning the biophysical environment and its associated problems, aware of how to help solve these problems, and motivated to work toward their solution.

The major sub-goals (Refer to Stapp, Environmental Education, Fall 1969.) of environmental education are to help individuals acquire:

1. A clear understanding that man is an inseparable part of a system, consisting of man, culture, and the biophysical environment, and that man has the ability to alter the interrelationships of this system.

2. A broad understanding of the biophysical environment, both natural and man-made, and its role in contemporary society.

3. A fundamental understanding of the biophysical environmental problems confronting man, how to help solve these problems, and the responsibility of citizens and government to work toward their solution.

4. Attitudes of concern for the quality of the biophysical environment which will motivate citizens to participate in biophysical environmental problem-solving.

Phase IV: Establish the Objectives[4] (in terms of behavioral predispositions) for an Environmental Education Program

There are various ways to state the expected and desired outcomes of an environmental education program. Perhaps the most significant and dynamic approach is to state them in terms of behavioral predispositions. In other words, the product of an environmental education program (K-12) should be a citizen who is:

1. Interested in his environment and its relationship to society.

2. Sensitive (total awareness) to his environment, both natural and man-made aspects of it.

3. Sensitive to the dimension of quality of his environment and able to recognize environmental problems.

4. Inclined to participate in coping with environmental problems.

Phase V: Review of the Literature Regarding Theories of Learning [5] and Instruction that Apply to the Formulation and Implementation of an Environmental Education Program

A recent review of the literature reveals the following points that should be considered in the formulation of an environmental education program:

. . . Behaviors which are reinforced are most likely to recur. It is important that desired behaviors be reinforced by the home, school, church, youth organizations, etc.

. . . The most effective effort is put forth by youth when they try tasks which fall in the "range of challenge"—not too easy and not too hard—where success seems likely but not certain.

. . . Youth are more likely to throw themselves wholeheartedly into any project if they themselves have a meaningful role in the selection and planning of the enterprise.

. . . Reaction to excessive direction of the teacher is likely to be: apathetic conformity; defiance; escape from the whole affair.

. . . What is learned is most likely to be available for use if it is learned in a situation much like that in which it is to be used and immediately preceding the time when it is needed. Learning in youth, then forgetting, and then relearning when need arises is not an efficient procedure.

. . . The learning process in school ought to involve dynamic methods of inquiry.

. . . Research shows little correlation between cognitive achievement and concern and values. Able students who achieve well in traditional "content-centered courses" do not necessarily demonstrate commitment to positive social goals.

. . . Learning takes place through the active behavior of the student. It is what he does that he learns, not what the teacher does. The essential means of an education are the experiences provided, not the things to which the student is merely exposed.

. . . One of the keys to motivation is a sense of excitement about discovering for one's self, rather than having a generalization presented by a teacher and requiring a student to prove it.

. . . Attitudes may not be formed through a rational process by which facts are gathered and a reasonable conclusion drawn, but rather through the repeated exposure to ideas.

. . . Helping citizens to acquire technical knowledge alone regarding an environmental problem, may not increase their concern for the problem.

. . . Citizens are more likely to become involved in environmental issues if they are aware of how they can have some effect upon decision-making.

Phase VI: Establish the Curriculum Organization [6] of the Environmental Education Program

An important criticism of our public school system is the lack of adequate articulation between the various divisions of the school organization. Instead of a well-developed series of instructional units and activities commencing at the kindergarten level and terminating at the twelfth grade, many school systems present a series of units that have little relationship between what has previously been taught and what will be taught in future years. The K-12 approach seems to be the most sound way to plan a curriculum for environmental education.

It is also important to plan curriculum projects horizontally as well as vertically. Disciplines, such as science and social studies, should not be studied in isolation. A curriculum should be planned so that students can see the contributions of interdisciplinary studies in assisting the learner to better understand the environment and to be more effective in solving environmental problems.

Furthermore, a curriculum program should recognize individual differences. There is no sequence that will meet the needs of all groups of youth. Therefore, a curriculum program should be flexible in design so that material can be presented in different ways depending on the background, needs, and aspirations of the students.

A set of guiding principles that should be considered when structuring an environmental education program are:

. . . Span the curriculum, kindergarten through the twelfth grade, so that environmental experiences can be presented at every grade level, thereby capitalizing on the cumulative effects of the program.

. . . Link subject areas that relate most closely to the environment, especially science and social studies, so that both the social and scientific knowledge important in understanding and solving environmental problems are properly developed.

. . . Integrate and correlate the program with the existing curriculum in a manner that will enhance the instructional goals of the school system.

. . . Focus on the local environment, but do not neglect regional, national, and international environmental issues.

. . . Stress attitudes and problem solving skills. The most important environmental impact that most of our urban citizens will have upon our environment is through their action as community citizens.

. . . The learner should play an active role in the learning process. The learner develops attitudes through personal experiences and thinking and not through the presentation of predigested conclusions.

. . . Provide a comprehensive in-service teacher education program which would operate throughout the school year and which is directed at assisting teachers to increase their understandings, interest, awareness, and teaching skills in environmental affairs and to involve them in curriculum development.

Phase VII: Establish the Curriculum [7] of the Environmental Education Program

In establishing an environmental education program for a school system (K-12), consideration should be given to the development of a series of environmental encounters. The encounters should focus the attention of elementary and secondary youth on their environment and in a manner that would link relevant ecological, economic, social, technological, and political information.

The environmental encounters could be designed to provide the learner with meaningful environmental experiences at each grade level, both elementary and secondary. The encounters could be used to enhance and extend an existing instructional program or to serve as the core of a comprehensive environmental education program.

Environmental encounters would provide the flexibility that a program needs to meet varying local environmental conditions and situations, as well as individual class needs.

Some examples of topics that the environmental encounters might focus upon, are: land resources, water resources, air resources, plant resources, animal resources, environmental design, environmental planning, transportation, solid waste disposal, and recreation. The class could select with the teacher environmental encounters to extend an existing class unit or to serve as the central thrust of a major teaching unit.

In developing environmental encounters, the following guidelines are recommended:

. . . At each grade level the learner should be exposed to meaningful environmental encounters that relate to relevant ecological, economic, political, technological, and social information. However, greater exphasis in the earlier grades should be toward developing in youth an interest, awareness, understanding and respect for the environment, and in the latter years emphasis should be on "honing" problem solving skills.

. . . Environmental encounters should provide the opportunity at each grade level for the learner to become personally involved in positive action toward the solution of environmental problems in which he has been exposed.

. . . The learner should play a major role in both selecting and designing environmental encounters.

. . . Environmental encounters should fall in the range of challenge—not too easy and not too hard.

. . . Environmental encounters should involve dynamic methods of inquiry.

. . . Environmental encounters that relate to environmental problems should expose the learner to the following problem solving procedure: (1) Define the environmental problem or issue. (2) Become informed about the problem. (3) State the alternative solutions. (4) Develop a plan of action. (5) Implement the plan of action.

Every environmental encounter should contain a list of the outcomes that are desired. The outcomes desired should be expressed as behavioral objectives. They (behavioral objectives) provide: direction for the learning process; guidance in selecting content and experiences; greater focus on the learner—what the learner does; and the opportunity to appraise (evaluate) the effectiveness of a particular learning experience and of the total program. Behavioral objectives can be stated at different levels of complexity and in the cognitive (knowledge), affective (concern), and action domains.

An example of an environmental encounter recommended for a sixth grade class, is as follows:

INVESTIGATING A POND COMMUNITY

"An Environmental Encounter
for a Sixth Grade Class"

Behavioral Objectives:

In the completion of a successful encounter, the student should be able to:

1. Draw an accurate map of the drainage area of the pond community.

2. Describe in writing four ways that the land in the drainage areas affects the pond community.

3. Draw two (2) food chains illustrating organisms observed in the pond community.

4. List (number) major problems affecting the pond community.

5. Describe in writing the major steps in solving one (1) of the problems noted in question 4.

Activity:

1. What is the bottom of the pond community like: How does the type of bottom affect the kinds of plants and animals found in the pond community?

2. As you look from the center of the pond community toward the shore, are there plants growing under water, on the surface, and out of the water? Why are plants important to the pond community?

3. Dip a small jar into the pond and note if there are small organisms (these are probably plankton organisms)? Why is plankton important to the pond community? What would cause plankton to increase or decrease?

4. Make or obtain a dip net and sample around the edge of the pond community. How are the animals you have caught important to the pond community? Draw a food chain linking some of the plants and animals you have noted in and around the pond community.

5. On a map of your community color in the land

area that drains toward the pond. How has the use of this land changed over the past 15 years? What changes are occurring at the present time? How does the use of this land affect the pond community?

6. Do both children and adults visit the pond community? What do people do when they visit the pond community?

7. Do you see any problems that are affecting the pond community? Who is responsible for creating the problems? What could your class do to help solve one of the problems noted above (define the problem, become informed about the problem, state alternative solutions, develop a plan of action, implement the plan)? Is your class motivated and concerned about one of the problems to the degree that they desire to work toward its solution?

An example of an environmental encounter recommended for a high school American Government class, is as follows:

FLOOD PLAIN ZONING

"An Environmental Encounter for an American Government Class"

Behavioral Objectives:

In the completion of a successful encounter, the student should be able to:

1. Draw on a map of his community the flood plains (50 year flood line) of the ___(name)___ River from ___(location)___ to ___(location)___ and record accurately how each flood plain is developed.

2. Describe in writing the number of floods and flood damage that has occurred on the flood plains of the ___(name)___ River from ___(location)___ to ___(location)___ over the past 60 years (or over the time that records have been filed).

3. Describe in writing the major provisions in the laws of his state and community regarding flood plain zoning.

4. Identify the power structure (pressure groups, governmental committees, governmental policy makers) of his community regarding who influences and makes policy on flood plain development and zoning.

Activities:

1. Take a tour (or illustrate by slides) along the ___(name)___ River from ___(location___ to ___(location)___ and note the following:

a. Are there a series of flood plains?

b. How are the flood plains developed?

c. Are there homes or buildings on the flood plain? Are they flood proofed?

d. Are there provisions for protecting the flood plains from flooding?

e. What trends regarding land development are occurring on the flood plains of your community?

2. Seek information from reliable sources regarding the flood plains of the ___(name)___ River from ___(location)___ to ___(location)___ :

a. Has flooding of the flood plains occurred during the past 60 years?

b. List the years in which flooding has occurred.

c. Approximately how much damage (dollars, lives, inconveniences) has occurred on the flood plains as a result of flooding over the past 60 years?

d. What does your state flood plain ordinance say? If none exists, is it considering an ordinance?

e. What does your community flood plain ordinance say? If none exists, is it considering such an ordinance?

f. How is the undeveloped land on the flood plain zoned?

g. Are there any current proposals to utilize the undeveloped flood plains of your river for recreational, residential, commercial, or industrial development?

h. What proposals seem wise or unwise in light of the hazards you have identified?

3. Draw on a map of your cummunity the flood plains (50 year flood line) of the ___(name)___ River from ___(location)___ to ___(location)___ and record how each flood plain is developed.

4. Determine by interviews the points of view of land developers, community citizens, realtors, chamber of commerce officials, planning commission members, city council members, and students of your class regarding the future development of the flood plains of the ___(name)___ River from ___(location)___ to ___(location)___ .

5. Based on the information collected, have the class formulate alternative solutions to the development (or preservation) of the flood plains on the ___(name)___ River from ___(location)___ to ___(location)___ .

6. Draw a chart of the power structure (pressure groups, governmental committees, governmental policy makers) of your community regarding who influences (underline the influencers) and makes policy (circle the policy makers) on flood plain development and zoning.

7. If the solution advocated by the class members is different from the point of view held by the planning commission and policy makers of your community, then develop and implement a plan of action (presentation to the appropriate authority, develop a fact sheet, publicize your position, etc.).

Each environmental encounter should also provide data regarding sources of additional information relevant to the topic.

If the environmental educational program for a school system revolved around environmental encounters, a twelfth grader may not be exposed to all aspects of the environment. However, through the inductive (inquiry) approach advocated by this system, a twelfth grader that had been exposed to this program should be more sensitive (total awareness) to his environment, better able to recognize environmental problems, more sophisticated in the utilization of problem solving skills essential to the solution of emerging environmental problems, and more inclined to participate in coping with environmental problems than the product of other forms of instruction known to the author. The learner would also have an understanding and should see the importance of relating ecological, economic, social, technological, and political information when working toward the solution of environmental problems.

The environmental encounters should be produced by the local environmental education committee and by youth and teachers from throughout the school system. The environmental encounters produced at the local level could be mimeographed and distributed to all schools in the system. Many school systems might need and desire consultant help (which is available) to orient the local environmental education committee to the task of developing environmental encounters. However, samples of environmental encounters could be developed and produced by a national publishing house according to elementary grade levels (lower elementary, middle elementary, upper elementary) and secondary subject matters (general science, American Government, biology, economics, social problems, etc.). Environmental encounters produced at the national level could be adapted to meet local needs and situations by the local environmental education committee.

Phase VIII: Establish a Comprehensive In-Service Teacher Education Program[5]

If our youth are to acquire the interest, awareness, understandings, and skills essential in understanding and contributing to the solution of environmental problems, then it is imperative that our schools provide environmental learning experiences. However, few teachers are prepared in our colleges and universities to use the environment to enrich instructional goals. For this reason a comprehensive in-service teacher education program is essential to a successful environmental education program (K-12).

An effective in-service teacher education program should be developed by the local environmental education committee. An early task would be to formulate a comprehensive in-service teacher education plan, which might include the following:

  a. Clear statement of objectives.

  b. Time sequence regarding when offerings will occur throughout the school year.

  c. Involvement of teachers at all grade levels and subject areas.

  d. Development of written material and instructional aids to assist the teacher in understanding and presenting environmental information.

  e. Blending of community environmental experiences with indoor presentations.

  f. Provisions for experiences to occur on school sites.

  g. Promotion and publicity of local collegiate offerings and scholarship programs.

The first stage of an in-service teacher training program would be to orient all teachers and administrators to the philosophy of environmental education, structure of the environmental education program, and ways to effectively utilize environmental encounters.

The second stage of an in-service teacher training program would be to plan a bus tour of the community to provide teachers with first hand experiences regarding their local environment and associated problems. Information should be provided to all teachers regarding community citizens and governmental officials knowledgeable on the environment and available to serve the school system as resource persons on environmental matters.

The third stage of the in-service teacher training program would be to assist the teachers in ways to effectively integrate environmental encounters into the school program.

Phase IX: Develop Instruments to Evaluate the Effectiveness of the Environmental Education Program

It is imperative that instruments be developed to evaluate the extent to which behavioral objectives are attained and the effectiveness of the total environmental education program. An evaluation should be a continuous process involving pupil and teacher feedback.

It is imperative that the evaluative instruments be objective, reliable, and valid. It should be noted that behavioral objectives provide an excellent opportunity to appraise the effectiveness of particular learning experiences and of the total program. The evaluative instrument could be developed by the local environmental education committee.

SUMMARY

If we are to bring urbanized man to a fuller understanding of his environment, our schools must embark on a comprehensive environmental education program. The program should be aimed at helping our youth to be more knowledgeable concerning the environment and associated problems, aware of how to help solve these problems, and motivated to work toward their solution.

One of the most important challenges of education today is to develop an effective method of implementing environmental education into our elementary and secondary school systems.

This paper provides one strategy as to how a school system might develop a comprehensive environmental education program (K-12). The environmental encounters could be used to enhance and extend existing class units or to serve as the core of a comprehensive environmental education program.

FOOTNOTES

1. The members of the seminar were: Donald Austin, Marion Baker, William Bryan, Ellen Jackson, Katherine Lien, Jean MacGregor, Paul Nowak, Cynthia Russell, Sara Segal, James Swan, and Professor William Stapp.

2. It should be recognized that part of the responsibility for developing and implementing an environmental education program might be assigned to an existing instructional committee.

3. The environmental education consultant could serve as chairman of the environmental education committee.

4. The local environmental education committee might consider the goals and sub-goals expressed in the following phase.

5. The local environmental education committee might consider the theories of learning and instruction expressed in the following section (these are not unique to environmental education).

6. The local environmental education committee might consider thoughts on curriculum organization expressed in this section.

7. The local environmental education committee might consider environmental encounters as an integral part of their program.

8. The local environmental education committee might consider the guidelines for developing a comprehensive environmental education program expressed below. ∎

IV Environmental Studies Come to the Campus

WHERE DO WE start in our national quest for environmental quality? What azimuths shall provide our orientation? Whose standard of quality shall we adopt? For what? When? Where? How indeed do we begin to make wise choices in land and water use? How do we develop without destroying? How do we protect without penalizing? Enter the university. For identifying the choices and for supplying the economic and ecological facts as well as the esthetic appreciations on which to make intelligent environmental decisions, perhaps no instrument of American society is potentially better equipped than a university. The university has basic research and teaching skills. The university is relatively objective. The university has growing resources. Yet the ordinary posture of a university may not be optimum for the task of contributing to the new conservation. For the university has become composed of highly individualistic professors organized into departmental enclaves, marked increasingly by what Laurence Veysey has called the breakup of knowledge into little pieces, with an accompanying "maiming and mutilation of the mind." The university has a number of disciplines concerned with conservation, for example, each with a highly developed yet essentially narrow approach. Some schools have taken out a patent on the term "conservation," defying colleagues of any other stripe to trespass. Some departments tend to fence off the field as a preserve for basic research. Other departments may rush in with action programs where scientists fear to tread. Still other professors may not recognize the extent of their involvement in the matter at all. In effect, universities both influence, and are influenced by, centrifugal forces at work in conservation. What patently is needed are university postures and instrumentalities that will influence, and be influenced by, centripetal changes in conservation. Fortunately, they are emerging, because universities inevitably reflect changes in the environment: a university is not something apart from the order to which it belongs; it is that order, shadow, and tint.

To describe American college and university efforts to come to grips with the degradation of man's interlaced surroundings, the term "environmental studies" is increasingly entering the lexicon of the campus. Some might say this term has sprung into being merely at the whim of phrase-makers, or to lend a charismatic quality to the matter with which it is associated. On the contrary, the term is coming into use to satisfy the very real need of scholars to describe, if not a new discipline, at least a new way of looking at a variety of old disciplines, their relationships, and their potential contributions.

While no pinpoint definition or delimitation of the term "environmental studies" is possible at this time, and indeed may never be desirable, we can list the factors or criteria that seem to be implicit in the use of the term by a university.

First, we are concerned with the environment of *man*. It is possible, of course, to study the physical nature or the biological characteristics of the environment on an infra-human basis, but the concept in "environmental studies" is the study of man as he affects and is affected by his environment, for good or ill. The focus, in addition, is upon the growing number of humans concentrating in increasing densities and bringing greater pressures to bear upon the environment.

Second, we are concerned with the *total* environment: its social, cultural, economic, and esthetic as well as its physical and biological, aspects. To seek an optimum total environment requires an understanding both of human needs and the needs of a healthy natural environment. Any discussion of the goals of society must draw upon knowledge of the nature of the world man lives in, just as any discussion of a balance of nature today must take into account the necessary impingements of man.

Third, we are concerned with *interdisciplinary* studies. The development and management of an optimum total human environment requires an understanding of the contributions which can and must be made individually and collectively by all the arts, sciences, and professions.

Fourth, we are concerned with integrated studies that have as their ultimate rationale the development of *long-term open-ended solutions* for environmental problems, rather than short-term unilateral approaches that may actually degrade the environment. We are concerned with the adjustment of designed time and space for optimum human performance within the carrying capacities of the environment. The desired objective is to bring conflicting forces into functional relationships, resulting in a unity called order, an order where human impact does not needlessly destroy environmental quality, and where environmental quality contributes to more fruitful human life, liberty, and pursuit of happiness.

Finally, while we recognize the essential importance of strengthening existing disciplines, we look toward teaching, research, and service configurations that will transcend traditional lines of endeavor, and be concerned with the wholeness of the relationship between man and the total environment. What we seek is *an integrated environmental ethic* based in the scientific method. To achieve such a goal we must literally develop a new university environment in which environmental studies can flourish and in which the fruits of such research can be reflected promptly in campus teaching and community service. The articles that follow suggest that such campus environments may indeed be evolving. ■

"At most institutions the resources are available; it is the mobilization and coordination of faculty and curriculum that are needed·"

A GLIMPSE AND ANALYSIS OF ENVIRONMENTAL EDUCATION OPPORTUNITIES IN AMERICAN HIGHER EDUCATION

Spenser W. Havlick

THE DETERIORATION of the quality of the physical environment in a democratic and informed nation continues in the face of a limited number of explanations. One of those explanations turns on what awareness, information, and political efficacy the educational system gives citizens and decision-makers about their environment. If institutions of higher learning are not providing relevant exposures about and possible solutions to environmental problems then a comprehensive appraisal would seem warrented. The objective of this preliminary investigation was to inventory what several selected universities and colleges are currently doing to provide effective environmental education learning experiences for undergraduate and graduate students. As particularly successful programs in environmental education are identified, new curricula, improved learning opportunities, and teaching innovations can be shared among institutions of higher learning throughout the United States.

More than 10 years ago the Conservation Foundation supported a rather thorough study of conservation education in the United States (Lively and Preiss, Conservation Education in American Colleges, Ronald Press, New York, 1957). Today, a fresh analysis of programs in the area of environmental education

stands out as a necessary and serious undertaking.

In 1968, under the chairmanship of Dr. Raymond Dasmann, the Conservation Foundation Committee on Environmental Education in American Universities undertook the task of identifying courses and programs which are available to the general student as well as persons training to be environmental specialists at graduate and undergraduate levels. With encouragement from the Committee the author selected a small number of institutions of higher education which served as a preliminary sample of what opportunities are available on American university campuses in the area of environmental education. (For a definition of environmental education as used in this paper see the article by Professor Stapp on page 30.)

METHODOLOGY

In preparation for an inventory of environmental education opportunities at several colleges and universities a pilot study was carried out at the University of Michigan. In order for a course to be considered relevant to environmental education, it was decided that the course must fall into at least one of the

Dr. Havlick is Assistant Professor of Resource Planning and Conservation, School of Natural Resources and Faculty Associate, Institute of Social Research, The University of Michigan, Ann Arbor. The study is being carried out with support from The Conservation Foundation, Washington, D. C.

following four categories: 1) the course must be a so-called "building block"—that is, it must contribute to a better understanding and knowledge of t h e physical-biological environment, 2) the course must be an "integrator" or relate man to his environment, 3) it must be a techniques or problem solving course which teaches problem solving techniques and stimulates students to work towards the solution of problems facing their environment, and 4) any remaining courses which were believed relevant to environmental education, but did not fall into the above three categories.

The pretest experience at The University of Michigan demonstrated the enormity of a nationwide effort to identify and evaluate effectiveness of courses and programs in environmental education. It was determined that selected faculty be contacted for a personal interview from a small number of institutions which offered specific programs or courses. Faculty members at designated institutions were chosen by reputational and positional techniques. The Conservation Foundation's Committee on Environmental Education in American Universities was particularly helpful in submitting names of schools and faculty throughout the United States who should be contacted during the study.

MAJOR FINDINGS OF THE STUDY

1. Most liberal arts colleges with a student population of less than 1,200 lack the depth of interdepartmental resources to sustain a multidisciplinary program required of a program in environmental education. Unusual cases do exist where seminars are offered in environmental problems (i. e. Springfield College, Massachusetts, and Beloit College, Wisconsin). In these situations team teaching often substitutes for single courses taught by different departments in the larger universities as in the example of Ohio State University, University of Washington, Massachusetts Institute of Technology, Colorado State University, Wisconsin State University, University of Utah, University of Wisconsin and others.

2. Many universities have a program or part of it which qualifies as environmental education in a department (or departments), school o r institute whose direction and policy are in keeping with a specific discipline such as political science, civil engineering, biology, geology, agricultural economics, or rural sociology. Under these administrative circumstances it remains unclear whether or not a program or curriculum in environmental education can have adequate breadth for the spectrum of students who may wish to enroll. Examples include Cornell University, Massachusetts Institute of Technology, and Indiana University.

3. The majority of students enrolled in comprehensive environmental education programs or courses

were apparently not training for primary or secondary teaching positions at the institutions observed. Most of the students interviewed in the Michigan pretest were not expecting to be teachers. In the nationwide inventory respondents indicated that students in courses related to environmental studies w e r e probably destined for professional positions in federal, state, and county (planning) agencies, various research activities, private business and industry, and universities.

4. The majority of schools under observation had three or fewer courses which qualified as comprehensive environmental education offerings. Without exception improvements and additions were being planned. It should be mentioned again that the criteria for judging a course were based on the definition given earlier which stresses the development of a citizenry that is knowledgeable about problems that affect our physical environment, understands how to be effective in helping to solve these problems, and is motivated to work toward their solution.

5. Several universities present what could be considered model opportunities in environmental education under the definition of the concept as used in this report. Harvard University via its Committee o n General Education, Clark University (Geography Department), University of Wisconsin (Environmental Studies Committee), Montana State University, University of Michigan (School of Natural Resources) and Colorado State University stand among the leaders. A number of schools are in the process of regrouping facilities and talents in the area of environmental education (University o f Wisconsin — Green Bay Center of Environmental Studies; O h i o State University's School of Natural Resources; and University of Colorado's Man-Environment Relationships Center will be worth watching).

6. Categorically all faculty members who were interviewed expressed a willingness to participate in a sharing of skills related to the area of environmental education. This emerged as an expression of wanting to learn from programs that were operational and to share whatever innovations may be helpful to others contemplating, beginning or reorganizing a course or program in environmental education. There was particular interest in what curriculum or faculty combinations had produced satisfactory results elsewhere in the country.

7. Every respondent mentioned or recognized environmental education as a serious and legitimate area of concern in light of the problems which face our biological-physical environment.

8. It appears that the success of an environmental education program depends on a capable and d e voted man or a faculty team that is able to coordinate the content and integrate the fundamental concepts of a program at a given institution. With the schools that were struggling to launch a new program or reorganize one that needs to become relevant t o t h e urban resource problems, "leadership" was given as one of the most vexing problems. Utah State University, University of Colorado, N e w Jersey

Commission on Higher Education and Ohio State University serve as illustrations.

RECOMMENDATIONS

From the findings and observations made during the initial inventory of environmental education opportunities in the United States certain general recommendations are presented. The suggestions which follow are made despite the omission of schools in geographic regions such as the Southeast and Pacific Coast. The reader is also cautioned about the intensity and scale of the inquiry which permitted only an identification of selected programs and courses. The project evaluation task was carried out at an exploratory level. Nevertheless certain patterns emerge from the general observations which call for the following recommendations:

1. If a program or curriculum in environmental education is to be successfully administered on any campus, the institution, through some mechanism of interdepartmental or interdisciplinary faculty should establish a coordination body where environmental education resources are pooled. The instrumentality could be in the form of an Institute or Foundation (University of Colorado), a Center (Cornell University), an Environmental Education Program (University of Wisconsin) or a committee (Harvard's Committee on General Education). When no formal curriculum coordination exists among contributing disciplines several disadvantages can occur. The Master's and Doctorate programs in Environmental Education at the University of Michigan can be strengthened, for example, by more formal faculty coordination in selected departments.

2. A strong plea is submitted for more graduate level courses in the major concept areas of environmental education. Several institutions are offering environmental education courses to undergraduates but none to graduate students. The specialization effort in graduate courses has tended to eliminate instead of refine, sophisticate and upgrade the environmental education listings in comparison with the undergraduate courses. It is suggested that the urgency of biological and physical problems in the environment requires awareness and understanding at least equivalent to the commonly accepted graduate skills of foreign language, computer programming, survey techniques, and communication (writing) abilities.

3. It is recommended that a depository for environmental education regional and national case studies be established. The proposal suggests the need for a file to be maintained that would list regional, state, or national problems which could serve as current research topics or case studies in need of study. Upon completion of a case study the newly gathered information would be placed in the depository which could serve as an informational clearing house for a wide array of physical problems of the environment from the local to the national level. The contents of the depository would be made available to interested institutions of higher education and

others on a regular basis. It is presumed that the environmental education "depository" could be housed in the Office of Education (HEW), in a Division of the AAAS, or at the Conservation Foundation, Washington, D.C.

4. It is suggested that American universities and colleges need to provide increased training programs in the form of course offerings, field work, and related studies in order to adequately meet the demand for more environmental educators expected in the decade ahead. For example, the New Jersey Council for Environmental Education in their April 1968 report revealed that 181 districts are engaged in or planning what are called environmental education programs. The upsurge in America's concern for a quality environment is expressed at the operational level by increased job opportunities for persons trained in environmental education. But American universities will fall short of supplying environmental educators which school systems and other agencies will need unless new environmental education training programs are initiated.

5. It is suggested that an inservice training and field seminar opportunity be provided for university-based environmental educators. An annual symposium is envisioned which would bring together researchers, university teachers and university administrators in an effort to exchange and explore new areas of mutual concern. Teaching strategies, literature and research findings, and other learning innovations could be shared. The symposia could be organized either nationally or regionally with divisions of graduate and undergraduate in separate sessions.

6. The suggestion is posed that an evaluation procedure be devised which enables graduates of environmental education programs to provide feedback to their parent institutions on how programs could be strengthened and made more relevant. This notion seems to be especially important in an area of academic attention as new as environmental education. With this suggestion the "graduate to alma-mater" reporting system promises to keep environmental education courses and programs dynamic and sensitive to the current issues not only as faculty members see the challenge but as practitioners at the community, agency, or other operational level see the need and the challenge of environmental education.

SUMMARY

The resolution of physical problems of America's urban and non-urban environments will continue in an ineffective, ad hoc basis until more and better programs in environmental education can be provided at the university level. College students who are destined to be decision makers in business and government, influentials in community life, and teachers at primary and secondary levels require a better understanding of the environment which they effect and which effects them.

Most current programs in conservation education are oriented primarily to basic resources; they do not focus on community environmental problems. Furthermore, few programs emphasize the role of the citizen, both individually and collectively, in working toward the solution of problems that affect our environment; very few of the programs are relevant to the learner because of the lack of personalized, problem-centered focus. There is a vital need for an educational approach that effectively educates man regarding his relationship to the total environment.

This pilot evaluation of a limited number of institutions of higher education revealed that no campus-wide mechanisms presently operate to plan for and coordinate programs in environmental education. Many of the schools have or had planning efforts underway. But very few universities provide or require a curriculum sequence in what could be termed environmental education. Harvard University is an example of the approach deemed satisfactory.

Several institutions offer a rather rigorous track (but lacking breadth) in environmental education related departments such as city and regional planning (Massachusetts Institute of Technology), civil engineering (University of Colorado; Massachusetts Institute of Technology). Another of the best examples is the Center for Environmental Systems Engineering at Cornell University.

Perhaps the most serious shortcoming that was observed during this study was the absence of any vigorous environmental education program in the Departments or Schools of Education. Qualified exceptions to this point occur at Wisconsin State University at Stevens Point and Eastern Montana University at Billings. Overall a very modest and uncoordinated teacher training effort in the area of environmental education was the rule at every institution studied in the inventory.

Including the University of Michigan pretest, ninety professors were interviewed or personally contacted from twenty-four institutions of higher education during the study. From the preliminary observations brought to light by this pilot study a workshop conference would provide the forum necessary for deans, faculty members, and selected students who were environmentally educated to share innovations and explore implementation procedures of new or revised courses and programs in environmental education.

A national workshop on environmental education would provide the forum for professors and administrators in American higher education to consider objectives and alternatives for reaching those objectives in what appears to be a new and synthesizing discipline. An overview of this study indicates that a thorough analysis of environmentally oriented programs and courses is in order on nearly all campuses where interviews were carried out. At most institutions the resources are available; it is the mobilization and coordination of faculty and curriculum that are needed after a rather thorough inventory is made. Readers of Environmental Education are invited to submit suggestions and additional examples of noteworthy approaches to the author in as much as the study is continuing.

The deterioration of the physical environment primarily in the urban regions of the United States is nearing a proportion where the citizenry is sensing the environmental illnesses but is bewildered about the causes and remedies at local, regional, and national levels. The availability of well-conceived, nationally recognized programs and courses in environmental education is a challenge institutions of higher education in the United States can ill afford to neglect any longer. Enough examples of good beginnings are available so that interested institutions and educators can share successes and innovations with others who are concerned about the future of man's environment.

"We must help the individual see himself as part of a vast living ecosystem."

THE PREPARATION OF THE INTERPRETIVE NATURALIST

AIN Task Force

THE ENVIRONMENT around us may be varied or monotonous, beautiful and exciting, or it may be ugly and depressing. The difference originates in our own minds and determines our subsequent action upon environment. What we understand, we value, protect, and cultivate; what we do not understand we neglect, waste, or fear.

The pressures of burgeoning population and technology upon the limited environment are already critical. The deprivations imposed upon most of us are great—loss of scenic beauty, of clean air and water, of contact with the once-fascinating diversity of other forms of life. Severe economic penalties may force us to obtain minimal corrections, but only an awareness, a positive understanding, and a love of the land, waters, and life around us can make possible the highest quality of environmental experiences.

Much of the customary conservation education and nature instruction has been narrowly conceived or directed to limited groups. Our concern must not be limited to stewardship of farmlands, or game management, or scouting skills. Most people of today are urban, largely ignorant, apathetic, or apprehensive of the land, yet hopeful of new experiences. Our concern, and therefore objective, is to bring to all of them the fullest realization possible of the life beyond self and to awaken the drive to preserve and experience all of "this curious world of ours."

The interpretive process should begin at an early age and as close as possible to home. Museum nature vans, green neighborhood parks, natural areas for schools are some of the opportunities. When young children enjoy these glimpses of life outside the immediate home surroundings, interpretation has begun. The next step is programs to allay fear and to arouse curiosity. The ultimate goal, after all, is to have and maintain a life supporting environment. An environment which man is rapidly fouling as much through ignorance as through sloth. So we must help the individual see himself as a part of a

vast living ecosystem. Each person must somehow find the thing of which he is a microcosmic part, safeguard it by understanding care, love it by a sensitivity to it. This is an involvement beyond self, beyond friends to the complete encompassing of the living environment. It takes interpretation.

The interpretive naturalist therefore needs the abilities to begin his service at very elemental levels and to extend his effort to life's largest dimensions. No profession has a greater challenge.

COMPETENCIES OF AN INTERPRETIVE NATURALIST

(1) Knowledge and understanding of the natural and man-made environment

> Botany and Zoology with an ecological orientation
> Natural History
> Vertebrate and invertebrate zoology (such as ornithology, mammology, entomology, and limnology)
> Local flora (including taxonomy, dendrology)
> Astronomy
> Physical and historical geology
> Natural Resources Conservation
> Ecology (with inclusion of man in ecosystems)
> Independent Field Study (with very practical application)

(2) Knowledge and understanding of the effective use of communicative skills

> Speech
> Expressive arts
> Writing (especially expository)
> Plastic and graphic
> Audio-visual aids
> Public Relations

(3) Knowledge and understandings related to:

This position paper has been developed by a special Association of Interpretive Naturalists task force under the chairmanship of J. Sanford Replinger.

A. How people react, think, mature, etc. (human behavior)

   Sociology
   History (American and world)
   Psychology, perhaps educational and social
   Anthropology (with emphasis on relevance of human history)

B. Economic functioning of the community

   Economics
   Political Science
   Demography
   Urban and Regional Planning
   Philosophical considerations

(4) Knowledge and understandings that relate to program planning and administration

   Interpretive Methods and Techniques
   Administration of Interpretive Programs
   Philosophy and Techniques of Environmental Resource Management (using resource personnel who are not teachers)

(5) Integrative considerations in a final seminar

   Seminar to consider Man, the Transformer of Environments, to deal with human ecology, i. e. man in terms of competition vs. adjustment relative to world goods, energy supply, life space, environmental contamination, religion, etc., nationally and internationally.

SUPPORTIVE COMMENTS

(1) Knowledge and understanding of the natural environment

The subject matter areas which are listed as being of great importance to the interpretive naturalist should be strongly field-oriented in presentation. In addition to the field work which may be incorporated into the course work offered by the training institution, summer terms should be utilized to gain practical experience and to provide opportunities for further extending the acquaintance with the out-of-doors. However, summer work experience alone should not be considered to be an adequate means of gaining field experience.

Courses in basic biological science should include strong emphasis on evolutionary and ecological aspects. The whole outlook of the interpretive naturalist must be that of the ecologist. Courses designed to enable students to identify common organisms and to understand their life history provide the foundation upon which this ecological understanding can be built with more advanced courses.

The geology, with strong emphasis on soils, should be field oriented and should include historical aspects of the subject. Natural resources conservation provides the bridge which connects this portion of the training with the "people oriented" portion of the curriculum.

(2) Knowledge and understanding of the effective use of communicative skills

Skill in the use of communicative arts can be used in a number of ways. Some ability and experience already acquired in this field is presupposed for persons who choose training for this vocation. It is not intended that all students take course work in all the areas mentioned, but to build on preexisting skills and to sharpen the ability to express their ideas. This field is expanding rapidly and those whose jobs are to communicate should be familiar with the newest and most effective techniques. This need is the reason for listing desirable competencies in the broadest terms. In addition, basic public relations is a "must" for (a) techniques and (b) understanding of the problems of management which hires interpreters.

(3) Knowledge and understandings related to people

a. In order to convey his message, the interpreter must not only know his subject, but he also must know and be interested in people, their needs and dynamic interrelationships. Thus the courses listed under this heading should make up a substantial portion of the curriculum.

In addition to course work, summer work in parks, group camps, and other situations where experiences working with people may be gained, is essential to the development of capabilities in this area. The practicum in the senior year is highly recommended.

b. Interpretation is dependent upon not only the natural environment, but also the human environment. This includes local institutions, man's changing use of the land, and historical backgrounds of the particular area in which interpretation takes place.

An understanding of man's dependence on the land, and problems related to future environments should be achieved through experience, in dialogue, action involvement, and related argumentation; not limited to course work.

(4) Knowledge and understandings that related to program planning and administration

A methods course in interpretive techniques should be developed as a part of any interpretive naturalist's curriculum. Training in administration of interpretive programs including program planning and the management of nature centers should be provided. Courses in the management of natural resources are essential to an understanding of the complex interactions of social and natural forces which mold the management planning and underlie the administrative programs of resource agencies.

Here as in come of the other areas, it is expected that a considerable amount of the needed skills could be gained by summer employment with appropriate organizations and appropriate personal follow-up.

Conservation training must involve ethics and esthetics quite as much as economics and ecology.

A FOCUS

IN THE HUMANITIES FOR RESOURCE MANAGEMENT EDUCATION

Philip N. Joranson

NATURAL RESOURCE management education is having growing pains of many kinds. Some have been diagnosed to a deficiency in exposure of students to the value concerns of the humanities. Aside from the basic business of teaching effective writing and speaking, with few exceptions there has been no compelling rationale about the specific relevance of the humanities in the education of a resource manager.

But society is changing and resource management is changing in ways that are placing some of the concerns of the humanities fields more and more obviously within the interest range and operational scope of the resource management professions. A good place to see this is in the current running contest on one issue after another between those who are strongly partisan to "preservationist" action and those who just as ardently support "conservationist" policy. Surely there is some truth in both points of view. But when either of these positions is promoted unbendingly, it betrays a failure to appreciate and understand very much about the total matrix of needs, values, and resources within which policy advocated would have to be pursued. Only certain kinds of needs, selected out of the total array of diverse needs by which man is related to nature, are seriously considered within each of these two competing interest groups. Really responsible citizenship today, however, must mean trying to recognize and appropriately value them all!

WIDER PERSPECTIVES

How can this actually be done in the professional life of resource managers as it is intermeshed within the structure of society? It must be done by working from a mental perspective that is wide enough to embrace all of the different kinds of considerations and values that need to be dealt with. This breadth is needed for operating realistically. It is also an indispensable condition for creativeness, and creativeness is expected in human evolution.

There are two principal departures by means of which we must expand our mental reach in natural resources curricula toward this end. First, we need to look at all of the different kinds of relationships between man and nature. They are of many types. This is suggested by the center portion of Figure 1.

FIGURE 1

FULL-SPECTRUM LIGHT ON MAN'S MULTIFORM RELATIONSHIPS WITH NATURE

(History, anthropology, political science, and law—all little used so far—also belong in this diagram. The perspectives in these fields deserve the same kind of emphasized attention that is here devoted to the four humanities fields.)

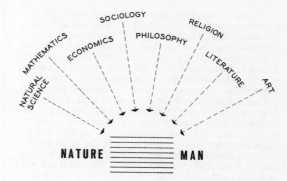

In attempting to size up these many kinds of relationships as to the kinds and importance of the values we will associate with each of them, we need, as a second major departure, to approach from a broader base of information and value perspective than we have used in the past. This will mean making full use of appropriate fields in the humanities, in addition to those fields of knowledge upon which we now rely. It will mean—as the arching portion of Figure 1 illustrates—adding to our usual approaches through natural science, mathematics, economics, and (latterly) sociology, some purposeful adventuring in philosophy, religion, literature, and art. No small part of the significance and richness of these fields consists in

Living at Cider Mill Road, Andover, Connecticut, the author is a private consultant and lecturer in forestry education.

concepts, attitudes, and appreciations that concern what nature is and the status and quality of man's relations with it. The questions we will ask in each of these fields are (1) What are the concepts or attitudes or feelings toward nature that are being advanced, and (2) What are the consequent implications for our understanding: how should particular types of man-nature relations—both individually and in relation to each other—be conceived and handled.

We will be accumulating a fund of ideas and attitudes with which to approach the whole range of relationships. Only with this kind of background can we claim the full respect of the public for the kinds of decisions we make on natural resource issues in which several types of man-nature relationship are involved and value priorities must be determined among them.

Such a program, including the humanities, as well as some other largely neglected fields not specifically dealt with here, would provide a highly purposeful and, I believe, very rewarding total approach for professional education in resource management. I see it as a challenge both to each individual and to the professions in approaching our many-sided land management decision responsibilities. It could go a long way toward overcoming a bondage of tightly held special interest within the resource management professions themselves, and I am thinking most particularly here of forestry, which is the field I know best. It would also make it possible for the trained forester to become a much more effective public advocate of balance and breadth in assigning priorities among nature-associated values.

"Nature" has been defined in many ways. What I mean by it here is the whole of the earth and the universe, both living and non-living, except mankind—all the rocks and waters and mountains and soil, the mineral and energy deposits and atmosphere, all the plants and animals and all that lies beyond this planet—but not human beings. Although this is a common and a useful definition, it needs some qualifying. In the most fundamental sense, man is part of nature. Like all other living things, he owes his origin to evolutionary process and is therefore kin to all other forms of life by ties as basic as the very DNA substance that guides the activity of the cells that compose both his body and theirs. Making very sure that we do not lose sight of this great biological and philosophical truth, it is still, however, very useful and necessary for the purposes of analysis to make the distinction between man and nature ("not-man") which the definition of "nature" we have adopted makes possible. We can now go ahead to distinguish and study each of the many varieties of relationship between man and those entities—living and non-living—in the world and the universe that are other than man. Together, these relationships constitute a vast and complex system within which each kind must be accorded due attention and importance if the system is to thrive.

Let us now become more specific and try to suggest the great reach and variety of man-nature relationships and associated values. From nature man receives the necessary physical and chemical conditions of biological existence, food, water for many uses, materials for shelter and to equip him for a productive, creative life in sufficient abundance to provide leisure for development of his higher capacities. Nature environs man with beauty, cosmic companionship, opportunity for recreational enjoyment, provides an originally mostly stable land surface for habitation, furnishes man with the evidences of his own evolutionary origin and relationships and contributes to man's self-understanding. But nature also produces the potential threats to life, health or property, of earthquakes, lava flows, droughts, extreme temperatures, hurricanes, floods, disease, skin irritations, insect depredations and nuisance effects, etc. These various interrelations between man and nature involve many specific activities: eating and drinking, breathing, keeping clean, managing and harvesting forests, researching, farming, gardening, mining, breeding plant and animal species, suppressing forest fires, regulating wildlife populations, hunting, fishing, vacationing, reserving and managing parks and wilderness areas, planning and building dams and managing watersheds, polluting the atmosphere, landscape, soil and water with wastes, designing and constructing buildings from natural materials, etc.

This is certainly not a complete list, but what it does include covers an enormous range in modes of interrelationship. All of these human activities are subject to social or personal ordering for maximum good, often through the use of a highly developed technology. In our rapidly moving society, generating many kinds of pressure and now subject to increasingly limited benefits of some of the kinds listed above, what are the most appropriate and creative principles and attitudes, where are the priorities as to the values to be achieved, what are the new directions? We are ready now to turn to the spectrum of disciplines which are open to our search for answers to such questions.

Let us first take some notice of the fields of knowledge—shown in the left half of the arching portion of Figure 1—on which we now rely: natural science, mathematics, economics and, most recently, sociology. These four types of approach yield indispensable kinds of guidance in understanding nature and dealing with man-nature relations as they are encountered in natural resource management.

But what about the humanities disciplines—religion, philosophy, literature, art? What can they contribute to a fund of ideas and attitudes useful to the graduate resource manager in reaching management decisions and formulating management policy? We will begin with religion.

WHAT THE HUMANITIES OFFER

Religion

There have been many definitions of religion. For our purposes here, a definition by Professor Theodore Gaster of Barnard College is useful, even though it is necessarily so general that it does not recognize in its language the distinctiveness of such faiths as Christianity and Judaism. He says religion is a "synthesis of thought, emotion, and behavior whereby, under sanction, men attempt to formulate and articulate their place in the scheme of things," and that it points to "dimension beyond the immediate." Under this definition, thought, emotion, and behavior will all be of interest in searching out the status of nature in a particular religious system. Thought here means creeds, theologies, and in a qualified sense-scriptures; emotion means quality and intensity of feeling; and behavior concerns personal and social ethics-in our present concern including personal and social ethics toward nature.

Now a word about what a theology is. By a recent definition of John B. Cobb, Jr., a theology is "any coherent statement about matters of ultimate concern that recognizes that the perspective by which it is governed is received from a community of faith." There have been many theologies in Christianity's history, as well as in our time, for each age needs to reinterpret in terms of its own time, problems, and resources for understanding.

Among religious systems and among theologies there is enormous variation in value discernment in nature and in the degree of concern with nature. Perhaps a good start among systems might be to look at Christianity, which is the faith most familiar to the majority in this country, and at some of the Far Eastern systems: Shintoism and Zen Buddhism in Japan; Taoism in China. Nature has a very prominent place in these Far Eastern systems.

And what theologies should we study? In the stress of today's critical conditions and projections concerning human abuse and ill use of nature, theologians are seeking as never before to understand, in Christian terms, the values involved in man's relations with nature. This has led to a new look at the Old and New Testaments and a restudy of theological development since the New Testament. During most of that long period influences were at work that discouraged emergence of positive attitudes toward nature in the Church. An outstanding exception was St. Francis of Assisi, a radically dedicated thirteenth century Christian. In his "Song of Brother Sun and All Creatures," all nature is on a "brother" and "sister" basis; God, man, and nature are brought very close together.

Coming down to our own times, many have been drawn by the writings of Albert Schweitzer and Pierre Teilhard de Chardin. Schweitzer makes an impressive case for ethical treatment of all living things. Teilhard sees a rising inwardness in the course of inorganic, organic, and finally human evolution, toward a point of final cosmic spiritual convergence. Among other directly relevant thinkers are Martin Buber, Conrad Bonifazi, Allan D. Galloway, Charles Hartshorne, Bernard E. Meland, Peter Schoonenberg, Paul Tillich, and Daniel D. Williams.

A common thread that unites a number of the religious writers, as well as some other writers, is their insistence that the entities of nature have integrity, value, and importance in their own right, and do not derive their value exclusively or necessarily from utility to man.

Philosophy

What is it that makes philosophy relevant in our search for tenable attitudes toward nature and man-nature relationships? We can get some hints by taking a look at the main characteristics of philosophy. In philosophy we find a constant attitude of radical inquiry with no predetermined conclusions; a scope which is all-embracing, spanning the whole of reality knowable to man and the entire reach of man's experience; a quest after ultimates, that is, after the most profound understanding of the physical and biological world, of human history, of art and beauty and of the goal of religious aspiration; and finally a method, called dialectical, that is simultaneously inductive and deductive in its relation to the other disciplines (after Theodore M. Greene).

DesCarte's philosophy went a long way toward freeing the world of nature for scientific study and toward ushering in the era of science. But it also devalued nature and contributed very substantially to our dominating modern view of nature as something material. One of the trends of reaction to this came in the organismic, evolutionary philosophies of Bergson, Alexander, Lloyd Morgan, and Smuts, some of the writings of James and Dewey, and finally in a flowering in the process philosophy of Alfred North Whitehead. Whitehead's was a monumental achievement in attempting to find common principles of explanation in terms of which all our experience and all natural events taking place in the universe might be understood in reference to what is ultimate. Charles Hartshorne, Bernard E. Meland, Daniel D. Williams, John B. Cobb, Jr., and others have explicated and carried forward his thought. Other modern philosophers such as Husserl and Scheler have taken a different tack.

Literature

In English and American literature much has been written about attitudes toward nature. Especially well known is the nineteenth century nature poetry of Wordsworth and Shelley. We should weigh the writings of such authors as Herbert Spencer and Thomas Huxley, Melville and Whitman, Thoreau and Emerson and Muir, Aldo Leopold and Joseph Krutch and many others; read what their critics have had to say; and decide for ourselves what we think of the suitability of their ideas and value judgments in view of the environmental facts and projections that we face today.

In literature, trends and interests reflect the cultural preoccupations of the times. Thus the poetry of Wordsworth and Shelley has been described by Whitehead in his Science and the Modern World as "a protest on behalf of the organic view of nature, and also as a protest against the exclusion of value from the essence of matter of fact." But are there not also some writings that seem to have an essentially ageless quality?

Art

Nature has been one of the best loved subjects of artists through the ages in both the East and the West. They have seen it in many different ways, and all of these are open to our study. Some critics are concerned today that it will be to its detriment if modern art strays too long and too far away from nature.

Much of art is the portrayal of beauty and an entire branch of philosophy, called aesthetics, is devoted to a conceptual understanding of beauty.

Summing Up

Let us again ask how the kinds of perspectives we have briefly described help us in approaching the whole range of interrelationship between man and nature. We see emerging from such a perspectival spectrum that includes the humanities a rich fund of information, theories, ideas, experiences, and attitudes which become our resources for understanding, according to their relevancy, each of the many modes of man-nature relationship. Then, after we have thought about the many modes and seen them in relationship to each other, we can narrow down from the big total picture to see where such a process brings us out on the values involved in specific decisions of the kinds that we must deal with in our professional work.

We will not suppose, of course, that if we have spent some time at this, we will have then arrived at some master plan for selecting and balancing discerned values in nature and in man that will henceforth supply confident answers to all our decision problems'. No, the human process is endless. It is up to each resource manager, I think, to continue his growth in value sensitivity and maturity and to do this with the help of all that he can learn and feel and appreciate from a sustained total spectrum approach.

And the same challenge also confronts every citizen. The approach outlined here is of course proposed also for general education and teacher education curricula. But the natural resource manager bears a special responsibility.

A PROGRAM FOR EDUCATION, RESEARCH, AND INTERDISCIPLINARY EXCHANGE

What we have outlined must become an enterprise for education, for research, and for new kinds of exchange between the familiar resource management fields of study and the newer disciplines. In a teaching program, there would be at least three essential features:

(1) Focusing of responsibility in the natural resources faculty, but a blend of instructorship from all the contributing disciplines. This means cultivating close relationships. There is no substitute for real interdisciplinary sharing between the instructors themselves. It's hard work, but it can be very exciting, and there should be time and money for it.

(2) A core of common content, drawn from all of the fields surveyed here and some others, but beyond this some leeway for the student to choose fields in which he wants to spend the most time.

(3) Challenge to the student to organize his own

total perspective and to apply it in his own decisions on specific current problems.

To run alongside and feed the educational process, this is also a field for a great deal of research. The elucidation of attitudes toward nature in the Hebrew and Christian traditions and in other religious systems needs much more of the scholar's attention than it has had. Much the same is true in philosophy. One of the main tasks of scholarship in all four of the humanities fields is to identify and make generally available and understandable the most relevant and creative of man's feelings and thoughts upon nature to be found in their literatures.

But not only does resource management need the humanities; the humanities people also need the resource managers. In order to be relevant and accurate, those whose creative work is done in the humanities often need to know something about the realms of nature in which our work as environmental managers is done and what our problems are in meeting today's challenges. Not a few philosophers and theologians today, for example, recognize that they cannot hope to accomplish their work without wide acquaintance in major fields of knowledge. So what we foresters, wildlife managers, and other resource managers work with and try to accomplish out in the field and in response to the wider challenges we face, needs to be communicated. The people in other fields of endeavor are usually as distant from us as we are from them.

And there is yet another step to be taken. Some resource managers, because of the lively and responsible situations where their work puts them, between nature and society, ought to take up their own places among the other critics of what has emerged and is now emerging in the humanities fields. We must not only inform, but we must also evaluate what others have done in other fields, where we can contribute a needed perspective or criticism.

A thoroughly reliable first principle for making ready for the future and its demands is to envision much greater cooperative flow between fields of learning that are logically and practically interrelated and that need each other every day if the challenges that are being generated in an ever-changing society are to be taken up and met creatively. To establish and cultivate these working relationships right now, in our age of highly critical environmental stress, therefore, is simply common sense. Whatever the difficulties of innovation and accommodation, this must not be postponed in resource management education! ∎

A plea for new methods and systems of ecological education.

THE LONG, WIDE VIEW OF BIOLOGY

H. Lewis Batts, Jr.

LIFE IS a quality, not a thing, and its essence is order—order as activity resulting in certain forms and processes. Biology is supposed to be the study of this quality, life, but in practice biologists study not life, but its attributes, its results—the certain forms and processes. These are studied at all known levels of complexity—some levels, the simpler ones, receiving more attention than others. All are equally important to an ultimate understanding of life, but much more is known about particles than about parts, about parts than wholes, about simple processes than complex systems. We do not need less study of simpler forms and processes than directed to them now, but we do need more consideration of complex systems, whole patterns, than they now receive.

The simplest form exhibiting characteristics we identify with life is a virus, and it seems to possess these only when situated inside a living cess—a rather direct and simple (although unknown) relationship of dependence. We know much about the forms and processes of cells and even of their molecules. We know what substances some bacteria must have in order to maintain normal life. We know what substances and conditions to provide in order to grow active yeasts, juicy tomatoes, gorgeous chrysanthemums, fat chickens, cuddly poodles, and contented cows. We may not fully understand it, but we recognize and accept the fact that there is a dependent relationship between these organisms and their environment.

Man goes to great lengths to learn and then to provide the proper environments for his yeasts, chrysanthemums, and cows. Man does not go to such great lengths to learn and then to provide the proper environment for himself.

Yes, we do know that as human animals, people, must have certain things in their environment in order to survive—water to drink, air to breathe, food to eat, and a place to live. We do not know, however, in what condition they must be. To what extent can we change our water, air, and food and still survive? To what extent can we change them and remain healthy, much less, happy? We do not know, but as we continually change our environment we act as though we know quite well. There are many indications that already we have made too much change in our environment; many people are suffering, many more are uncomfortable. Lives are being lost because of this ignorance.

Cancer is being more and more referred to as an indicator of civilization, a disease induced by the artificial environment. Primitive tribes of people in Africa and Australia rarely have cancer, yet it kills more children in the United States each year than any other disease; and it has been diagnosed well enough and long enough so that it is obvious that it is on the increase. In addition to cancer, diseases of the lungs, liver, and heart, and mental disorders are on the increase, even in young people, in the United States.

There are population "explosions" of blackbird and insect pests; and the war against crop-eating insects in the United States gets harder and more costly each year, instead of easier. We lost our chestnut trees and passenger pigeons some time ago, and we are about to lose our elms and whooping cranes. What will be next, perhaps robins, oak trees, people? The importance of learning the causes of increased incidence of human disease and increased populations of destructive pests is obvious. The importance of learning how to save elm trees, whooping cranes, and other forms, may not be so obvious, if indeed it is important at all. They are, however, parts of man's natural environment, and may be links in his chain of survival.

Increasing numbers of people are being deprived quickly of the opportunity to live in even a semblance of the environment to which the human animal, man, has gradually adapted over very long periods of time. Even though we do not know what they are, from observations of other animals it is inconceivable that there are no limits to our adaptability.

Biology as pure science may have no obligation beyond the discovery and description of natural phenomena pertaining to life, but biologists do. Someone needs to interpret the results of scientific inquiry and apply them toward improving the quality of living for people. Much of this, of course, is being done, but far too little and in too limited a perspective; and much of what is being done is done by technologists who rummage through the masses of data gleaning isolated bits and pieces primarily for economic reasons and secondarily for immediate benefit of mankind. More research concerned with cancer, insect pests, and elm tree disease has been aimed at finding commercially manufacturable substances for use in curing them rather than aimed at finding causes and preventing these conditions. There is much less immediate economic profit in discovering a naturally operating system of checks and balances than there is in manufacturing an artificial substance. As Dr. Donald A. Spencer of the Pesticides Regulation Division of the U. S. Department of Agriculture recently commented, the government has "no control over industrial research, of course. The economics of the country dictate this."

Manufacturers and producers of things and services, and their advertisers, determine to a larger extent than any other influence how people live, the very quality of our living. They persuade us what to consider important: powerful gasoline-fueled automobiles and boats; color TV sets; large green lawns of closely cropped, uniform, weedless grass; the looks of fruits and vegetables; the amounts of artificially added nutrients in packaged foods, etc. The

Dr. Batts is Professor of Biology at Kalamazoo College, Kalamazoo, Michigan, and Executive Director of the Kalamazoo Nature Center for Environmental Education, 7000 North Westedge Avenue, Kalamazoo.

public is just beginning to learn that there are higher, hidden costs in addition to the purchase price attached to these things we are convinced we need. Our gasoline engines pollute the atmosphere with toxic substances and noise; some TV sets now admittedly leak X-radiation. The tremendous amounts of fertilizers and pesticides required to produce homogeneous lawns and unblemished fruits and vegetables are killing unbelievable numbers of bees, fish, oysters, birds, and mammals—the importance of at least some of these we already know.

Many people have exploited the long-held belief that nature is here for man to do with as he pleases—a forest exists to be cut down and a stream exists to be used as a sewer—believing that no price need be paid for such behavior. As a consequence of this belief we allow and contribute to the pollution of our own environment:

Yearly we release millions of tons of pollutants into the air (approximately one ton per person in the United States), pollutants which damage buildings, vehicles, crops, lungs, etc. Yearly we discharge billions of tons of pollutants into our creeks, rivers, lakes, and oceans, some of which is returned to us in our food. Yearly we apply millions of tons of some of the most toxic chemicals known to man onto our crops and on soil in which they grow, and some of this we eat, also. Yearly we kill outright or contaminate the homes and food of wildlife—plants and animals whose importance in the environment of man we do not know.

When confronted by the growing concern of public health scientists and conservationists over the fact that residues of certain insecticides called chlorinated hydrocarbons (DDT, dieldrin, aldrin, endrin, etc.) are building up to higher and higher levels in our environment and in our own livers, fatty tissue, and brains, technological apologists point with pride to the tremendous contribution to our economy made by the widespread use of these highly toxic substances. Not only is the manufacture and sale of these poisonous chemicals contributing directly to our economy (the public paid $1 billion for pesticides in the United States in 1965), but through their use crop yield is much greater, populations of these disease-carrying flies and mosquitoes have been decimated, etc. These economic and public health results have been produced in the short view, but there are other results that should be considered (even economically) in the long view.

Furthermore, target insects such as flies and malaria-carrying mosquitoes have built up resistance to DDT to the point where they are again becoming serious threats to human health. Short-range battles with these and other insects have been won, but apparently the war has only begun; as resistance develops, subsequent battles get harder to win and thus the problem is increased by the so-called solution.

No one knows the effects on us of any one of these substances as they accumulate in our own tissues. The recently established federal monitoring program has indicated that the average human already carries pesticide residues in his fatty tissues alone in the amount of 12 parts per million, and we cannot avoid increasing this amount. These poisons are in our food, air, water, and soil, where their residues are known to remain toxic for many years. DDT reportedly has been found in every animal tested for it from the Arctic to the Antarctic, and no DDT has been applied anywhere near these two polar areas.

Now systemic pesticides are beginning to be used. These poisons are meant to be taken up internally by plants and the insect pest is killed when it feeds on the plants—plants that are being grown for food for humans and for animals that are to be eaten by humans. DDT, systemic poisons, etc., even though they obviously get into human tissue, do not have to be tested by or for the manufacturers for internal effects of small amounts on humans, as do drugs, because "they are not intended for use in the body." Fortunately, and due almost entirely to growing pressure from an increasingly enlightened and alarmed public, insect control research is moving away from broad-spectrum persistent poisons to highly specific natural substances such as an insect's own growth-regulating hormone. This is an ecologically sound approach and, when synthesized, such substances can be produced commercially and thus contribute to the economy.

Biologists often appear to abdicate to technologists, or perhaps they are only out-shouted. There is no reason at all why the technology that produces the goods and services man wants cannot produce them without polluting his environment. In the rush to get the economic advantage over a competitor, the extra care necessary to avoid polluting the environment may not be taken. However, wherever it has been demanded by the public it has been taken, and easily.

When the public demanded that detergents be made so that foaming action would not be evident in streams and lakes, manufacturers quickly produced the more desirable degradable detergents. Upon demand, manufacturers of gasoline engines are finding ways to reduce noxious exhaust gases; and pesticide manufacturers are finding excellent substitutes for chlorinated hydrocarbons. We will stop threats to our well-being only when we see true relationships and insist that man's total welfare be put above that of purely economic considerations. Only then will we refuse to accept the proposition that a polluted environment is a necessary price to pay for having the goods and services we want.

This is a challenge to our methods and systems of education. The body of scientific knowledge is growing so large so rapidly that it is not possible to learn or to teach more than small fractions of any scientific field. It is these tiny fragments that are not only inadequate, but misleading. Students are thereby prevented from seeing wholes and overall order. We need to teach the broad perspective so that, whether the student becomes a farmer, lawyer, physician, or biologist, he realizes that whenever changes are made anywhere in our environment, other changes will result. Therefore, utmost care must be taken to understand the consequences of changes before they are attempted. Attitudes and perspectives are therefore far more important to teach than are facts: for the facts of today change into tomorrow's fiction. Knowledge must serve the future.

A broader perspective is needed, and who are better equipped, and therefore more obligated, to provide this wider view if not biologists? Research and interpretation to the public are desperately needed at levels of interacting systems of individuals, populations, communities, and their total environments.

Many of the problems we face today, whether political, economic, sociological, or biological, result from the expediency of yesterday—taking the short, fragmented glimpse rather than the long, wide view. ∎

"The energies of the campus must be redirected."

THE UNIVERSITY AND ENVIRONMENTAL EDUCATION

The Editor

TO SUPPORT and sustain the third American rev-olution—the search for environmental quality—we need new integrated programs that will discover, dissem-inate, and apply the ecological and economic facts, en-gineering techniques, and esthetic appreciations basic to an applied conservation conscience. Each Ameri-can institution must adjust itself accordingly. The implications for our institutions of higher education are particularly clear. The energies of the campus must be so redirected that environmental management will share in the skills and resources the university can contribute to the solution of public problems, and the university in turn can profit from the stimulation that comes from confronting a pressing public issue.

About how best to involve the university in a broad strategic campaign against the pervasive degradation of the American environment, there is considerable discussion and experimentation. Because goals vary, institutions vary, traditions vary, perceptions of prob-lems vary, and terms are imprecise, there is a lack of consensus. The aspects of the problem defy easy pigeonholing. They keep slipping out of the discrete departments into which universities tend to be organ-ized, and out of the tight compartments into which action agencies tend to consign their tasks.

One approach, for example, would be to examine environmental education from the perspective of uni-versity organization. The trouble here is that the prob-lems of environmental quality defy the traditional pat-tern of the division of labor within the university which arranges knowledge into a series of subject matter areas concerned with segments of the physical, bio-logical, and social sciences and the humanities. An-other approach would be to examine environmental education from the perspective of such conservation objectives as outdoor recreation opportunity, water quality and supply, forest and field yield, urban beau-ty, and so on. The trouble here again is that conflicts among competing resource demands are frequent and intense, and it is becoming increasingly difficult to draw any clear quantitative or qualitative lines among the problems. Each specific resource use raises a congeries of questions about man's relationship to his total environment, and the choice of alternatives among competing resource uses involves legal, economic, social, administrative, technological, esthetic, eco-logical, and ethical considerations which in turn span manifold governmental agency and university depart-ment lines (1).

Any attempt to dissect environmental education in-deed runs the risk of so multilating the specimen that it loses its essential characteristic—its multidisciplin-ary, multi-process nature. Yet it is necessary that we collate its contents and goals in some way if we are at least to agree on what to disagree. One ap-proach is simply to ask the question:

> With respect to environmental education,
> what are the needs and demands of the mar-
> ket for the goods and services of the university?

The university engages in basic research, and in applied research and development. The university supports elementary and secondary education, and supports and may even engage in 2-year terminal vo-cational training. The university performs under-graduate instruction, professional education, and advanced scientific training. The university engag-es in formal adult education, informal counseling, and extension services. Environmental education should be an aspect of all of these levels of enter-prise:

New Knowledge and New Knowledge-Seekers

The conservation, redevelopment, and mainte-nance of environmental quality requires more knowl-edge than we now possess. The things we do not know about the earth machine and its denizens are stag-gering. At the level of fundamental knowledge, we are desperate for criteria and tools with which to measure environmental quality in an ecological sense and in an economic sense. At the level of technolo-gy, we lack means and ways of abating, restoring, controlling. Actually it is rather fruitless to worry whether the research to be performed is termed ba-sic or applied, or whether we start with a stated re-quirement and proceed to a solution or start with a concept and proceed to an application. The impor-tant thing is that we ask the right questions; in other words, that the research be cast in a problem-solv-ing climate—the problem being the achievement of environmental quality. Much of such research can be initiated by existing university departments; some will require development of hybrid departments or at least of special task forces. Again, it would seem fruitless to worry about the "home" of the research. The important thing is that each scholar, regardless of his stripe, accept a redefinition of his role and his conceptual approach that recognizes the problem of environmental quality and its interdisciplinary nature.

Professor Schoenfeld's article is based upon testimony given before the House of Representatives Select Sub-Committee in behalf of the Brademus Environmental Quality Education Bill, 26 March 1970, Washington, D.C.

Intimately associated with the university's search for new environmental knowledge will of course be the graduate training of researchers equipped to fill the public and private stations where environmental studies will be pursued in the physical, biological, and social sciences. How in fact to train such scholars in a more productive cross-fertilization of ideas poses a vital question for the modern university. It is one of those striking anomalies that at the very moment that the problems of the environment are seen as being inextricably related, the university's specialists are becoming ever more specialized. Clearly the watchword of environmental studies must be the production of multidisciplinary knowldege a n d multidisciplinary knowledge-seekers.

More and Better Professionals

The conservation, redevelopment, and maintenance of environmental quality requires more managers or operators better equipped to apply present and emerging knowledge. At least three broad types of professionals can be identified. First, there are the resource technicians like park managers, geologists, ecologists, meteorologists, foresters, geographers, economists, sociologists, architects, hydrologists, game managers, engineers, and so on. Not only must they be well grounded in their specialty if they are to be immediately employable, but if they are to be promotable they must be able to relate their discipline or function to that of other professionals and to the larger questions of human values and environmental policy. Second, there is the need for the broad resource generalist, perhaps the rarest of all species, who can deal effectively and creatively with whole policy issues in all of their complexity in a staff or executive role. Third, there must be "change agents" equipped with an understanding of the interrelationships involved between their callings and total environmental management, and with a knowledge of the tools of the trade in energizing land and water u s e controls—lawyers with pertinent legal skills, designers and planners with a grasp of resource policy implementation, communicators and educators equipped to interpret resource problems in such a way as to achieve consensus rather than conflict (2).

In the production of new professionals, are we talking about 4-year, 5-year, or 6-year programs? Do we start with generalists and make specialists out of some or do we start with specialists and make generalists out of some? Do we modify, expand, broaden, intensify the curricula of existing departments and schools, or do we invent custom configurations? These are some of the questions presently agitating the university as it faces the training of environmental technicians, public policy formulators, and change agents.

One promising form of environmental management training involves the bringing back to the campus of operational personnel for more specialization or more broadening, depending on the needs and goals of the selected individual. Such programs may be of the non-credit professional refresher type, or they may involve the granting of advanced degrees. Whatever the type or level of professional environmental management education, the product should be specialized enough to be viable in field operations and broad enough to appreciate the complicated biotic and human phenomena over which he presides. It is no small challenge.

Citizenship Education

In the final analysis, environmental quality management will proceed only as far and as fast as public opinion will sanction. The university can assist in three ways in the achievement of a mass conservation literacy. First, in its undergraduate education it can confront all students—not just career majors—with the kinds of resource management conflicts about which as citizens and voters they will render crucial judgments; it can attempt to instill a desire for constructive change; it can suggest biosocial standards of values, and it can offer practical guidelines to action. Second, the university can assist the public schools in the development of K-12 scope and sequence concepts and materials that will lift conservation education out of any rut of irrelevant or inadequate approaches and techniques. Third, the university can assist 2-year terminal technical institutions in developing sound curricula for the field aides who must increasingly be produced to fill sub-professional positions in resource management agencies of many types.

Technical Counsel and Services

Growing national programs of environmental quality management depend increasingly on regional and local initiative and responsibility. It is only at the intra-state level that most federal policies can be translated into public and private practices, yet it is at this level where the forces of wise resource management continue to be ill-equipped to deal with the forces of exploitation. The inefficiency with which public agencies and private citizens go about performing the socially essential tasks of environmental house-keeping stem largely from the fact that the technical and organizational skills available to the land conserver or rational planner are normally inferior to those available to the land exploiter. In its traditional extension mode, the university must reinforce local leaders with improved educational materials and professional consultation on environmental quality. While we continue to search for more environmental facts and to train more environmental managers, we can help apply what we already do know by rifling skills and resources to the local level. Those contending for environmental quality need data to show that economically we can afford such surroundings and that biologically we cannot afford anything less. The facts and techniques need to be made applicable and available in localities where the problems exist and where the issues a r e fought. Local leadership needs a fund of information and special talents on which to draw, including the effective stimulus that would come from knowing the experiences of other leaders in other communities who have met and overcome some of the common problems. Interdisciplinary teams of university extension personnel can collect, collate, and disseminate practical guidelines to community organization and action in l a n d and water use controls (4).

A Federal Role

While it would be nice to think that the university would or could engage in a self-energizing program of environmental education of adequate scope and depth sans outside help, the fact remains that in the absence of federal funds such is likely not to happen, particularly in the presence of federal support for educational programs that actually mitigate against the development of interdisciplinary research, teaching, and extension focused on environmental quality. Federal funds, for example, support some water pollution abatement research that is too unilateral; they support some highway engineer training that is too narrow; they support some agricultural extension work in environmental degradation; they support elementary and secondary education programs that have nothing to say about conservation. Until Congress reviews its broad authorizations and appropriations for w a t e r management, agriculture, transportation, and urban redevelopment in the context of environmental quality goals, and particularly until Congress invests specifically in broad environmental education, it is unlikely that the universities will have the will and the way to enter the picture before substantial sectors of our environment reach a state of perturbation which will be difficult if not impossible to correct at reasonable cost and within reasonable time limits.

In sum, we need a federal Environmental Education Act which will state unequivocally a commitment to environmental quality research, teaching, and extension, and provide segregated funds. The rationale for such an Act would be simple: it is unthinking people who pollute the environment, and it is thinking people who can bring about environmental quality conservation redevelopment and maintenance (5).

REFERENCES

1. Cooley, Richard A. , Graduate Educational Research in Natural Resources Public Policy, The University of Washington, Seattle, 1966, p. 6.

2. Schoenfeld, Clay, "Educating the Public in Natural Resources," Journal of Soil and Water Conservation, November-December, 1968, p. 17.

3. Schoenfeld, Clay, "Environmental Education and the University," Educational Record, Summer, 1968, p. 306.

4. Schoenfeld, Clay, "Regional Environmental Education Centers," Environmental Education, i n press.

5. Schoenfeld, Clay, "Toward a National Strategy for Environmental Education," The Journal of Educational Research, in press. ▪

History, archaeology, anthropology, political science, sociology, economics, geography –
all are in the act.

ROLES FOR SOCIAL SCIENTISTS IN ENVIRONMENTAL EDUCATION

Robert N. Saveland

WHO STARTED the parade? There is no doubt that it is moving. Ecology as a word has even been turning up in the comic strips. Ecologists who have been talking about environmental quality for years are suddenly finding themselves on the bandwagon. Not only are they up front with all the fanfare, they are also slapping the reins. What's more, there are plenty of others seeking a place beside them.

Popular media has taken up the cause of environmental quality. Each of the major weekly newsmagazines gives substantial space, if not entire issues, to environmental problems. Saturday Review has started a supplement on the environment. Even Sports Illustrated came through and reprinted Lord Richie-Calder's article, "Mortgaging the Old Homestead," which appeared originally in Foreign Affairs.

In these days of managed news, one is inclined to view such hoopla with some misgivings. Is the danger real? While the President's State of the Union message has made environmental quality a national issue, how long can the public interest in these problems be sustained? It is in this context that the role of the social sciences in environmental quality needs to be evaluated, for environmental problems have not always been thought of as a social science concern.

Whether a humanity or a social science, the discipline of history is related to environmental quality. Beacon Hill, Georgetown, Lookout Mountain, The Saarinen Gateway Arch in St. Louis, Glacier National Park, Alcatraz, and countless historical sites and monuments are outward manifestations of that relationship. The work of the historian is inextricably linked with the development of our value systems. By our sets of values we determine what we want to preserve of our environment and heritage. In the rebuilding of American cities, structures are often torn down because they are old. In the process, we have sometimes exchanged a part of our character for a glass facade, or for the blacktop of a parking lot. By communicating with architects and city planners, historians can assist in the decision-making process relative to the kinds of surroundings which will reflect the values of our society.

The historian also has a role as a chronicler of the environmental-quality movement. As such, he perceives that it did not spring full-blown onto the American scene, but had its antecedents in earlier conservation activities. John Muir, Gifford Pinchot, and Theodore Roosevelt are known as pioneers in this movement. Fairfield Osborn (2), William Vogt (5), and Rachael Carson (1) are latter-day exponents whose contributions deserve a place in this chronicle.

Because a concern with the dead past and primitive cultures is frequently attributed to archaeology and anthropology, these fields may not at first appear to relate to environmental quality. Italian subway builders might take issue with this proposition. Repeated attempts to build a new tunnel in downtown Rome have been thwarted when old ruins have been encountered. Each time, alternative routes had to be planned. Recently in Atlanta, Georgia, construction work on a new shopping center was delayed for weeks in order to give archaeologists time to complete a "dig" when Indian relics were uncovered by bulldozers. Anthropological studies of present-day communities of people who live in harmony with their environment will be increasingly important as social and technological changes bring more manipulation of those environments, as on Nauru island where phosphate mining is eating away the island itself (3). Anthropologists, as well as other social scientists, are especially concerned with how man perceives his environment, and with the customs, institutions, and mores he conceives in an effort to rationalize that environment.

Among the social scientists, the political scientist now has one of the more important roles in relation to environmental quality. Many of our laws are based on traditional freedoms, such as riparian rights, mineral rights, and sovereignty of the seas, which come in conflict with emerging attitudes toward

Dr. Saveland is Professor of Social Science Education, University of Georgia, 127 Fain Hall, Athens. He is author of World Resources.

At the Pruitt-Igoe Housing Complex in St. Louis, $1,700 a day is spent in an effort to cope with vandalism. The Complex comprises 33 high-rise buildings with a 50 percent vacancy rate.

environmental quality. Legislation which established soil conservancy districts can be referred to as a model of how an environmental problem can be approached by legal means. New federal and state laws are establishing standards of quality for our air and water, and providing the means for achieving and enforcing those standards. Beyond the letter of the law lies the power structure of our society. The political scientist is aware of the means by which pressure groups work to achieve their desired goals.

The sociologist is also concerned with the group structure of our society. Race, caste, and prejudice play a part in the quality of our environments. During the same month as the President's State of the Union message on environmental quality, vandals roamed through the Pruitt-Igoe housing project in St. Louis. They smashed windows that ordinarily protect water pipes from freezing. Burst pipes caused 10,000 residents to spend a weekend in freezing misery. Subsequent renovation will cost close to a million dollars. At the time of its opening in 1954, the Pruitt-Igoe housing project was widely acclaimed for its design. The public looks to the sociologist and psychologist for some explanations of the motivations, frustrations, and fears which have transformed so much of our public housing into monsterous high-rise slums.

The rural landscape is not without its sociological problems related to the quality of the environment. Mechanization and farm consolidation are the basis for migrations leading to ghettos. The underemployed and destitute who remain on the land may suffer malnutrition and hunger in substandard housing which gives little credit to the world's most prosperous nation.

Sociologists and demographers study the age-sex composition of various populations. Data on birth rates are indicative of trends in population growth, a basic factor in environmental problems. Warning signs have gone up, the outcomes of population control lies in unpredictable areas of human behavior relative to contraception, abortion, hunger, disease, and nuclear warfare.

Economists point to the disparity between unlimited wants and limited resources as a factor in environmental quality. Plainly, many of our environmental problems are an outgrowth of the industrial and technological revolution. They are complicated by the high rate of product consumption within our society. The costs of alleviating industrial pollution of our air and water are ultimately borne by the consumer. Now, however, these costs are being taken into consideration more and more in determining the profit to a community and region in locating an industrial facility within the area. By the use of simulations and a systems approach, economists can contribute to intelligent planning and zoning.

Last but not least, the geographer has traditionally called for the conservation of our natural resources (4). In essence, the cultural geographer is a human ecologist (6). As such he is vitally concerned with myriads of interrelationships within the ecosystem. His particular skill in analyzing site factors, routes, and land-uses especially equip him to deal with problems of environmental quality. Paradoxically, on the issues of environmental quality, geographers have not been in the public eye to the extent that ecologists have.

Two branches of geography deserve particular mention in connection with environmental quality. Historical geography, with its emphasis on sequent occupance, can demonstrate the changes which occur in the environmental quality of an area through time. Settlement geography, in part, focuses on frontier areas of the world where man is beginning to impinge upon his environment in sufficient numbers to cause problems.

From the foregoing, an overriding idea becomes clear. Whereas each of the social science disciplines has its particular point of view regarding problems of environmental quality, the problems themselves are a common concern. Thus, concerted action regarding these problems calls for interdisciplinary cooperation, not just among the social scientists, but also between social scientists and natural scientists.

In addition to a role within a discipline, social scientists also function as researchers, technicians, and teachers. Some of the areas for exploring human behavior as related to environmental quality have been indicated. In delving into these areas, researchers will test hypotheses and accumulate more data leading to new insights into environmental problems.

The social science technician actually works on day-to-day problems associated with environmental quality. He maps the blighted areas of cities or seeks alternative expressway locations. As a social worker, he or she may work directly with people, especially in trying to improve home environments. Not only in government, but also in business, can persons trained in the social sciences contribute to the better management of our surroundings.

Teachers have a special responsibility in the matter of environmental quality. The time lag between cause and effect in environmental matters can be compared to the gap that separates the high school student from the adult. The battleship Arizona went to its grave almost 30 years ago. Oil from its sunken hulk still seeps to the surface at Pearl Harbor. If all use of DDT were stopped now, some would still reach Antarctic penguins 10 years hence. Further effects of the population explosion lie ahead.

Under such circumstances, the civics teacher cannot confine his classes to the content of the constitution. History teachers cannot simply rehash former happenings. Geography teachers must do more than girdle the globe. Social science instruction will have to operate in the affective domain. Students "turn on" when it comes to problems of environmental quality, like the Ohio high schoolers who wound up a study of pollution in Lake Erie by appearing before a Senate committee. Or they become involved like the students in a school in Connecticut who gained national recognition for their PYE (Protect Your Environment) Club.[1] Through study trips and first-hand contact with decision makers, classes can enter the affective domain.

In the last analysis, all social scientists operate in the role of citizens. Currently the wolf cry is being raised on environmental problems. Is the danger real? As in the fable about the boy who cried wolf, will citizens disregard the warnings after a time? The social scientist as a citizen has an obligation to help bring about better human responses that will result in a higher quality of life for the people of this earth.

FOOTNOTE

1. Thomas School, 40 Highland Avenue, Rowayton, Connecticut 06853.

REFERENCES

1. Carson, Rachael, Silent Spring, Houghton Mifflin, Boston, Massachusetts, 1962.

2. Osborn, Fairfield, Our Plundered Planet, Little, Brown, and Company, Boston, Massachusetts, 1948.

3. Saveland, R. N., World Resources, Eastern Hemisphere, Ginn-Xerox, Boston, Massachusetts, p. 246.

4. Thompson, J. L.; Thompson, B. R., "The Concept of Conservation Needs Revision," The Journal of Geography, pp. 516-517, December 1969.

5. Vogt, William, Road to Survival, W. Sloan Associates, 1948.

6. White, C. L.; Renner, G. F., Human Geography: An Ecological Study of Society, Appleton-Century-Crofts, New York, New York, p. v, 1948. ∎

A call for reform in the preparation of teachers for the new conservation.

THE <u>EDUCATION</u> IN ENVIRONMENTAL EDUCATION

Ira Winn

TWO DOMINANT and interrelated themes are found in the new conservation movement in American education: (1) the integrated or interdisciplinary approach as a substitute for narrow and traditional departmentalized offerings; and (2) the corresponding necessity to implement programs that will give people not only an understanding of the ecological facts of life, but will move them to action in helping to prevent and solve environmental problems. The first theme underlies many problems of higher education. It signals the need for a basic reappraisal of educational structure and better organization and administration of curricula. But it is the second theme that in many ways is the more difficult to act upon, for the planning involved can easily fall into the category of wishful thinking that so often widens and clouds the gap between felt needs and effective educational programming.

Havlick's survey of environmental education opportunities in American higher education indicates that the most serious weakness is "the absence of any vigorous environmental education program in the Departments or Schools of Education . . . very modest and uncoordinated teacher training effort at every institution studied"(2). At the same time, interestingly, the study notes that few students now in the field of environmental education plan to enter teaching. And when they arrive in training, doubtless those few teacher candidates are highly specialized as biologists or geographers. Thus develops the vicious cycle that must be broken before the training of teachers for the new conservation movement becomes adequate for the needs and realistic for the times. The departments of education, biology, city planning and architecture, recreation, agriculture, sociology, etc. will have to work cooperatively or they will fail in the difficult task of environmental education because they deny the interdependence of educational life even as they affirm it for life in general.

THE ENVIRONMENTAL EDUCATION TEACHER

For one thing there are few teacher education specialists who are adequately trained in the evnrionmental sciences. For another, there are few scientists who have a grasp of the difficulties of mounting an effective teacher training program. Commonly, training is seen as the giving of courses—the filling of the pitcher of the mind with facts about the environment that can be learned in the various departments. But what must be quickly learned by environmental educators is an old dictum of Plutarch: The mind should not be seen as a pitcher to be filled, but as a flame to be kindled and fueled. The fact that man does not act simply on the basis of his knowledge accounts not only for the high rate of drug use among doctors or the ease with which advertisers and highway engineers fool housewives and house owners; this fact affects the entire fabric of our being and raises questions about out perception of the way the world really works and what we are prepared to do about it. The purpose of this article is to offer some perspectives for effective training programs in environmental education, to set the sights and raise some standards, and to point out some of the pitfalls that lie along the way.

It would be utopian to assume that most university education in the near future will take a fully integrated tack. Interdisciplinary seminars, however, can be set into the more general departmentalized framework and thus serve as a vitalizing force and a link between subject specialists. Of course, the environmental education major, whatever his particular subject specialty, will take a broad spectrum of course work involving both physical and social sciences and the humanistic studies which raise fundamental questions of esthetics, values and ethics. Most important during the upper division and graduate years, interdisciplinary seminars and symposia should be made a part of the requirement for all subject majors in fields involving the environment. In fact, this is no more than to say that at least a 1-year seminar on environmental problems be made a part of the minimum requirements for a university degree.

CASE STUDIES

The educational dialogues of the new conservation must be strongly problem-oriented. Environmental educators should lean heavily on the use of case studies in order to bring field realities into the classroom and to cause diverse subject specialists to rub shoulders and broaden their perspectives. The decisional character of case study is of particularly vital significance to environmental education (3). The approach not only forces cross-disciplinary thinking in the course of problem solving, but it is strongly directed toward consideration of fundamental value problems inherent in the development of democratic political life. Illustrative is the recent study by Erickson and Reynolds of the ecology of the Quabbin reservoir (1), a case analysis that moves thinking and discussion beyond the preliminary level of problem description and data collection, where so much of education today lies stagnant. The focus on judgment (the solution of the case problem) helps the participants in the case discussion to adopt the reflective-questioning attitude so vital to the new conservation. As the authors conclude, "The ecological system of a reservoir includes our own sociology. If it is scientifically possible to dredge a reservoir, for example, is it sociologically wise to 'dirty up' a fisherman's favorite lake? If it is scientifically feasible to reduce nutrient levels in a res-

Dr. Winn is Associate Professor of Education, San Fernando Valley State College, Los Angeles, California.

ervoir by strict surveillance of sewage disposal and fertilizer use in areas surrounding a reservoir, is it politically feasible to do so? These are obviously questions that the biologist and engineer cannot answer—but it is often within the framework of just this kind of question that their proposals must be built" (1).

The teacher candidate who is nurtured through such an interdisciplinary sharpening process will be primed to enter into the modern currents of inductive teaching. Those trends are now beginning to revitalize teacher education as a force for social change. First, the goals of teacher training for environmental education need to be written from an operational standpoint, rather than in terms of glittering generalities and traditionally vague objectives such as "appreciation of nature" or "understanding the importance of conservation." A more appropriately written lesson goal for the new conservation might be: "Students will be able to point out political factors influencing decision on a given park localization or choice of freeway routing"; or, "Students will be able to find examples of environmental contaminants in home or neighborhood store and be able to explain to their class and the owner the reason for their danger." The student teacher in environmental education should thus become proficient in lesson planning for behavioral change. While there will still be room for a general statement of objectives, incorporating a rationale or a general philosophy, modern educational experience dictates a break away from the common fixation on lesson planning at the abstract level. The second point of departure from tradition is the need for stress on practice of problem solving techniques and innovative approaches that both stimulate intellectual curiousity and practical wisdom. Peer teaching critique sessions, perhaps using video tape, can be "traded" for factual knowledge with subject specialists in the sciences and in other areas where schools of education will likely be in short supply.

The use of combined teams and visiting consultants will further the healthy exchange of ideas as well as give the necessary substantive boost in what will constitute a mutual learning phase over the next few years. Social science teacher trainers should have little difficulty adapting to the political economic, and sociological side of environmental education, while science trainers will easily learn to handle approaches to the physical aspects of environmental problems. But the real trick is to combine these forces with all the other esthetic and value perspectives that make up the whole of the new conservation—and life in general.

ADOLESCENCE OF ENVIRONMENTAL EDUCATION

During the coming (and inevitable) 3-5-year period of adolescence and early adulthood of the environmental education movement, there will be need for special and summer projects, federally and privately financed, to develop training programs and new educational techniques and to set standards for assessing progress. As the Report to the President's Council on Environmental Quality has noted, not only is there "excessive reliance on traditional classroom methodology," but environmental projects in the past have lacked evaluation and articulation, and it is nearly impossible to tell what works best and why (4).

This admission of past deficiencies, this need to experiment anew and to borrow in order to build a new field of knowledge is not as gloomy a course as first it may appear. The new conservation has the advantage of not being bound by the constraints of traditional subject organization and methodology. And the changes in teacher training will help force corresponding reform in the secondary schools, as physical, social sciences, and recreation are brought into better articulation. Financial support seems to be steadily increasing, and, hopefully, the foundations and government agencies concerned will increase their aid in order to institutionalize and expand environmental education centers in the universities. Naturally, failures can be expected to occur, if only because the field is still emerging from its infancy. But in a more basic sense, learning is a form of borrowing and profiting from error, and often the best learning occurs in the act of teaching others while teaching oneself.

What larger outcomes can be expected from such an educational reform movement? Properly administered, what should result is not only a transformation in the structure of education but new perspectives, new perceptions, new actions by the general public (5). The awakening of the citizenry to the delicate ecological fabric of life will bring into being a political body much more resistant to the blandishments of the hucksters, aware of long run consequences of short run plans, and alive to the dangers of patchwork approaches to problems of food supply and population, energy sources, underdevelopment, pollution, and other social issues. Students of the new conservation will inevitably be activists, oriented toward involvement in the world community and its problems. Thus will be created or recreated that which gave heart to Tocqueville as he weighed the promise of the American scene—a community of publics, now engaged in thinking about the nature of their education and their environment, questioning the kinds of cities they are living or going to live in, and concerned about the kind of life they are leading. Are we, those most concerned with environmental education, fully ready to accept these changes?

REFERENCES

1. Erickson, Paul A.; Reynolds, John T., "The Ecology of a Reservoir," Natural History, 78:(no. 9) 52, November, 1969.

2. Havlick, Spenser W., "A Glimpse and Analysis of Environmental Education Opportunities in American Higher Education," Environmental Education, 1:(no. 1)21-24, Fall 1969.

3. Hunt, Pearson, "The Case Method of Instruction," Harvard Education Review, 21:177-178, 1951; Winn, Ira, The Case Study Reform Movement in American Civil Education: Educational Implications of Political Apathy, doctoral dissertation, University of California, 1966, pp. 109-166; Oliver Donald; Shaver, James P., The Analysis of Public Controversy, Harvard Graduate School of Education Report, chapters X-XI, 1962.

4. Rockefeller, Laurance and others, "Report to the President and the President's Council on Environmental Quality," pp. 13, 31-32, August, 1969.

5. Winn, Ira, "Public Parks and Private Lives," Natural History, 78:(no. 8)20-26, October, 1969; Ferry, W. H., "The Technophiliacs," The Center Magazine, Center for the study of Democratic Institutions, Santa Barbara, 1:(no. 5)45-49, July 1968.

"An integrated effort to combine bits and pieces of research into broad understanding."

THE MAN - ENVIRONMENT SYSTEM APPROACH

Reid A. Bryson

THROUGHOUT some 3 billion years of evolution, living things have adapted to the environment by an intricate network of interaction and reaction. The threads of this web are so closely interwoven and complex that discord in one section usually spreads like a wave into every corner of the pattern. Today degradation of the earth's physical and biological environment poses grave threats to all living organisms. This degradation has serious social, cultural, economic, and esthetic, as well as biological, consequences for mankind. Indeed, there is growing evidence that these threats could reach catastrophic levels. Within recent decades, man has rapidly proliferated in numbers, cleared forest and prairie for agriculture, covered lands with highways and cities, stripped the wilderness of minerals and resources, and perhaps most disastrous of all, has endlessly polluted the waters, air, and lands. It is apparent that man has begun to tear apart the fine fabric of the very resources upon which he is so totally dependent. Yet the environment is rapidly deteriorating at a time when ever increasing numbers of people depend upon it and are seeking greater uses of it.

We need a better understanding of the physical and biological effects of the natural and man-made environment upon man. We must gain a clearer understanding of the relationship of all living things to their physical and biological surroundings. We must learn how to keep the earth's environment in a condition capable of maintaining life throughout the decades and centuries of the future. We can no longer afford the luxury of assuming that the future will take care of itself.

The university has a major responsibility to mobilize its resources to aid in the solution of environmental problems. It has a clear responsibility for the survival and improvement of life for civilized man. In addition, our entire educational system has a responsibility not only to preserve and transmit the knowledge, wisdom, and values of the past, but to discover and develop that which will ensure the survival of the present and future generations with improvement in the quality of life. The educational system must have a mandate to develop a commonly held body of knowledge about the whole man-environment system so a national environmental ethic can emerge.

To deal effectively with the intricate interrelationships among features of the physical and biological environment and their social, economic, and political consequences requires a measure of integration of intellectual effort rarely achieved in the past. The knowledge and analytical tools of many disciplines must be utilized, but more critically, a true interdisciplinary effort is required to solve some of the more intractable problems and to design effective policies to deal with them. The investment of effort must be multiplied through established disciplines and also must be expanded through the development of comprehensive interdisciplinary programs of education and research which integrate the various disciplines.

There has been serious discussion on organization for environmental studies among students and faculty at The University of Wisconsin-Madison through a series of committees, beginning as early as 1966. Actually, The University of Wisconsin had a long-standing reputation as a leader in environmental studies, beginning in the early 1900's with the pioneering research of Birge and Juday on the limnological problems of Madison's lakes. Since those early investigations, Wisconsin has become a national "center of excellence" for research on eutrophication, the accelerated aging of natural waters due to man's activities, the contamination of natural waters, and pollution abatement. The University also is a leader in research on legal aspects of environmental quality, computer modeling of lakes and streams, and sewage treatment methods. Wisconsin experts have pioneered in rural land zoning and environmental diseases. The University is one of the leading centers for research on food poisoning and how bacterial organisms affect food. Our earth scientists continue their search for an adequate understanding of the basic geophysical and ecological principles which govern the relationship of life in its environment—particularly that of man to the earth. Wisconsin meteorologists are studying the physics of the atmosphere to better understand the mechanisms of energy distribution that power the weather and account for climatic change. Climatic change is of interest particularly for understanding world patterns of climate and the impact of climate on ecological systems. University climatologists are studying the possibility that atmospheric pollution from industry, large-scale man-made changes in vegetation over the earth, or the triggering of cloud formation by jet contrails may intervene in the delicate balance of atmospheric forces and result in climatic changes of great significance.

Widespread interest in the broad area of environmental studies at The University of Wisconsin in the past decades has generated dozens of centers and programs in the biological, physical, and social sciences on the Madison Campus, and many faculty members have been engaged in teaching and research in environmental studies. A number of programs have developed cooperation and participation of faculty from several disciplines, and will continue to do so. Yet

---

A distinguished meteorologist in his own right, Dr. Bryson is the Director of The University of Wisconsin's new Institute for Environmental Studies at Madison.

despite this impressive array of scientific and technical competence, we have felt that something significant was missing—the massive integrative effort to combine the bits and pieces of research into a broad understanding of the total man-environment system, in all its biological, physical, social, and cultural aspects. We also felt there was a need to develop several kinds of teaching programs: (1) broad undergraduate programs concerned with the environment which would contribute to a knowledgable and ecologically perceptive citizenry; (2) a more advanced masters level program for the training of environmental managers; (3) a doctoral research and education program directed particularly at those interdisciplinary environmental areas which have been largely neglected in discipline-oriented research, and (4) a strong adult education and extension program to carry the results of research to application on the many pressing environmental problems, and to provide an interchange of ideas between university and citizens.

To these ends, The University of Wisconsin this year reconstituted its Institute for Environmental Studies as a divisional unit responsible to the Chancellor of the Madison Campus. The Institute, which had been a research unit within the Graduate School, now has been administratively restructured to provide improved leadership and impetus to the University's teaching and research efforts in the environmental studies area. Functions of the Institute are threefold:

1. Provide leadership in interdisciplinary environmental research by initiating new, and coordinating existing, research programs;

2. Initiate and support cross-disciplinary undergraduate and graduate courses and degree programs;

3. Improve communication among groups and individual faculty members involved in environmental research, training, and extension programs, and with the public. (The Institute will develop and foster programs of external communication to concerned publics through University Extension.)

Many of these activities are already underway, and the Institute will assist in their further development toward closer cross-disciplinary ties and greater public awareness. The integrating focus of the Institute for Environmental Studies is the man-environment system: the relationships between man, individually and collectively, and his natural and man-made environment. We are concerned particularly with quantitative answers, for the problems are so complex that we must know which factors are more important and which actions may have consequences far larger than their apparent significance.

The above mentioned concerns and conclusions prompt the following observations:

First, there is a general lack of understanding of the nature of the man-environment system and the need for ecological balance by professional academicians and by the public. There is widespread public concern over environmental quality today, which will continue and increase, but there is considerable dissonance because of the complexity of the problems and the lack of knowledge. Much of the attention on environmental problems so far has resulted from a growing recognition that there are problems. This recognition ranges from awareness of things around us that are unhealthy or unpleasant to awareness of some global environmental problems. There has been less attention to rational solutions of individual, local, or nonlocal problems. This is a source of frustration. Individuals can gather up aluminum cans in a spring cleanup, or choose low-phosphate detergents, but they can't by themselves deal with the large sources of environmental perturbation, or set up the social, economic, and legal institutions that will be able to do so. Many people are aware of their individual impotence. Environmental education that elucidates problems or makes people more aware of them will only increase this frustration unless it also deals with means and methods for solution.

Second, much of the material on environmental problems has been rhetorical. There is a need to quantify as many of the factors influencing the environment as possible and a need for the construction of models. The educational process must also deal with this need to quantify. People must understand interrelationships in ecosystems. Decision makers must understand the consequences of alternative decisions throughout the system. It should be pointed out that modeling work on environmental systems is a young science in which students can be involved. This means that new curricula at all levels should aim at developing on the one hand an appreciation of the interrelation of all parts of the web of life, but on the other a feel for which interactions are most sensitive. The totality of nature is too much for the single human mind to comprehend, but the well-educated citizen must understand the essential framework and how much stress is tolerable.

The above two points also say that new curricula aimed at environmental understanding and ecological awareness should not be composed of "shopping lists" of traditional courses and subjects, for the lack of integration of discipline-oriented courses and research is probably the most important reason for the general lack of understanding of man as an integral element of a complex system. It is clear that a prime purpose of education is to help the citizen discover who he is and how he relates to the rest of the world. Integrative environmental curricula, properly designed, can do much to alleviate the general failure of traditional curricula to achieve this goal. There is a general lack of understanding of what is meant by "ecology." It is a term used in both narrow and broad senses. There is also great variation in the use of the term "environmental quality." Both should mean more than conservation of wildlife and abatement of pollution.

Many of our current environmental problems are a function of population growth and increasing percapita consumption of resources. That is to say that not all our problems are poor-housekeeping problems. This means that the educational program needs to establish the relationships between population, pollution, and ecology. Further, the public needs to be in a position where it can make intelligent value judgments about what kind of life it really wants; that it is no longer possible to "let technology take its course." Because if we do, nature will surely respond and take its course.■

"A disciplinary beachhead in the no-man's-land between the two cultures of science."

ECOGRAPHY: A NEW SCIENTIFIC DISCIPLINE

Everett M. Hafner

SEVEN-TENTHS of the way through the 20th century, we are suddenly all discussing the possibility that man may be breeding and poisoning himself out of existence. Food shortages, limited mineral resources, water and air pollution, energy consumption, chemical and radioactive contamination, noise generation, deforestation, and many other problems suddenly seem to be growing faster than the rapidly growing population itself. We are also suddenly aware that our attack on the environment is an attack upon ourselves. Even as our technology expands, it appears to threaten physical and mental health of men everywhere. Thus, we are beginning to see that a dramatic change in man's attitude toward himself and his planet is necessary for his survival.

Each of us has his own dreadful vision, his scenario as it were, of what can happen to us if we continue along our present course. A brief but violent nuclear war, brought on by the rage and frustration of hungry millions or by tyranny or even by simple ineptitude, is the most familiar fantasy. Mine is very different from this and in some respects even more dreadful. It is based loosely on our recent observations of Venus, a planet of Earth-like size, but whose atmosphere is grotesquely different from ours. In my image, the cloud of dense water and carbon dioxide enveloping the planet is the result of massive pollution of the air by runaway processes started by an ancient technology.

In the light of what we now suddenly know about ourselves and the natural world, the story of what might have happened on Venus a billion years ago is not unbelievable. Life evolved from lower to higher forms in a warm but otherwise benign habitat; an intelligent species arose to exploit its resources for the sake of power and growth; a point was reached where the balance of life was endangered by insults to the environment. Increasing amounts of carbon dioxide in the atmosphere, coming from large-scale combustion of hydrocarbons, began to raise the temperature of the planet by the familiar "greenhouse" effect until it became clear to all thinking people that life itself would soon be threatened. Despite the most imaginative efforts on the part of her scientists to alleviate the problem, Venus grew steadily less habitable as the temperature rose. A strange and uncontrollable panic gripped the planet, leading eventually to the revival of old and discredited superstitions. One of these had been the worship of Earth, a blue and conspicuously beautiful neighbor in the sky, long recognized by scientists as an abode of life and a possible haven for the overpopulated societies of Venus.

It was already too late to develop more than pathetic and abortive attempts to send large colonies of Venutians to Earth. But under the spell of panic and superstition, and with vast resources to support them, engineers designed a monstrous project. Their idea was to bring about a dramatic change in the spin of Venus. Huge jets were erected on the equator and enormous amounts of fuel burned for many years in order to slow down and ultimately to reverse the rotation. When the engines finally stopped, more than one percent of the total mass of the planet had been sent into space; a fraction of the exhausts remained as the atmosphere that we now see. In the final state of rotation, Venus was spinning slowly backward at just such a rate that, once every 584 days, at the time of closest approach of the two planets, a space station fixed on Venus had Earth shining at the zenith. But all life had vanished.

I do not mean to propose this as a serious theory for the explanation of the atmosphere of Venus or of its strange and anomalous rotation. I am only suggesting something that is within the realm of possibility not only for the history of that planet, but also for our own future. We are already well along the road toward irreversible change in the quality of the Earth, brought about by our own insatiable greed and our inability to control our own growth. If we reach a point of no return, it is not inconceivable to me that we shall react to the pressure of a variety of frightening circumstances by going mad as a species. Then Earth, too, may grow a dense opaque atmospheric shroud which for all I know is the sign of the death of planets.

But fortunately we seem to have some time in which to reverse the march toward the destruction of our world. We are also fortunate in witnessing the emergence of a new generation of young people deeply concerned for a wide range of social problems and equipped with energy and good sense to act out their roles as responsible citizens for our time. I have had the privilege of meeting and working with many students who represent the movement toward restoration of the environment, and I am convinced that they deserve all the help that we can find for them. My own small contribution is a proposal that they

Dr. Hafner is Dean, School of Natural Science and Mathematics, Hampshire College, Amherst, Massachusetts. This paper is from a Symposium on Undergraduate Studies in Environmental Science in connection with the American Association for the Advancement of Science annual meeting in Boston in December 1969, and from a National Science Foundation Project Directors' meeting in Washington February 1970. The paper has also appeared in Ecotatics, Simon and Schuster, 1970.

learn to think of science in a broader and more comfortable sense than their experience has so far suggested to them.

It is, of course, not the fault of young people alone that science is now widely viewed with hostility, as a cold and insensitive instrument whose work is devoid of or even antagonistic to social and humanistic value. This is a picture that scientists themselves, perhaps inadvertently, have helped to create. But we are beginning to see vigorous signs of a change. While much of the traditional hard science of the past is now losing support, other areas which bear most heavily on the condition of man are now coming strongly forward. First among them is ecology—the branch of biology which deals with mutual relations between organisms and their environment. It is a science with a long and venerable history, but only recently, in the presence of acute distress in the ecology of man, has it come to prominence with the sense of excitement and promise that I recall when nuclear physics burst upon us more than three decades ago. But ecology by itself, even with strong emphasis on the human species, will not be sufficient to handle the grave problems that confront us now, since many of them appear to have their roots in social and political behavior. In the remarks that follow, therefore, I attempt to delineate a new field of science standing midway between what we now recognize as the natural sciences and the social sciences, combining insights of both and developing its own fundamental technique.

History tells us that ideas, like organisms, follow a pattern of evolution that we do well to understand. In religion, in philosophy, in art and music and literature, and in history itself, newborn ideas may or may not be strong enough to mature and wise enough to age gracefully. Mutation and replication are working processes in the history of ideas, as are symbiosis, parasitism, slow disease, and sudden death. Academic people are, or ought to be, midwives at the birth of ideas and coroners at their death. Too often do we neglect those roles. Many a conceptual rose is born to blush unseen; many a corpse languishes in the academy denied of its right to be buried.

Communities of ideas, gathered together around central themes deeply rooted in human consciousness, form the "disciplines" of academic life. At a given stage of our development, each academic discipline represents a consensus on questions of priority, feasibility, research technique, continuity, and academic prestige. The enterprise of learning works best when we nurse and nourish the newborn, while burying the dead with minimum expense and ceremony.

Nowhere are these processes more vivid than in the history of science. My own most familiar discipline—physics—regarded sometimes as a central kingdom in the larger world of natural science, formed itself slowly and painfully from a set of powerful ideas in philosophy, mathematics, astronomy, experimental design, chemistry, engineering, and military science. Galileo sensed the birth of discipline when he constructed dialogues on "Two New Sciences," but it was not until much later that physics emerged in recognizable form. Even now there is some difficulty with its definition: there are dictionaries that describe it in negative terms only as "the study of inanimate matter in which no chemical change occurs." There is also extraordinary variety in the

work that physicists do, from bottom to top of the energy scale and from the smallest to the largest of natural systems. Yet it is fair to say that physicists share more than a label and a professional society; they collect around a set of problems and modes of inquiry most usefully identified as a single discipline. This may, by the way, not always continue to be so.

If physics were forming today, we should of necessity have to see it as "interdisciplinary" since physicists would not yet exist. Academic departments of philosophy, mathematics, and so on, would be uncomfortable hiding places for people concentrating on the study of energy for its own sake. A university here and there, supported by grants from special panels of the National Science Foundation, would set up a Center for Research on the Laws of Motion (CRLM), devoted mainly to graduate studies directed by the faculties of various schools and departments. Undergraduate students, sensing a crisis of leadership, would devote summer and weekends to mechanics and radioactivity. The American Association for the Advancement of Science would sponsor symposia on ways of organizing these activities into respectable courses and programs.

It is in this perspective that I see our present concern for the development of environmental science. My own mail—hundreds of papers and reports, dozens of books, thousands of letters—brings me mounting news of responsible and intelligent concern for the future of the Earth as a home for life, and of proposals for tooling up in response to that concern. Although some of what I read is simple-minded or self-serving or otherwise useless, the mainstream is strong and full of honest purpose. Take, for example the question of Environmental Law. Whereas a few years ago it was hardly identifiable as a subject of serious study, it now commands the attention of professional lawyers, graduate students of law, and undergraduates who look toward careers in the field.

An enormous academic movement, supported by students of all kinds from the most to the least revolutionary, by faculty in all areas of study, by deans and presidents and authoritative figures in government, is pulling us forward. The movement is so strong as to be hazardous in itself. Garrett Hardin (Professor of Biology, University of California at Santa Barbara) has spoken of the dangers of a "euphoria . . . likely to make us lower our critical guard, to indulge in ill-considered enthusiasms." I sense this too, and I add to it the hazard of inadequate or irresponsible leadership. Much depends, especially for the long future of environmental action, on the guidance of the academic community.

This brings me to my point. It seems to be regarded as inescapable that environmental science is interdisciplinary. And so it is, in the sense that it connects almost all fields of study, ranging from architecture to zoology. But chemistry or mathematics or economics is interdisciplinary in the same sense; in my brief history of physics, I do not suggest that its emergence as a discipline removes it from contact with everything else. On the contrary, and paradoxically, intensive concentration on the fundamental laws of nature clarifies our view of the whole world of reason, in a way that would be impossible otherwise. The lesson of experience, perhaps explicable in psychological terms, is that specialization is essential to our progress. A sense of discipline, by which I mean a devotion to a concentrated community of closely related ideas, is our most productive scholarly tool.

Given the truth of this principle, we might spend some effort on building, or perhaps simply recognizing, a new discipline within environmental science. I wish to call it "Ecography" as a way of recognizing that it is new, and as a suggestion of its basic meaning. The name is unimportant, but the conception of discipline is vital.

Instead of listing the dozens of existing disciplines from which ecography has grown, let us simply ask about its central and deeply rooted theme. We are engaged in a study of facts and values which describe and control man's interaction with his habitat. In what respect, then, does ecography differ from human ecology or, for that matter, geography as it is currently understood? The answer I give you is that ecology, for its own scholarly purposes, must carry too great a burden of biology, while geography must carry too little. If you wish, ecology is too close to the exclusively natural sciences while geography is too close to the social sciences. Thus, the role of ecography, as its name suggests, is to establish a disciplinary beachhead in what appears to be a critical no-man's land between the two cultures of science.

I earnestly believe that the new discipline has already been born, but that it is a foundling, crying for adoption. In view of the rapidly growing severity of man's ecological crisis, we—students and teachers alike—cannot afford to overlook the chance that our new baby is a Wunderkind whose future strength depends upon our feeding him properly now. With this in mind, I propose that the colleges and universities take action. In the case of the "multiversities," whose structures are rigid and jealously guarded, it is neither feasible nor necessary to build interdisciplinary centers in order to provide an ecographical setting. The better way is for each to organize its Department of Ecography with the usual spectrum of people and facilities: chairman, faculty, budget, laboratory, undergraduate and graduate programs, and degrees. It is only through the conventional structure, which has worked so well for other disciplines of science, that most universities can respond to the demand for professional recognition now building up among young students and teachers. And this is certainly one way in which our environmental problems can be adequately studied and ultimately solved.

Perhaps there is a better way, open only to institutions newly forming and therefore free from prior structural commitment. They can listen to Robert Hutchins, criticizing our universities:

> Civilization and culture cannot be preserved and expanded without another institution that is missing. Today we have no centers of independent thought and criticism. The multiversity is not independent: it is the result of the parallelogram of forces at work in the community. It is not engaged as an institution in thought or criticism. . . . It is compartmentalized both vertically and horizontally into departments and divisions that are in competition for money and students. A multipurpose institution can by definition have no unifying principle.

Instead, says Hutchins, we must look to the college, or cluster of colleges, in which departments of study are never permitted to organize. The college is a small community of teachers and students, using their special talents to achieve clearly defined goals. It is possible, even necessary, in such a setting to combine a sense of discipline with the respectability of change. A new discipline, like ecography, can find a natural and immediate place; so can an old one, like chemistry. And some disciplines can be permitted to die without endangering the lives of people.

Whatever modes of reform they choose to adopt, the colleges and universities of the world will be moving toward definition of this new discipline in a response to a variety of forces. One is the emergence of ecography as an interesting and challenging subject of study. Another is the collective voice of thousands of students, demanding academic recognition of their concern. But the greatest force of all is the threat of our own destruction, which we must continue to face until the gap between the sciences is filled. Beryl Crowe (1) says:

> There has developed in the contemporary natural sciences a recognition that there is a subset of problems, such as population, atomic war, and environmental corruption, for which there are no technical solutions. There is also an increasing recognition among contemporary social scientists that there is a subset of problems, such as population, atomic war, environmental corruption and the recovery of a livable urban environment, for which there are no current political solutions. . . . The common areas shared by these two subsets contain most of the critical problems that threaten the very existence of contemporary man.

Professor Crowe ends his piece in pessimism, without being able to suggest any feasible way out of the impasse. But two important things ought not to be overlooked in the analysis: the steady evolution of academic form, and the insistent voice of the students. "The waters are rising," said a student at the recent Nobel Conference in Stockholm, "and we have no boats." It is our responsibility to make the boats possible by providing tools for so many outstretched hands. We possess the tools, but we must learn to use them in new ways.

My proposal is not put forth with the suggestion that it is in any way unique. I know that many simultaneous attacks will be made on the question of developing environmental science, and I suspect that more than one of them will yield effective results. My main purpose is a more general one: to urge students toward a revision and revitalization of their conception of science and to develop scientific expertness as a means of balancing and substantiating their talent for social and political action which they now seem most naturally willing to exercise. I firmly believe that both activities must go forward together. Science without a sense of social commitment will always be a part of academic life, but it will not answer the gravest questions now before us. And political action, however wisely and humanely directed, will fail equally badly if it is uninformed by science.

REFERENCE

1. Crowe, Beryl, "Tragedy of the Commons Revisited," Science, 166:1103, November 28, 1969.■

The forestry student faces a new era.

FORESTRY'S CHANGING ECOLOGY

Richard W. Jones

THE CHRONICLES of North America, from initial settlement by Western Europeans until the early 20th century, reveal that man's relationship to the forest has been primarily utilitarian. From the era of settlement and land clearing, through that of lumbering and exploitation, to the period of timber management—the forest served, first as a barrier to civilization and, later, as a tappable reservoir of useful raw materials to satisfy many of man's economic demands.

Pushed by the puritan tradition to have dominion over the wilderness and the desire to establish an environment more nearly like that to which they had been accustomed in the Old World, settlers abided by a frontier ethic which encouraged domination of the primeval forest that covered much of the continent. It was apparent that they clearly understood man's role as prescribed in the edict of Genesis 1:28: "... and subdue it and have dominion over the fish of the sea and fowl of the air and over every living thing."

In reaction to the conquest of the wilderness, some championed the cause of "preservation" during the 19th century. Among the leaders of the movement were Henry David Thoreau, the transcendentalist; Horace Greeley, the preservationist; and John Muir, the publicist. The first half of the 20th century has seen the preservation flag waved by Aldo Leopold, who pointed out the value of preserves for scientific study, as well as other noncommercial pursuits. History will, no doubt, shed light on others who have been individually instrumental in fostering wilderness preservation.

Of course, the "wise use" compromise was spawned during the same period of time. This philosophy proffered the notion that, through management, renewable forest resources could be conserved, that is, used judiciously without exhausting them. The founding of the American Forestry Association in 1875, the Society of American Foresters in 1900, and the establishment of the U. S. Forest Service within the Department of Agriculture in 1905 crystalized the development of this concept in the United States.

Through the bias of historians, the lack of functional organizations, or the charismatic leadership of early advocates, it appears that the doctrines of both preservation and conservation were initially propagated by outspoken individuals. In today's highly, and perhaps overly, organized society, groups rather than individuals are shaping opinion for the right- and left-wing interests of forest resources philosophy.

There is an increasing demand for the amenities provided by wild lands. Pressures exerted by urban living and availability of unprecedented leisure time have generated within teeming millions of Americans both the desire and the means to escape from their workaday routine to the "great outdoors." Here the objectives they seek vary from the purist's complete isolation on the one hand, to the family camper's mere transfer of normally experienced social relationships into a different ecological setting—that which is perceived as "the forest"—on the other.

Regardless of some practitioners' reluctance to change, the profession of forestry has been forced to adapt to the pulsebeat of the times and public opinion. Increasingly, foresters are having to recognize and accommodate the non-utilitarian functions of the forest environment in response to demands expressed by its users—the electorate and stockholders. Many of these demands may seem alien to or incompatible with classical forestry; nonetheless, in the context of man's relation to his forested environment, the allegedly non-utilitarian functions are perceived by many forest users as utilitarian indeed. As technological advances have made possible the introduction of substitutes for tree-derived products, and changing sociological profiles have pointed up the forest's uniqueness in providing amenity values, the timber production role of forests has in many cases become secondary to aesthetics or other considerations. Demand for water, fish and game, recreation, and forage attests to the importance of the non-timber resources.

What may be construed as a threat to many forest resource managers is not so much the resource-demand mix but, rather, the changing characteristics,

---

The author is Assistant Professor, School of Forest Resources, University of Georgia, Athens.

interests, and attitudes of the forest users, that is, those who have been largely responsible for that mix. The tradition-bound forester is trained to cope with a changing demand for forest resources. His diversified skills enable him to manipulate the natural resources produced in the forest. He can provide more and better wildlife habitat; he can build roads f o r timber access in remote areas; he can construct facilities for what he thinks the recreating public wants; he can insist on timber harvesting practices which improve water quality and affect its quantity and timing. In short, he is well qualified to manage the forest resources, but how well equipped is he to manage the people who use those resources?

"Forestry" has been defined as "t h e scientific management of forests for the continuous production of goods and services." In lieu of this, we could just as adequately define this pursuit as "the protection, management, and utilization of forest resources." This simpler, broadened definition is more amenable to the ensuing description which derives from Figure 1. It shows how forestry is changing from a production to a consumption orientation. It depicts the dynamics of present-day emphases as compared with those formerly stressed, both at operational and policy-making levels. It reveals a new purpose for its various thrusts.

PROTECTION

Last generation's forester was required to spend much of his time in fire control or other forest protection activities. These could be viewed as custodial or remedial in nature. Little time was available for him to combat the causes of forest destruction; his efforts were geared primarily to the suppression of its effects.

Forest managers have long been engaged in t h e protection of renewable resources from three principal destructive agents: insects, disease, and fire. Protection from pests and pathogens is still largely a matter of control "after the fact." Biological and chemical countermeasures offer hope that entomologists and pathologists may take the offensive, thereby becoming involved in the prevention as w e l l a s control of insect and disease infestations.

Fire, of course, is for the most part a man-caused phenomenon. In fact, only about one of each ten wildfire occurrences are of natural origin. Considerably more effort is now being expended on the prevention of man-caused fires. Effective in the endeavors have been information and education programs designed to change people's attitudes from carelessness to awareness, from apathy to concern, and from malice to responsibility. The would-be woods burner's personal economic stake has also been emphasized. Law enforcement has been reserved as a last resort while effective public relations has been recognized as the best means of preventing unwanted fires. Successful prevention has depended upon unclogged channels of communication, attitude modification, a favorable press, advertising, and other human-directed pursuits. There is a growing realization that forest protection is for human benefits and not just from destructive agents.

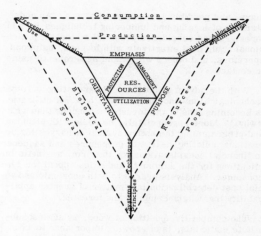

FIGURE 1

THE DEVELOPMENT OF FORESTRY

MANAGEMENT

Classically, management of f o r e s t resources meant manipulating or regulating their harvest and assuring their replacement for a sustained yield of raw material. The timber management plan rationalized much of the decision making such that it almost seemed that trees or other resources were being produced for the sake of themselves rather than their u s e r s. Not that managed commercial timberlands went uncut—on the contrary, low stumpage prices and an accelerating demand for wood by industry effectively kept this from happening.

Outside pressures—technological, demographic, economic, and political-are expanding the dimensions of forestry. Land use decisions are no longer determined solely on the basis of the probable financial return on the investment, cost/benefit ratio, or other justifiable tangibles. Whereas "current annual increment" may once have been, independently, a suitable assessment for timber regulation, external factors such as the ballot box, pressure group activity, and taxation policies may have far more bearing today on resource management decision alternatives. Land use allocation for the optimum production of benefits-not always measurable in board feet, cords, or other quantifiable parameters- is becoming a primary determinant of resource management policy. An accurate appraisal of voting behavior is fully as important as that of fiber yield today. Accordingly, the need for information from behavioral scientists cannot be over-emphasized. Sociopolitics is a very real force, and the resource manager must be attuned to its demands as well as its "modus operandi." Public opinion is a force which the forester must be able to harness; ideally, he should be molding it.

UTILIZATION

Traditionally, foresters needed to be knowledgeable about the conversion of raw materials into pri-

mary, and possibly secondary, products. An understanding of logging and lumbering techniques by all
foresters was considered essential so that the professional could deal effectively with loggers, pulpwood
operators, and others with whom he frequently came
in contact.

With the advent of mechanical harvesting and other
technological advancements, the "how" of utilization
is becoming less of the forester's concern than t h e
"why." More appropriately, he deals with planning
and programming the entire system of harvesting operations, relating the flow of procedures and sequences
to financial considerations for the firm, aesthetic implications for the motorist, and sales appeal for t h e
consumer. Analysis geared to both economic and social cost determination is a matter of greater applicability than engineering for the forester.

The competitive position of wood, as against substitute materials, is of growing importance to t h e
profession. Technological improvements in the development of substitute products are of much m o r e
than casual interest to the forester of today. Perhaps,
if yesterday's forest utilization specialist had been as
concerned and well financed as today's, wood products
used in construction would have a better image than
they currently hold in some quarters. A much greater emphasis is upon the consumer than was in evidence
a decade ago and earlier.

BIO-ECONOMIC TO SOCIOPOLITICAL
REORIENTATION; THEN WHAT?

A review of American forestry's annals discloses
several characteristics about the trails which p r o -
fessional foresters have trod. Not all have taken the
same path; if they had done so, it would not need to
be brushed out periodically.

Undeniably, the profession's plight over the last
quarter-century reflects a broadening of the base of
competence a m o n g resource managers. Notwithstanding the constant expressions of need for more
specialization in applying land management skills, an
even more resounding outcry for near-prophetic discernment of decision impacts is being uttered. Could
it be that the nature of professional activities h a s
made a complete orbit and now approximates the one
established during forestry's infancy? Back then the
"ranger" could do anything and everything—he was
a jack-of-all-trades! Judging by users' demands today, that's what he's supposed to be now.

Perhaps the professionals of 1909, 1939, and 1969
shared some common traits. They were generalists;
they put in long hours facing a wide variety of somewhat similar problems. But the sources of those
problems differed. The forester during the profession's first decade had the impossible task of running
his forest on a shoestring. Time, funds, and priorities permitted his practicing only the most extensive
of forestry operations. He was often the sole custodian of millions of acres of forest land. Resource-
fully bringing practical means to bear on the problems he encountered, America's early forester made
significant tangible contributions to the recognition
and advancement of the profession, albeit he implemented rather unsophisticated forestry practices.

During the 30's, 40's, and 50's the tide of professional activity turned to an emphasis on technical
aspects. Economic analysis proved important in the
justification of land management decisions as technology made it possible to convert forest biota into
forest resources. Forestry was intensified during
this period, and production-oriented foresters dominated the professional scene.

The postwar era has ushered in complexities from
which the forest resource manager was formerly fairly
well insulated. "People problems," as they h a v e
come to be called, are mounting daily as displays of
affluence and desires for influence are being translated into sociopolitical pressures upon the forester,
his profession, and the environment in which he operates. Policy issues relating to natural beauty, open
spaces, wilderness preservation, property taxation,
outdoor recreation, and land acquisition are but a
few indicators attesting to man's concern for his natural resource heritage. The resource manager i s
caught in the middle and, logically, should be instrumental in the resolution of conflicts arising f r o m
controversies. Insofar as they are sensitive to demands of forest users, foresters should be uniquely
equipped to assess the benefits or liabilities resulting from land management decisions.

Popular in the latter decades of the 19th century,
restrictive usage of forest lands became subordinate
to wise-use in this century. But current trends, such
as burgeoning wilderness preservation demands, indicate that restricted use is once again in v o g u e.
Continued population expansion and shrinkage of the
available land base could dictate a swing of the resource philosophy pendulum back toward what some
would brand "exploitation" before the next century
begins. An informed majority can help policy makers stay on a rational, moderate course by muffling
the din of the vocal minority, of whichever persuasion they may be.

THE RESOURCE MANAGER'S MISSION

In light of current conditions, and these are probably only a foretaste of those that can be expected,
what is the forester's reason-for-being? What i s
his mission in the much wider culture or environment he operates in today? Digested into s i m p l e
terms, it may be posited that the l a n d manager's
function is:

to optimize human benefits from forest resources through . . .

 (1) comprehension of the forest environment;

 (2) application of professional skills;

 (3) interpretation of the philosophy, goals, and
     techniques of forest resource management
     and science to society at large.

How well foresters attain these objectives will
reflect the extent to which they have accomplished
their mission—through adjusting themselves to a r e -
oriented profession. ∎

Environmental design art as an entre to interpretation.

VISUAL CONSERVATION

Doris M. Carter

OUR ENVIRONMENT is a visual and concrete reality. It consists of nature and of man-made objects–and nothing more! As a culture, motivation, or the desire to control natural resources and technological-products, is dependent upon our level of sensory development–or, in other words, upon our quality of sensory-esthetics.

The need to develop a sensory awareness of the environment exists at all age levels. Since our environment is a visual phenomena, education concerning it can be channeled directly through vision as the mode of communication. Educators on any level who are attuned to their environment might attempt to stimulate visual awareness in their students by exploring the following areas: (1) the environment–past, present, and future; (2) the disappearance of natural resources–flora and fauna; (3) visual noise created by pollutants; (4) community planning; (5) visual grouping patterns–man and animal; (6) organic and inorganic relationships; (7) camouflague techniques; and (8) technological synthetics. Taking each of these areas in sequence, some suggestions follow to motivate the educator or to act as a catalyst or springboard.

1. The environment–past, present, and future. Visually evaluate your local environment. Go on a field trip with map in hand. Using a color-key code as a value point system, evaluate: pedestrian annoyances; traffic control; recreation areas; places for people, street furniture, civic art; points of references; upkeep of historical buildings; and reconstruction areas. Create an aerial view of a self-sustaining human environment for the year 2000 A.D. and for a given population. Use a key system to denote the various organizations employed such as residential, educational, commercial, civic, agricultural, transportation, industrial, and recreation.

2. The disappearance of natural resources. Find out how various flora, fauna, and resources have disappeared from the American scene. Visually express, through a series, the process of disappearance as caused by man's neglect.

3. Visual pollutants. In your community, take photographs of the ugliest area you can find. Choose a small place and take photos from all angles. In class redesign that space free from visual pollution. Build a 3-dimensional model and display it in the community to show what could be done with the tract.

4. Community planning. Employing visual examples, trace the cross-cultural development of the use of the following plans: grideron, ring, radial, and organic. Make several sketches of the plans used for Garden Cities, Ville Radieuse, Broadacre City, Williamsburg, Newtown, and Cumbernauld. Evaluate these plans in relation to possible use in your own environment.

5. Visual grouping patterns. Study and sketch the visual grouping patterns or the natural arrangement of organic forms. A group of snails on a rock, a group of flowers growing, a group of cells through a microscope, a group of animals in a herd, a group of rocks washed up on a beach–can these group systems be applied to town planning? Try to design a small town based on the sketches. Can these group systems relate to population problems? Does man abide by the same rules as nature in regard to physical space needed for a good life?

6. Organic and inorganic relationships. Analyze an organic object to find out its basic skeletal structure. Find a man-made object that is based on the same framework. Create an object of your own based on this skeletal articulation. Bring a man-made object to class. Take it outdoors and look for the same form in nature. Investigate the links or archetypes existing between the organic and the inorganic. For example, what is the link between a daisy, a Rosette window, and a Ferris wheel? What is the link between a fossil shell, an Ionic column, and a spiral staircase? Search into the most minute organic unit of these objects and discover the feature that is repeated over and over again. Compare these structures to those found in ecology. Find other visual-organic relationships.

7. Camouflague techniques. Study camouflague techniques used by insects and animals. Apply these tactics to the use of man-made objects for the purpose of camouflaguing visual noise created by technology.

8. Technological synthetics. Technology is turning our visual world into a phoney world. We live in a land of double-talk, of double-value standards. Even paper money has become "plastic money." Give visual examples of the ways in which real materials are being substituted by the synthetics of technology. Some examples: real flowers–plastic flowers, real wood grain–formica, real wood–contact paper with wood-like pattern, real Christmas trees–plastic trees.

This material has been presented in a broad manner, suggestive, out of focus, and unlimited in scope. This was done with sharp intent so that the inventive educator from grade 1 to the college professor might adapt the material to his own personal needs. The age of the student is insignificant; the need for curriculum material is momentous and immediate. Salvador Dali's "Persistance of Memory" forever reminds us that it is truly the eleventh hour! Unless we educate rapidly, Dali's surrealistic landscape will be our natural habitat. ∎

The author is an Instructor in the Art Department of Worcester State College, Chandler Street, Worcester, Massachusetts, and a consultant to the National Park Service.

An instructional approach for learning and involvement.

ENVIRONMENT AND THE COLLEGE STUDENT

Frank M. Corrado

SINCE MAN, as we know him, is a buying, selling, building, wrecking, eating, excreting, gregarious, lonely, semi-rational animal, it would follow that any study so broad as to encompass man's "environment" must be broached from many points of view. In other words, if we want to study environmental problems and issues, we must look at the problem from a business, political, engineering, philosophical, communication, and scientific point of view, to name only a few.

The interdisciplinary aspects of the environmental crisis have already become accepted in the minds of student leaders and college activist groups. They are approaching the crisis from many academic points of view. A study by the author of 15 college environmental groups in the Midwest in December of 1969 shows a wide divergence of origin: biology, engineering, law, urban studies, and medicine. Typical groups with mass appeal were the Northwestern Students for a Better Society at Northwestern University and the Environmental Action for Survival (ENACT) at the University of Michigan. At present, however, there is no truly interdisciplinary approach or 4-year curriculum at any American university.

The federal government, which for years has funded numerous scatter-gun research projects on environment problems, has only recently recognized its shortcomings in doing this and the shortcomings it has engendered on the campus.

A report to the President's Environmental Quality Council (5) noted that "federal funds being expended at universities for environmental problems do not encourage establishment of such programs." The report suggested that the federal government, through its grant programs, is encouraging "paper institutes" which hardly present "a satisfactory model for interdisciplinary research." If there is any interdisciplinary work going on, the report stated, it is the result of "sheer willpower on the parts of participants."

The report asked the federal government to support formation of Schools of the Human Environment at colleges and universities. The purpose of such schools "should be problem-focused education and research directed toward people—their needs and desires for a satisfying life in pleasant surroundings." The report recommended that a faculty reward structure and control over curriculum development and degrees be made part of the program.

The University of Michigan was recently awarded a $750,000 grant by the Rockefeller Foundation to expand its graduate training in environmental problems. The University said the grant would allow the school to coordinate its scattered efforts in this area.

The purpose of this article is to present a plan for a single course of instruction on environmental issues for students of all disciplines. It is no substitute for development of Schools of Human Environment, but it could serve two purposes: (1) offer an interim, experimental framework for developing a wider curriculum and eventually a school of environmental studies; (2) offer the small college an opportunity to present a balanced course in environmental studies.

The 1-course approach to environmental issues suggested here offers students an overview of environmental problems, serves as a basis for putting students of many disciplines on common ground, attempts to show interrelationships of the problems, and not the least of all, telegraphs the message that the university or college is keeping on top of contemporary issues. The 1-course plan could also play a role in adult continuing education programs.

The plan presented here outlines a framework for developing a teaching outline. It also urges use of multiple techniques for presenting the material. The Course Plan:

1. Crisis in the Environment—Man and His Relation to Nature
2. Ecology
3. Air
4. Land (Congestion, solid waste, open space, cityscape)
5. Water
6. Movement
7. Noise
8. Environmental Planning
9. Inner-city Environments
10. Involvement and Participation

CRISIS IN THE ENVIRONMENT—MAN AND HIS RELATION TO NATURE

The beginning lecture is a naming session. A laundry list of environmental problems is exposed to give the student an idea of the extent of the crisis. During this session the student is presented with a picture of man—at war with nature and at the same time dependent on nature for his existence.

By a continuous, careful scanning of the local newspapers, it is quite possible to come up with many examples that will give students a feel for the current problems. The author has found that many students don't read pollution stories in the newspapers.

ECOLOGY

As Dr. Eugene Odum has stated (4), ecology is concerned with the levels of life beyond the individu-

The author is Public Information Officer, Federal Water Pollution Control Administration, 718 West Briar Place, Chicago, Illinois. He is also an Instructor in Environmental Studies at Roosevelt University, Chicago.

al organism. It is the study of systems, relationships between producers, consumers, decomposers,
and abiotic substances. When ecology is applied to
the urban situation, the basic principles remain the
same. A theoretical approach to ecology is pointless
in an environmental issues course unless each issue
introduced relates to ecology and specifically human
ecology. Among the serious pollution issues to be presented in the Ecology portion are the damaging effects
of pesticides and radioactivity on the entire biosphere.

AIR

Air, like water pollution, is obviously a difficult
subject to teach to an interdisciplinary group. Even
a superficial understanding requires the study of biology, chemistry, and engineering. There is no easy
way around it. Discussion of specific pollution problems will require the presenting of understandable
scientific explanations. But this is not enough. The
explanation will be meaningless unless the explanation is followed up by relating the problem to the human experience. Unless the student is shown the
medical and ecological importance of clean air, clean
water, and low noise levels he cannot be motivated
for involvement. Unless the student sufficiently understands the scientific principles of a pollution problem, he cannot become an effective activist. These
three approaches to presenting environmental information dove-tail one another and follow from one another.

Possibly the best way to tie these three approaches
together is to attempt to answer a series of questions.
For example:

(1) What is air pollution? What are its many
forms?

(2) What is its history?

(3) What is its effect on man?

(4) What governmental approaches are being used
to combat it?

(5) What technological answers are available?

(6) How does air pollution relate to other environmental problems?

(7) What is the future prospect?

WATER

The same questions applied to air pollution should
also be applied when considering water pollution.
There are differences though. The national–state
water pollution program is much further along than
the fight against air pollution. The technology is
more complex because of the biochemical aspects of
water pollution. In other words, there is more to
talk about at this point in time.

LAND

There are a number of sub-categories that fall
under the general topic of land. Among the ones
which should be studied are: solid waste, cityscape,
open space, and congestion.

Solid Waste. Of the major pollution problems,
solid waste disposal is perhaps the most technologically backward. Open burning, sanitary landfills,
and incineration are still the commonly practiced
forms of disposal throughout the U. S. Nevertheless,
the study of solid waste disposal techniques offers an
excellent means of integrating the different environmental problems. Incineration often causes air pollution. Landfills often pollute groundwater supplies.
The major cost in solid waste disposal is transportation, another environmental issue. Abandoned vehicles and litter are genuine aesthetic problems,
which brings up the issue of cityscape.

Cityscape. Cityscape refers to the visual city.
It is the morphology of the city, the urban landscape.
It is the architecture, the neon commercialism, the
billboards on the highways. Man has for too long
viewed his environment in economic terms. The student must be shown the possibilities of good planning
and be introduced to the character and charm of the
great streets and public edifices, which give the city
a sense of "place." The student must be made aware
of the loss of great historic buildings by the corro-
sive batterings of air and water pollution and of man's
plain neglect for the city as a distinct environment.
The student must be made aware of the possibilities
that good planning offers for improving the quality of
urban life, and for improving its cohesiveness as well.

Open Space. There is plenty of open space. But
not in the cities where it should be. The continuing
economic exploitation of land has been responsible
for the continuing low priority placed on parks and
open space in our cities. The great public places
are deserted. Urban man only gathers in the market
areas. Cafes on piazzas, promenades in the sunset
along the edge or in the city's center are disappearing. In many instances they were never there. The
landscape is Dickensian. It is necessary to acquaint
the student with the means available for saving bits
and pieces of the landscape from completely disappearing in our cities. There are alternatives to the
sprawl of the suburbs and the implosions in the city.
Both open space and cityscape have similar messages,
but open space emphasizes the need for quantitative
space, while cityscape emphasizes the qualitative
aspects.

Congestion. The population implosion in the central city is having dangerous environmental effects on
human beings. Violence, mental illness, and sickness
are the effects. The question that must be answered
here is what are we going to do with so many people
in the central cities? What are the planning alternatives? What happens if we continue to do nothing?

MOVEMENT

Transportation is the national nightmare. Cars
are jammed daily in traffic. Mass transit is in financial difficulty. One-third of the city is devoted
to transportation facilities. Airports are unable to
handle increasing volume. The effects: air pollution from combustion engines, oil spills from massive
tankers, and water pollution from urban runoff, noise
pollution from congestion, and solid waste problems
from junked autos. The student must attempt to find
the solutions, but he must first understand the issue.

NOISE

Sonic booms, subways, traffic, inferior building
codes—all contribute to noise pollution. Dr. Gerald

Dorman of the AMA says that noise is more than an annoyance, it can be a physical and psychological danger (2). The student of the environment must realize, however, that noise is more than a medical subject. Engineers, planners, and architects must become concerned. And the public must demand more research into long-term pathological effects.

ENVIRONMENTAL PLANNING

The classic concept of urban planning was physical—the city beautiful, the city functional. The concern for man was health. Open spaces meant health.

The decade of the '60's widened the horizons of planning to include social stability and development as reasonably attainable goals. From all indications, the '70's will focus on health concerns once again, which in essence would be a return to late 19th century thinking. Environmental pollution cannot serve as a planning consideration. It is negative. It has technologically available answers.

Planning for the '70's should be based on: (1) the social-physical answers developed in the '60's; (2) the total ecological realities. What I am saying is this: you can't go off on a new tangent and forget what has gone before. Planning must now be oriented toward providing millions of humans a method for remaining in balance with the biosphere. But the planning of the '70's—you might call it environmental planning—must incorporate and stress physical design and inner-city problems as well. Environmental planning must cover all bases.

If there is a bible for this new type of planning, it is Design With Nature by Ian McHarg (3). His sermons emphasize the need to assign values to the air, water, and land, and he preaches that we must plan for ending the sick pathology of the inner city.

INNER-CITY ENVIRONMENTS

Columnist Charles Bartlett, in the Chicago Sun Times, January 12, 1970, warns that concern about the environment might be used "to diminish the public's concern with the plight of the inner cities." He feels that a Theodore Roosevelt-like approach "will mean more competition for the attention and emotions of the young who have been crucial supporters of the urban cause." He observes that the politicians may feel much more secure if the issues of traffic and pollution can be separated from the issues of the inner-city.

If you were to overlay the incidence of physical disease, social disease, pollution, mental disease, and the economic and racial composition of a major city as was done in Philadelphia by Ian McHarg, you would find that the poor, the black, and the sick inhabit the same environment. This environmental fact of life has also been shown in Chicago by Pierre De Vise (1).

It might seem that a student concerned with environmental issues is being taken deeper into the heart of environmental "darkness" by studying inner-city environments. And it might be argued that the major environmental problems are the problems of the suburb and countryside as well. However, since the greatest concentration of environmental problems appear to overlay on the center city, it would follow that

a closer look must be taken. The closer look will involve the student with the realities of urban pathology in a most concrete and brutal way.

INVOLVEMENT AND PARTICIPATION

The Nelson-McCloskey teach-in on April 22, 1970 and the 500 plus college groups which formed ad hoc to participate in it suggests that the environmental movement on American campuses is well under way. On December 29 and 30, 1969, thousands of college students from dozens of newly formed environmental groups participated in teach-ins sponsored by the Department of Interior's Federal Water Pollution Control Administration.

Activism has also taken other forms. Students are marching on major industrial polluters and on their own statehouses. They've held mock funerals for the automobile, planted trees, cleaned debris from rivers and creeks. Groups range from the conservative Northwestern Students for a Better Environment to the radical Friends of the Earth.

Participation cuts across student political, social, racial, ethnic, religious, and vocational lines. While activism appears strongest in California, students in the Midwest and East have made headlines also for their Vietnam-like stance on environmental pollution.

At least a third of the students who attended and critiqued the Department of Interior Chicago teach-in December 29, 1969, expressed a strong desire to become involved in pollution cleanup. Critiques were offered by a total of 26 of the 337 students who registered for the 1-day teach-in. A 5-member Student Council on Pollution and the Environment (SCOPE) was formed to serve as a link between the Department of Interior and college activists.

Some typical remarks: "There should have been more emphasis on what students can do." "Please put more emphasis on high school students. We can do a lot!" "I wish that a list of these (conservation) organizations be mailed to us as quickly as possible so that we know who to turn to in the future." ". . . get people involved."

What this all means is that higher education must provide students with ways of becoming actively involved in environmental issues, by presenting a curriculum that stresses participation and involvement. The involvement can take a number of forms: scientific (pollution sampling), political (presenting statements at conferences), action (cleaning up a stream, picketing, holding workshops), and technical (developing a computer model for lake pollution) just to cite some examples.

TECHNIQUES OF INSTRUCTION

There are many ways to present material in a course on environmental issues. As many ways as possible should be attempted:

(1) Guest Lecturers—It is obvious that there are not many people who can handle all the topics presented here in depth. Guest lecturers should be used whenever possible. One rule to remember is that such lecturers should come from different fields. For example, a scientist might be brought in for an air pollution lecture, a politician for a water pollution

lecture, a city official for a lecture on solid waste. A novel approach might be to find an industrialist who would be willing to explain the business point of view to the students and subject himself to some grilling.

(2) Field Trips—The visual experience, that is, seeing things for yourself, is and always has been recognized as one of the best means of learning. The city is the laboratory for environmental problems, just as much as the countryside is. Almost every city has a sewage treatment plant and also some method for disposing of solid wastes. Most industrial communities have an air pollution problem, and somebody in local or state government is working on it. Visits to these places can serve as a learning experience. The traditional reference points for ecology—the visit to the pond or forest preserve—are normally within close reach. Also there are numerous public meetings held quite regularly on environmental topics. Students can attend these meetings, and with some preparation they can participate actively.

(3) Labs—The outgrowth of a field trip could be a lab experience. Labs can be a 1-shot affair or held on a recurring basis during the course. If a class were to take a boat trip, they might also want to take some water samples and analyze them later in a lab.

When facilities are limited, one night might be set aside for lab work. A series of four stations—on air, water, solid waste, and noise—might be set up and manned. Students could be rotated, spending 15 minutes at each station.

(4) Game Theory—Students might develop a game corresponding to a pollution abatement conference or city council meeting. The scenario might be a crucial hearing and vote on pollution abatement. Students could be assigned various roles, representing business, politics, activists, etc.

(5) Outside Assignments—Two directions might be taken on assignments. If possible, the best approach would seem to be one in which students cooperate in a single project, like developing the overlays for an inner-city area or investigating the political, economic, and social aspects of a pollution problem. The alternative approach is a problem-oriented one with assignments going to students in line with their academic pursuits. Some suggestions:

a. Learn about the workings of a local conservation group. Tell about the job they are doing. Explain how they might improve.

b. Conduct a survey of air and/or water pollution legislation introduced in your state legislature within the last 2 years. Explain the factors involved in passing and defeating such legislation.

c. Develop a computer model for a local pollution situation and explain its workings.

d. Describe the state of the art in advanced waste treatment.

e. Develop a national policy on preserving and expanding genetic pools for wildlife in urban areas.

f. Conduct your own sampling of local industrial outfalls and compare your results with similar information obtained by pollution control agencies.

g. Describe the effects of thermal pollution on food chains.

h. Compare the background noise levels for a cross section of residential areas in the city.

i. Measure air pollution at the local airport.

j. Investigate and report on the environmental problems of a 1-mile square residential section of the city.

k. Discuss research and demonstration projects underway to improve techniques of solid waste disposal.

l. Speculate on possible radical citizen approaches for environmental improvement.

m. Report on computer applications for highway movement control.

n. Discuss alternatives for the automobile powered by a combustion engine.

o. What laws are on the books in your state at the present time for preservation of open space.

p. Discuss some successful attempts used locally to sway public opinion in favor of a conservation project.

These are but a few ideas for outside assignments for students; there are hundreds more. Original research and syntheses should be stressed in all cases.

A SUGGESTED LIST OF REQUIRED READINGS

Class Texts

Shepard, Paul; McKinley, Daniel, (eds.), The Subversive Science, Essays Toward An Ecology of Man, Houghton Mifflin Company, New York, 1969.

The President's Council on Recreation and Natural Beauty, From Sea to Shining Sea, A Report on the American Environment—Our Cultural Heritage, Government Printing Office, Washington, D. C., 1968.

Crisis in the Environment

Rienow, Robert; Train, Leona, Moment in the Sun, Ballantine, New York, 1969.

Ecology

Carson, Rachel, Silent Spring, Houghton Mifflin Company, Boston, 1962.

Commoner, Barry, Science and Survival, Viking Compass, paperback, New York, 1963.

Storer, John, The Web of Life, Signet Science Library, New York, 1963.

Air

Cleaning Our Environment, The Chemical Basis for Action, The Subcommittee on Environmental Improvement, American Chemical Society, Washington, D. C., 1969.

Air Pollution Primer, National Tuberculosis and Respiratory Disease Association, New York, 1969.

National Air Pollution Control Administration: "The Citizens Role in Air Pollution," 1967; "Needed: Clean Air"; "NAPCA, Public Policy and Air Pollution Control," June 1969; The Ambient Air, Iglauer, Edith, New Yorker reprint, April 13, 1968; Air Pollution Act, November 21, 1967.

Water

Cleaning Our Environment, National Air Pollution Control Administration.

The Practice of Water Pollution, Federal Water Pollution Control Administration, Biology, Government Printing Office, Washington, D.C., 1969.

Federal Water Pollution Control Administration: "A Primer on Waste Treatment," 1969; Showdown... for Water," 1968; "Water Pollution, The Blighted Great Lakes," 1968; "Lake Erie Report," 1968; "Heat Can Hurt," 1969; Water Pollution Control Act, 1966.

Land

Cleaning our Environment, National Air Pollution Control Administration.

Lynch, Kevin, The Image of the City, MIT Press, Cambridge, Massachusetts, 1966.

Jacobs, Jane, The Death and Life of Great American Cities, Vintage, New York, 1961.

Whyte, William H., The Last Landscape, Doubleday and Company, Garden City, New York, 1968.

Bureau of Solid Waste Management, Department of Health, Education, and Welfare: "Solid Wastes: A List of Available Literature," October '68–April '69; "Summaries, Solid Wastes Demonstration Grant Projects," 1968; "Sanitary Landfill Facts," 1968; The Solid Waste Disposal Act, 1965; "An Interim Report, 1968 National Survey of Community Solid Waste Practices."

Congestion

Dubos, Rene, Man Adapting, Yale University Press, New Haven, Connecticut, 1965.

Erlich, Paul, The Population Bomb, Ballantine Books, New York, 1968.

Noise

"Noise Pollution," American Medical Association papers from Congress on Environmental Health, April 28-29, 1968.

Chermayeff, Serge; Christopher, Alexander, Community and Privacy, Doubleday and Co., New York.

Movement

"The Coming Revolution in Transportation," National Geographic, 136:3, Appel, Fredric Co., September 1969.

The Proposed Chicago Crosstown Expressway, Transportation Advisory Group, City of Chicago, November 30, 1965.

United States Department of Transportation: Public Law 890670, October 15, 1966; Federal Highway Administration Publications, 1969.

Inner-city Environments/Environmental Planning

McHarg, Ian L., Design With Nature, The Natural History Press, Garden City, New York, 1969.

Three Approaches to Environmental Resource Analysis, The Conservation Foundation, Washington, D.C., 1967.

Involvement and Participation

Farrell, Richard J., "Let the Polluter Beware!" Standard Oil Company, Chicago, 1969.

The League of Women Voters, Land and Water for Tomorrow, Training Community Leaders, A Handbook, League of Women Voters Education Fund, Washington, D.C.

CONCLUSION

This is a concrete proposal, designed to serve as a road map for college teachers and curriculum planners in establishing an environmental program at the college level. It is rather broad; it tries to cover all the bases. It is not the solution or the answer to environmental curriculum planning, but rather an approach, a point of departure.

The emphasis I have tried to give is on bringing the various urban disciplines together, on bringing the students from different fields together. If the course achieves nothing else, it hopefully will weld a link of communication between students in many academic fields and create a dialogue on the quality of life.

REFERENCES

1. DeVise, Pierre, Slum Medicine: Chicago's Apartheid Health System, Community and Family Study Center, University of Chicago, Chicago, 1969, 91 pp.

2. Dorman, Gerald, "Welcoming Remarks" to the American Medical Association's Sixth Congress on Environmental Health, American Medical Association, Chicago, April 28-29, 1969.

3. McHarg, Ian L., Design With Nature, The Natural History Press, Garden City, New York, 1969, 198 pp.

4. Odum, Eugene P., Ecology, Holt, Rinehart, and Winston, Chicago, 1963, 152 pp.

5. Steinhart, John S.; Cherniack, Stacie, "The Universities and Environmental Quality, Commitment to Problem Focused Education," Government Printing Office, Washington, D.C., September 1969, 22 pp. ∎

An experiment in undergraduate education for environmental policy formulation.

DARTMOUTH'S COLLEGE COURSE I

Alvin O. Converse, S. Lawrence Dingman, and Malcolm Lewis

WITH INCREASING demands on our resources of land, water, and energy, problems of allocation are assuming vital importance. Policies must be formulated to deal with these problems, which are generally complex, multidisciplinary, and sometimes poorly defined. Traditional undergraduate curricula, even in liberal arts colleges, tend to be analytical and to focus on disciplines. They give students insufficient background for dealing with the multidisciplinary problems that characterize real life, where solutions require an ability to synthesize. Dartmouth's College Course I—"Introduction to Policy Formulation"—was designed to give undergraduates from varied academic backgrounds an opportunity to arrive at solutions to such real problems.[1]

OBJECTIVES AND PHILOSOPHY

The students were asked to select and study aspects of the Connecticut River Basin for the purpose of formulating a public policy that best satisfied needs which they identified. The specific educational objectives of College Course I were to: (1) give students an opportunity to apply their knowledge in a synthetic rather than an analytic or critical manner; (2) give students an opportunity to disregard discipline boundaries and study on a need-to-know basis; and (3) provide a forum for discussion of important public problems.

An important aspect of such a synthetic approach is the knowledge of the more or less formal aspects of problem solving. It is convenient to consider three phases in problem solving. First, one must study an existing situation and phrase what is always a limited and theoretical version of the needs and constraints that are apparent. The job is rather difficult, because one can overlook some aspects of the problem and also because it is difficult to formulate an adequate written statement of the situation. The second phase of problem solving involves solving the theoretical problem. Here one must devise alternative policies or courses of action (and it is always possible to omit various desirable alternatives) and

show that in theory one of the alternatives is the best solution. Finally, the third step is to implement the solution of the theoretical problem in the real world. In this course the students were asked to carry out these steps. They were asked to dig out what they felt to be significant needs from a general study of the river system. They were then asked to prepare a recommended policy or course of action giving justification. Finally they were asked to put this recommended course of action in a form which appeared capable of implementation.

We asked the student to pay particular attention to the formulation of the theoretical version of the problem. It is not uncommon that heated discussion or argument about particular courses of action occurs before objectives are clearly defined. This seems particularly true in regard to environmental questions. To overcome this, the formalism of optimization theory was used as the vehicle for theoretical problem formulation. While we are quite aware of its limitations, optimization theory emphasizes the definition of objectives, identification of factors under one's control as well as constraints, and listing of alternative courses of action to achieve the objectives. Ideally the choices among alternatives can be made on the basis of some quasi-objective scalar criterion, such as a benefit/cost ratio, although it is more often a vector. A formal symbolic statement of the problem has the advantage that with each stage in the process a participant knows exactly what has been said. Objectives can be argued, but it is useless to proceed in discussing alternative courses of action until they are agreed upon.

There is an analogy between functioning in this way and aspects of the philosophy of pragmatism as discussed by William James. In Pragmatism (2), James considers the problem scene of a squirrel in a tree and a hunter arriving. The squirrel is on the opposite side of the tree from the hunter, and as the hunter moves in a circle around the tree, the squirrel moves so that he is always on the opposite side of the tree, facing the hunter. The question is,

The senior author is an Associate Professor in Dartmouth's Thayer School of Engineering. Mr. Dingman is attached to Dartmouth's Public Affairs Center. Mr. Lewis is a graduate student in engineering at Dartmouth, which is in Hanover, New Hampshire.

"Does the hunter go around the squirrel?" The answer is, "yes" if by "around" one means that the hunter at various times occupies the circumference of the circle with the squirrel near the center. However, if "around" means that the hunter is at various times to the front, sides, and back of the squirrel, the answer is "no." If "around" is not defined, there is no answer, and the argument can continue indefinitely; if "around" is defined, there is no question (i.e., the answer is trivial). In more complex problems, of course, careful definition does not always automatically provide an answer.

Thus, an essential objective of our course was to acquaint undergraduates with this approach to policy formulation, and to let them evaluate its power and limitations in a fairly complex real problem of their own selection.

The broad topic we chose to examine was that of the water and related land resources of the Connecticut River Watershed. This choice was initially made by the instructors for the following reasons: it fulfilled the three objectives stated above; Dartmouth is located on the river; the instructors all had some knowledge and professional experience dealing with particular problems of the watershed. As indicated in the students' responses to questionnaires at the completion of the course, this choice was fortunate. Their principal comment was that the course was valuable because it was relevant. They were very conscious of the relevance of resource management problems in general; the Connecticut River in particular was the subject of a current comprehensive planning effort. The physical closeness of the river added further to the pertinence of the subject. Furthermore, the students were very keen to visit the specific area they had chosen to study and to discuss the problem with the people involved. In fact, it was this aspect of their work that the students found most attractive.

ORGANIZATION

College Course I was offered to all upper classmen and graduate students without prerequisites or regard for their major subject. It satisfied no requirements for a major unless an agreement between the student and his major subject advisors was made. The course could not be used to fulfill distributive requirements. It did, however, count in the total course requirement. Eight sophomores, 12 juniors, 14 seniors, and four graduate students took the course; majors from 12 different departments were represented—with 13 science majors, 11 social science majors, seven engineering students, and five English majors.

Experience in the introductory engineering course (See 3) indicated that the objectives of College course I could best be achieved by having the students work in groups, each group to select an aspect of the larger problem as a topic. Since it was felt that the groups should be sufficiently small to be tractable and so that an individual's part in the group effort could be ascertained by the group and its instructor, group size was limited to eight. For guidance and evaluation groups met each week with their advisors for about 2 hours.

The course met en masse three times each week for a total of 24 lecture sessions. Lectures and their topics are listed in Table 1. Seven of the lectures were by off-campus speakers.

Early in the course, Professor Theriault, a specialist in human relations, conducted a session in small group dynamics. A group of eight student volunteers were given a classic problem in management to discuss in front of the class. Several observers in the audience were asked (without the discussants' knowledge) to record aspects of the interactions among the panel members, and their observations were discussed after the panel had reached a decision. This experience proved to be most valuable in subsequent group work.

It was hoped that the lectures would present information on many topics useful to the groups in attacking their problems. Although it was somewhat difficult to maintain continuity among the lecturers, we did, for instance, have a former commissioner of the Federal Power Commission and a representative of the electric power industry speak on succeeding days, and there were several lectures on planning in general and river basin planning in particular.

Each group was required to submit a proposal outlining the topic it had selected by the third week of the 10-week course. Each proposal was reviewed by the instructors and discussed with the groups, with revised proposals due the following week. Progress reports for each group were due half way through the course. Final reports were to be submitted in written form and summarized in a 45-minute oral presentation before a 5-member panel, each of whom had professional experience pertinent to the general topic. This panel included a lawyer, an authority on resource management and government institutions, an ecologist, an engineer, and a planner.

A final examination, directed largely at testing the student's ability to formulate problems and evaluate alternatives, was also given. Some problem sets, encouraging the gathering of more information on topics covered in lectures, were also required. One of these involved the manipulation of a rather complicated computer model of a reservoir system to produce maximum value of power produced and sold. One of the instructors developed a bibliographic computer program using Dartmouth's BASIC time-sharing system. This was conceived to provide a readily available, up-to-date list of references, cataloged by topic. The list included review comments on each reference. Students could add comments, and this enabled them to take advantage of references others had found. This was one of the attempts to share the knowledge of the "experts" in the course with the other members of the class, so that information in some depth on any topic was available to all. This approach was found to be especially useful during the initial stages of research but less so later on because of the time required to keep the files up to date. To further facilitate the groups' operations, a budget of $100 was provided to each group to cover mileage, phone calls, and reproduction services.

TABLE 1

LECTURERS AND TOPICS, COLLEGE COURSE I, WINTER 1969

Number	Topic	Lecturer	Affiliation
1	Introduction—The Vermont Yankee Problem: Problems in Policy Formulation	J. Brownell	Former Assistant Attorney General for Vermont
2	Problem Formulation	A. O. Converse	Professor of Engineering, Dartmouth
3	Small Group Dynamics	G. F. Theriault	Professor of Sociology, Dartmouth
4	The Connecticut River Watershed: Physical Setting	S. L. Dingman	Lecturer in Earth Sciences, Dartmouth
5	History of Institutional Arrangements for River Basin Management	H. N. Scheiber	Professor of History, Dartmouth
6	The New England River Basin Commission	Frank Gregg	Commissioner, New England River Basin Commission
7, 8	Aquatic Ecology	G. E. Likens	Professor of Biology, Dartmouth
9	Human-Waste Treatment	E. S. Brown	Professor of Engineering, Dartmouth
10	Interstate Arrangements for River Basin Management	F. Gutheim	Consultant, Washington, D. C.
11	Remote Sensing as a Tool in River Basin Management	R. B. Simpson	Professor of Geography, Dartmouth
12	Economic Analysis	L. G. Hines	Professor of Economics, Dartmouth
13	The Role of the Federal Power Commission in River Basin Management	C. Ross	Former Commissioner, Federal Power Commission
14	The Role of The Electric Power Industry in the Connecticut River Basin	H. J. Cadwell	Executive Vice-president, Northeast Utilities, Inc.
15	Mathematics of Economic Evaluation	A. O. Converse	Professor of Engineering, Dartmouth
16	State Planning	D. C. Hoeh	Lecturer in Social Science, Dartmouth
17	Computer Simulation 1	A. O. Converse	Professor of Engineering, Dartmouth
18	Decision Making in the Face of Uncertainty	M. O. Tribus	Dean of Engineering, Dartmouth
19	Community Planning	H. Kent	Planning Consultant, Norwich, Vermont
20	Computer Simulation 2	A. O. Converse	Professor of Engineering, Dartmouth
		S. L. Dingman	Lecturer in Earth Science, Dartmouth
21	Connecticut River Basin Culture	J. W. Fernandez	Professor of Anthropology, Dartmouth
22	Tax Policy and Environmental Management	G. S. Witherspoon	Former Tax Commissioner, Vermont
23	Transportation Planning	R. S. Stearns	Professor of Engineering, Dartmouth
24	Federal Science Policy	E. M. Lyons	Professor of Government, Dartmouth

RESULTS

The topics selected for intensive study by the groups were: (1) "A Recreational and Environmental Protection Plan for Wilder Lake" (a portion of the Connecticut River near Hanover); (2) "A Proposal for the Restoration of Salmon and Shad into the Connecticut River System"; (3) "Aspects of Planning in the Ottauquechee River Valley, Vermont"; (4) The Impact of a Nuclear Power Plant in a Rural Community" (Vernon, Vermont); and (5) "Resource Development of an Upper Connecticut River Tributary" (the Mascoma River).

The study of Wilder Lake revealed a rather large recreation potential that was largely unfulfilled, due to limited public access and conflicts among various recreational uses. The group felt that the present pollution problem in the lake would be alleviated in the near future by the actions of the two bordering states. They recommended purchase of easements by the state and the towns along the lake to provide access and maintain scenic values. A series of trails, campsites, swimming areas, and boat access points was also recommended, as were regulations regarding boating use, so that various recreational interests could be served without conflict. This plan was to be implemented by a cooperative arrangement between the states of New Hampshire and Vermont and the New England River Basins Commission.

The second group examined the costs and benefits associated with restoring the salmon and shad sport and commercial fisheries of the Connecticut River. They investigated the effects of possible constraints on reintroducing these fish (dams, reverse flows, pollution, effects on other fish life) and decided that the problems associated with these could be circumvented. Options associated with fishway design, hatchery design, flow re-regulation, and tributaries suitable for breeding were investigated, as were legal aspects—funding and fishing laws. The costs and benefits of restoring the fishery in successive upstream segments were calculated; a maximum benefit/cost ratio of 1.44 was found for runs of 2 million shad and 40,000 salmon, supported by five fishways and a salmon hatchery. Specific recommendations were made for managing and financing the recommended policy.

Problems of planning in the watershed of the Ottauquechee River, a large tributary to the Connecticut near Hanover, were examined by the third group. Particular emphasis was placed on recreation and tourism, since these are the major "industries" in this area. The present opportunities for the use of recreational facilities in the area were described. Problems which are tending to limit its future recreational potential were identified as: (1) lack of coordination among planning groups; (2) insufficient attention to the needs of watershed residents; and (3) rural sprawl and strip development. Recommendations for alleviating these problems were made, including formation of a powerful regional planning commission with members elected by watershed residents and strong ties with the state planning office, economic analysis of the recreation industry to determine how and by whom money is spent and who benefits thereby, and a policy of cluster residential and particularly commercial development off scenic roads.

Problems associated with the siting of nuclear power plants in rural areas are becoming increasingly important, as reactors will supply most of the future electricity needs in New England. The need for a comprehensive study of the economic, social, and environmental impacts of such plans was recognized by the fourth group, which examined the situation in Vernon, Vermont, where a large nuclear plant is under construction. Through extensive interviews with power company officials, state and local government officials, private citizens, biologists, and others, they detailed the impact of the plant with regard to politics, economics, labor, planning and zoning, transportation, schools, and the environment. Problems associated with the dual role of the Atomic Energy Commission as a promoter of peaceful uses of atomic energy and as a regulatory agency were recognized, as was the lack of a mechanism for effectively considering the environmental effects (e.g., thermal pollution) of a nuclear plant. Specific changes in plant licensing procedures were recommended, involving the Federal Power Commission as a reviewer of these effects. The group also recommended a plan whereby the state, rather than the town, would tax the plant and return tax monies to several towns in the area. These monies would be returned in proportion to the plant's effects on each town, assuring more equitable regional balance between costs and benefits associated with the plant, and would avoid the problem of surplus tax revenues which would otherwise face the town of Vernon. Several other recommendations were made, and this report in particular received a good deal of attention from public officials in Vermont and New Hampshire.

Aspects of the management of the water and related land resources of a nearby tributary of the Connecticut River (the Mascoma River) were investigated by the fifth group. In this study, present and future problems associated with flooding, water supply, and pollution were examined. Industrial and municipal pollution were recognized as major problems with serious effects on the future industrial and, particularly, recreational development of the watershed. The group provided detailed discussions, with cost analyses, of how this pollution could be abated by various arrangements of regional treatment facilities. Lack of public access to the numerous water bodies in the basin was seen as an impediment to future recreational use, and purchase of easements and cluster zoning were recommended as policies which would encourage the fuller use yet retain the attractive rural open-space qualities of the region.

The instructors felt that College Course I fulfilled its three principal objectives very well. On the basis of the reports and final exam results, they were less sure that the fundamentals of problem analysis had been widely assimilated. However, replies by the students to questionnaires indicated that learning about problem formulation was one of the more valuable experiences of the course. The relevance of the topics examined was considered by the students to be one of the outstanding course features, and this was helped by having each group select its own topic.

Almost every student thought that the opportunity to work in a group was an extremely valuable experience, and one which was largely unavailable in other courses. This response was not anticipated by the instructors, and indicated that this might well be considered a valid objective for future courses of this type. The opportunity to hear speakers from outside of academic life was also frequently cited as a good feature of the course.

There was little consistency among the responses to the question "What were the worst features of the course?" A few cited irrelevant or poor lectures, and some complained that some members of their group were uncooperative and did little work. There was also some dissatisfaction with the final exam and problem sets, which several students felt interfered with the main objective—to analyze a problem and produce a report recommending a policy. Recommendations for improvement of the course in future years were also very diverse, but included making it longer (2 terms), using smaller groups, and eliminating the pass-fail (ungraded) option so that group members would be more highly motivated. There was an overwhelming consensus that each group should be free to select its own topic, but several students indicated that a list of suggested topics would be helpful.

IMPLICATIONS FOR THE FUTURE

College Course I clearly fulfilled several needs felt by the students which were not being satisfied in other courses. Principal among these were an opportunity to direct themselves to a real problem with multidisciplinary dimensions and the opportunity to work in groups, which many students recognized as frustrating, yet as something they would have to do often after finishing their formal education. Other courses which fulfill these goals should be highly successful and, indeed, necessary.

An environmental science program is almost by definition problem-oriented, and courses of this type would seem to be an essential part of such a program. Success in allowing students of virtually any academic background to participate indicates that such a course could be used early in an environmental science program. In that role, it might do much to foster a student's interest in particular areas, which he could satisfy later in specialized courses. However, College Course I was extremely satisfying to junior and senior science majors, who had a chance to apply some of their disciplinary knowledge to a larger and real problem. Whether regarded as a summary or introduction, such courses do in our opinion have real value in allowing the students an opportunity to see where individual disciplines fit together, and in providing an environment in which they can be thoughtful and creative.

CONCLUDING REMARKS

We close by quoting from a memo written by one of the authors on the subject of managing our technical society. It is a statement of the general philosophy behind the course.

Decision making or design problems involve objectives by which to measure the desirability of a certain course of action, factors under the problem solver's control (i.e., power),

and factors not under his control which we shall call constraints. One cannot think about objectives very long before becoming interested in philosophy. Constraints include political laws, customers, psychological limitations, as well as the empiricism of natural science. Controllers are just as concerned with stability and feedback whether they be servo-mechanisms or the President's Council of Economic Advisors.

Unfolded in this manner, it is apparent that such problems are not interdisciplinary, they are just not disciplinary. Solution demands people who will follow where the problem leads. These people must have access to knowledge on a need-to-know basis rather than on an expert know-it-all basis. Thanks to the computer or information processor, this will be possible to a much greater extent in the future.

Wisdom, or the lack of it, is found in the application of knowledge. If we are to escape Franny's indictment (in Salinger's Franny and Zooey) of piling up knowledge for its own sake and never mentioning wisdom, then we must seriously consider application. It seems that one of the worst misconceptions about liberal education is that it's not to be applied.

FOOTNOTE

1. The idea for an undergraduate course in Policy Formulation (College Course I) at Dartmouth College originated with Professor A. O. Converse of the Thayer School of Engineering. His interest in presenting such a course grew out of a knowledge of optimization theory and an earlier attempt to apply some of its precepts to a problem in public policy—the establishment of state criteria for acceptable levels of thermal alteration in the Connecticut River (1). In addition, Professor Converse had been associated with Thayer School's introductory engineering course, in which students work in groups toward the solution of a specific engineering problem (3). Many of the organizational features of that course were adopted in College Course 1.

REFERENCES

1. Converse, A. O., Thermal Energy Disposal Methods for the Proposed Nuclear Power Plant at Vernon, Thayer School of Engineering, Dartmouth College, Hanover, New Hampshire, 1967.

2. James, William, Pragmatism, Meridian Books, Inc., New York, 1955.

3. Stearns, S. R., Education Today for Environmental Challenges Tomorrow, paper presented at the American Society of Civil Engineers Annual Meeting, (Meeting Preprint 1046), Chicago, Illinois, 1969. ■

A university course dealing with environmental quality as an issue of public policy.

THE POLITICS OF ENVIRONMENTAL QUALITY

John Baden

THERE is probably no public policy issue so universally and fundamentally important as the quality of the life support system of earth. Thus, given that the impact of man upon his environment increases with his numbers and his technology, mounting attention is being given to the condition of man's environment and to its probable future.

To the critical observer it may appear that many commentators on the environment use the sanctity of their scientific-academic posts to legitimate and buttress their claims of impending disaster. Catastrophic pronouncements are the hallmarks of this group. Members claim that we will see massive famine by 1975; that industry is generating so much CO_2 that the "greenhouse effect" will overheat the earth or, conversely, that so much atmospheric dust is being generated that sunlight will be blocked, giving rise to a new ice age. Concurrently they claim our production of heavy metals such as lead and boron and of chlorinated hydrocarbons is so excessive that the entire earth is becoming toxic. For the average citizen there are strong incentives to avoid or dismiss such predictions.

In marked contrast to the preceding claims of impending disaster is the cornucopian theory of economics. The optimistic proponents of this theory believe that man's increased ability to control nature has placed him on the threshold of utopia. From this perspective the future is indeed bright. For example, electric power production will double each decade, and even more Americans will live better electrically. Incomes will continue to rise in America, fostering the elimination of poverty. Genetic engineering and the "green revolution" will bring nutritional improvements to the underdeveloped countries. Increased automation will nearly eliminate drudgery and the accompanying leisure will produce and enhance "culture." Existing problems of environment will be solved and new ones precluded by the same technological-information advancement that serves as a foundation for the impending economic progress. There are strong incentives to believe those who promise such a future.

One might seriously doubt if any fully facultied person would consider these disparate possibilities of only idle importance. Further, since either set of possibilities will fundamentally influence relations throughout the entire society, it is clear that an investment directed toward an understanding of these potentialities is decidedly worthwhile.

It is equally clear that environmental problems are public problems in the broadest sense of the term. Although isolation or wealth may mitigate direct environmental impact, the matrix of interdependencies is so complete that Eskimos have suffered excessive radiation exposure while those on Park Avenue have high concentrations of lead in their nerve cells. When the effects of action rebound upon third parties in this manner, political action can be expected.

THE BIOLOGICAL FOUNDATIONS

With all due respect, the reader is reminded that he is an animal. From this fact, several others follow. First, man can exist only within certain environmental parameters. Above or below a relatively narrow range of temperatures, pressures, and atmospheric mixtures, man is a nonviable species.

Second, man is a participant in a dynamic system. As such he is dependent upon other members of the system (species of plants and animals, sunlight) for their contributions to the maintenance of the system. There is no way man can escape this dependence.

Third, man has not always had an easy time of it. From the perspective of mid-century America, the modal condition of most men in most societies throughout history has been one of extreme hardship, uncertainty, and deprivation. Exceptions, such as those found on the northwest coast of aboriginal North America and on a few of the benign Pacific islands, were primarily fortuitous. But even in those exceedingly hospitable circumstances, nearly half of the mature population was engaged in the protracted, hazardous activity of child

---

Dr. Baden is Assistant Professor of Political Science at Montana State University. He has been a Visiting Professor at Indiana University.

bearing. The fact that few of those born in primitive societies lived to see the extension of their lineage serves as grim testimony to the tenuous relationship of man to his environment.

Although man must acknowledge the set of interdependencies in which he is affixed, he has the demonstrated capacity to significantly influence the system. Yet he tinkers with the system, consciously or otherwise; if prudent, he will keep in mind that he is a fragile biological organism.

ENVIRONMENTAL IMPACT UPON SOCIETY

Not all men live in an identical environment. This fact is reflected in differing social responses to differing environmental circumstances. As a general rule, the more modernized (or developed) a society, the less obvious is the impact of the natural environment. Thus, while the Kung Bushmen or tribal peoples from the interior of New Guinea must continually adjust their social processes to immediate environmental factors; more highly developed societies have the potential to defer the reality checks imposed by natural processes. If the societies at both poles of development or anywhere between are to have long run viability, their socioeconomic activities must harmonize with the natural energy exchange systems in which they are inextricably enmeshed. However arrogantly modern man approaches nature, there exist reality checks that cannot be indefinitely postponed. Accepting this, it is only reasonable to turn to a cursory examination of modern man's current impact upon his environment.

SOCIETAL IMPACT UPON THE ENVIRONMENT

Science, operationalized as technology, has enabled man to significantly reduce environmental uncertainty. This fact is expressed in the actuary tables of insurance companies. These tables demonstrate the feasibility of altering man's circumstances in such a way as to enable the modal individual to complete the life cycle as culturally defined in his society.

Technical development, however, need not coincide with long-run improvements in man's condition. Indeed the problems inherent to technology and the management of its implications are receiving increased attention. " To me it seems possible that the new amount of technological power let loose in an overcrowded world may overload any system we might devise for its control; the possibility of a complete and apocalyptic end of civilization cannot be dismissed as a morbid fantasy. " (1) Taking cognizance of such spillovers is the core of an ecological approach to problems of social organization and collective action; the recognition that events are interdependent is central to an ecological perspective. In brief, this approach recognizes the systemic aspects of seemingly isolated activities. These systematic spillovers and disruptive externalities may be subsumed under three headings.

First are the unintended consequences of technological advancement. For example, while American Cyanide, Inc. , by the development of numerous herbicides and pesticides, has contributed to the 200 percent increase in corn production, this contribution is neither isolatable nor fully beneficial. Neither, a prudent man may insist, is it fully understood. The long range implications of such tinkerings with ecological systems may be crucial—in the strongest sense of that term. In this context the need for remedial public policy arises when there exist activities or processes with a high potential for significant negative spillovers.

The second set of problems, those resulting from man's increased fecundity and successful nuturing, are the most obvious. This stress of growth is beyond the unguent of simple technological remedy. It is clear that institutional adjustments with regard to population pressures must derive from ecological considerations.

The third category deals with the interdependence of societies and the potential imposition of environmental costs. It is clear that a society can be autonomous, and hence independent, only to the degree that it is self sustaining: autonomy is a function of capacity for self-sufficiency. With this in mind, consider that the scope of man's ecological disturbances have increased. Thus, the buffering capacity (or remedial qualities) of the world's ecosystem have become more heavily taxed. As a result of the potential for such worldwide disturbance and man's fundamental dependencies on the environment, the capacity for self-sufficiency is precluded at ever broader geographic levels and ever higher levels of political organization. As an extreme example, if a country ruins its rivers by contamination, that act, in a sense, is an internal problem; that country must suffer the consequences. If in the process of river flow, however, the life support system of the oceans are destroyed, then the original polluting acts are worldwide in scope. In the latter case, costs are visited upon all oxygen-using organisms. Only recently has man developed the technical prowess that permits one society to impose environmental costs on a worldwide scale. With our current potential, an effective policy response must be applied at ever greater levels of generality, i.e, the jurisdictional scope must be congruent with the natural systems affected.

Although environmental issues are highly interrelated, it is convenient to segregate them for purposes of study (and is necessary for purposes of analysis). There is substantial agreement that excessive human population constitutes the fundamental problem, for it exacerbates all others. There is, of course, considerable disagreement regarding the seriousness of population as a problem. Further, some individuals, ranging from communalistic hippies to conservative Roman Catholics, maintain that there is no morally acceptable solution to the problem of excessive human population—if such a problem should exist. Given that matters of public policy usually have an underlying moral justification, this normative issue, in addition to the neutral demographic and resource projections, should be examined.

Environmental pollution is the second topic. For the purposes at hand, pollution may be considered to be of two types, natural and man-caused. The leaves of deciduous trees and the needles of red cedar both pollute water and have caused fish kills. In sharp contrast with man's sources of pollution, components of nature's pollution are naturally, as opposed to man's chemical means, biodegradable and are normally found in ecosystems. Thus, our focus is upon man made pollution.

Resource depletion is the third aspect of environmental deterioration considered in this course. As a hunting and gathering animal, man makes minimal demands upon the inanimate resources of the earth and has relatively small impact upon the animate.

When environmental exploitation is limited to hunting and gathering, however, only a very low population density can be sustained. To maintain high populations, a pattern of more pervasive and intensive resource utilization must be developed. Our current industrial practices impose very high demands upon resources.

VALUES, BELIEFS, AND THE ENVIRONMENT

Values have been described as the selectors and regulators of behavior. Thus, if one wishes a handle for an understanding of behavior. Thus, if one wishes a handle for an understanding of man's orientation toward his environment, he will be advantaged by insight into the values of the men in question. While an appreciation of prevailing values fails to grant deterministic analytic leverage, subjective insight should be enhanced.

While the environment is global in one sense, human values are global in another, and everything cannot be covered. In brief, a focus is required. By restricting our consideration to the relatively specific topic of American orientations toward wilderness, the perspective should be manageable. Hopefully, given that America was approached as pristine wilderness, our view should not be myopic.

POLITICS, POWER, AND ENVIRONMENTAL QUALITY

While in " normal " times most people believe they can avoid all but ritualized participation in politics, the environment, in fact, impinges upon everyone at all times. In reality so does politics. To understand the social forces which influence patterns of environmental exploitation, it is essential to understand the politics involved in the allocation of exploitation rights and responsibilities.

Political power is the ability to influence the outcomes of social events. It may be defined as the capacity to modify the conduct of others. Within any society there are differentials in the quantity and scope of power held by persons. Politics involves the competition for this power. All societies are stratified as to the quantity and the type of power held by persons within them. And, in all societies this distribution is patterned. That pattern may be referred to as the government of that society (and part of it, the Government of that society). Under all governments persons enjoy certain rights and hold certain obligations. As with power, these rights and obligations are also differentially allocated. At this point it is only reasonable to ask what bearing a sketch of political theory holds for the environment.

At virtually any point in history, everyone has wanted to be better off. " Better off " has always included material items and has always been evaluated in a context of scarcity and competition. Further, the production of material items always involves environmental inputs and outputs. Thus, as persons strive to become better off, e. g., increase their production of mouse traps, they exert an environmental influence. But the effects of this influence are not entirely absorbed by the producing unit. Their production involves spillovers (or externalities) into the environment. The environment may be considered as a type of public resource. Another name for a public resource is " public good. " Examples of public goods include roads, the provision of law and order, and national defense. Thus, it is clear that the environmental externalities (or spillovers) from private production affect a public good. And, if an issue is public in this sense, it is clearly within the scope of governmental action. This in brief is the theoretical underpinning of environmental legislation.

GOVERNMENTAL REFORM AND ENVIRONMENTAL QUALITY

The political system of the U. S. evolved in a wilderness context and with low population densities. Those who were responsible for establishing and embellishing our political institutions developed a framework highly conducive to rapid development. In the process, however, there was little, if any, attention given to environmental externalities. The right to a high quality environment was lacking in the Bill of Rights. At this late stage of development its inclusion would be primarily symbolic.

Most acts which diminish the quality of the environment (and hence lessen the quality of a public good) are discrete, are specific, and leave the actor at least momentarily better off. Given the latter characteristic, there is little reason to expect strictly voluntary modifications in behavior to improve circumstances unless the structure of incentives is changed.

BASIC READINGS

1. Anderson, Walt, Politics and Environment, Goodyear, Pacific Palisades, California, 1970.

2. The Annals, 389, May 1970.

3. Caldwell, L. K. , Environment: A Challenge for Modern Society, Natural History Press, New York, New York, September 1970.

4. Ehrenfeld, David W. , Biological Conservation, Holt Rinehart, and Winston, New York, 1970.

5. Hardin, Garrett, Population, Evolution, and Birth Control, Freeman and Company, San Francisco, California, 1969.

6. Nash, Roderick, Wilderness and the American Mind, Yale University Press, New Haven, Connecticut, 1967.

7. Watson, R. A. ; Watson, P. J. , Man and Nature: An Anthropological Essay in Human Ecology, Harcourt, Brace, and World, New York, 1969.

RECOMMENDED READINGS

1. Ehrlich, Paul R; Ehrlich, Anne H. , Population, Resources, Environment—Issues in Human Ecology, W. H. Freeman and Company, San Francisco, California, 1970.

2. Graham, Frank Jr. , Since Silent Spring, Houghton Mifflin Company, Boston, Massachusetts, 1970.

REFERENCE

1. Price, Don K. , "Purist and Politicians, " address before the American Association for the Advancement of Science 1969, Science, 163: 25-31, January 3, 1969. ∎

A novel aid to undergraduate instruction in environmental biology.

A DEMONSTRATION OF ECOSYSTEM STRESS

R. A. Coler and H. B. Gunner

THE TOXIC effects of pollutants have hitherto been largely assessed by their impact on individual target species or on artifically grouped populations. Little is known, however, regarding the community dynamics precipitated by a sustained low level stress, and the multiple ramifications it may orchestrate over the entire aquatic community. In effect, this arises from the difficulty of observing the inherently u n - wieldy total ecosystem.

This restriction has been recently obviated, however, by the authors' resort to the rhizosphere microbiocoenosis of duckweed (Lemna minor), a float-ing pollution tolerant angiosperm (2). The most casual scrutiny of these plants dramatically reveals a spectrum of biological interactions. The underside of leaves and roots teem with protozoa, rotifers, gastrotrichs, flatworms, nematodes, and crustaceans, all vigorously striving for living space and food (see Figure 1).

Further, the duckweed rhizosphere provides a readily accessible ecosystem whose constituent populations may be maintained, observed, and sampled without violating the integrity of their microenvironment (4). By housing the plants in disposable tissue-culture flasks (see Figure 2), the authors have been able to mount the long term runs essential for tracing the subtle population shifts characterizing chronic toxicity (3, 4). The optically clear chambers permit microscopic examination of Lemna without its removal, thus circumventing the ecological disruption inherent in handling and desiccation.

FIGURE 1

RHIZOSPHERE POPULATIONS (ROTIFERS AND FLATWORMS) ON UNDERSIDE OF LEMNA MINOR

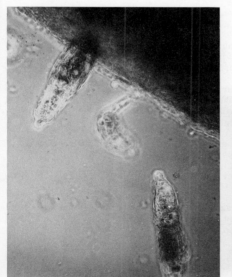

FIGURE 2

A BANK OF TISSUE-CULTURE FLASKS

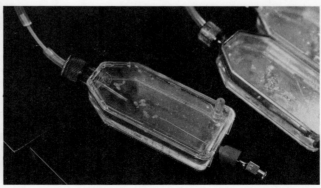

The authors are associated with the Environmental Technicians Training Program, Department of Environmental Sciences, Mershale Hall, University of Massachusetts, Amherst. Dr. Coler is Director of the Program.

This paper outlines a series of laboratory experiments for an undergraduate environmental biology course, adapting the above research tool to demonstrate the inter- and intraspecific dynamics of competition, predation, applied stress, and succession.

Preliminary:

1. Take class to organically enriched, eutrophic pond to collect duckweed and observe plant in natural habitat.

2. Transfer duckweed to Hutner's Culture Media (8) (previously prepared) and aerate at an illumination of 75-100 footcandles.

3. Allow populations to stabilize for 7 to 10 days.

4. Have class, in the interim, familiarize itself with the biology of L. minor and the rhizosphere phenomenon (1, 7, 9). While the references listed offer a starting point, the students should be encouraged to search the literature.

Exercise I. Construct chambers (2/student) – charge each with 20 cc of fresh Hutner's medium and stock with ten uniform plants (5).

Exercise II. Using standard taxonomic keys (6, 10), instruct students to familiarize themselves with dominant rhizosphere populations. Depending on student competence, limit the inventory to protista or metazoa, and the identifications to order or to family level designations. Each student must record identifications and population densities every day upon his instructor's preliminary confirmation of identifications.

The instructor will compile a checklist, distribute it among the class, and designate which flasks will be controls, which will be experimentals, and which will be discarded because of atypical community composition. For each concentration there should be at least one replicate.

Exercise III. Expose rhizosphere biota to a selected stress (oil, pesticides, detergents, etc.) graduating the concentrations at intervals of ten from (for example) 1 ppm. to 100 ppm. (3, 4). Tally resident biota every other day the first week, and once a week thereafter.

Exercise IV. After 2 or 3 months collate accumulated data with each student tabulating, graphing, and summarizing his results. A discussion should follow in which the biological response to the poison is reviewed. The basis for grading will reflect his ability to accumulate, interpret, and present meaningful data.

Because the instructor can exercise many options, the laboratories may be readily tailored to the interests and potential of each student. The laboratory experience consequently, supported by appropriate classroom lectures, will provide:

1. A research perspective,

2. An appreciation of the physiological and ecological response to acute and chronic toxicity,

3. A degree of taxonomic competence.

In these times when the thrust generated to halt the exploitation of our resources is being dissipated by "bandwagoneering" politicians, attempts to implement corrective measures seem fated to flounder in a morass of jargon. It would appear that an educational experience providing direction and perspective would be of value.

REFERENCES

1. Alexander, M. , Introduction to Soil Microbiology, John Wiley and Sons, Inc., New York, 1961, 472 pp.

2. Coler, R. A. ; Gunner, H. B. , "The Rhizosphere of an Aquatic Plant (Lemna minor)," Canadian Journal of Microbiology, 15:(no. 8)964-966, 1969.

3. Coler, R. A. ; Gunner, H. B. , "The Response of a Specialized Aquatic Ecosystem, the Duckweed Rhizosphere, to Selected Environmental Influences," Water Research, in press, 1970.

4. Coler, R. A. ; Gunner, H. B. , "Laboratory Measure of an Ecosystem Response to a Sustained Stress," Applied Microbiology, in press, 1970.

5. Coler, R. A. ; Gunner, H. B. , "Pesticide-induced Population Changes in an Aquatic Rhizosphere," Bacteriological Proceedings, p. 18, 1970.

6. Edmondson, W. T.(ed.), Fresh-Water Biology, John Wiley and Sons, Inc., New York, 1959, 1248 pp.

7. Hillman, W. S. , "The Lemnaceae, or Duckweeds. A Review of the Descriptive and Experimental Literature," Botanical Review, 27:221-287, 1961.

8. Hutner, S. H., "Comparative Physiology of Heterotrophic Growth in Plants," in Loomis, W. E. (ed.), Growth and Differentiation in Plants, Iowa State College Press, Ames, 1953.

9. Katznelson, H. , "Nature and Importance of the Rhizosphere," in Baker, K. F. ; Snyder, W. C. (eds.), Ecology of Soil-borne Plant Pathogens, University of California Press, Berkeley, pp. 187-209, 1965.

10. Pennak, R. W. , Fresh-water Invertebrates of the United States, Ronald Press Co. , New York, 1953, 769 pp. ∎

A WHOLE UNIVERSITY GOES ENVIRONMENTAL

Edward W. Weidner

WE ARE in the midst of an ecological crisis. City and countryside are spoiled. Air and water are polluted. Everywhere we look, man's abuse of his environment is evident. The accelerating public awareness of this crisis is all to the good. Without such awareness there would be no hope of mobilizing the great concentrations of resources and manpower that are going to be required to save us from world-wide environmental calamity.

Few if any of us, however, can have any accurate concept of the effort, the ingenuity, the determination, and the cost that will be required to translate this awareness into effective action in support of environmental quality. The reason is that we are dealing with a situation that requires us to abandon or substantially modify certain attitudes and beliefs that have been a part of our conventional wisdom for generations, even for centuries. To mention a single and extremely troublesome example, there is the problem of population control. Its ramifications reach into every area of our lives, including the most personal. If basic changes in our individual and societal attitudes in this area are to be made, we face an educational task that dwarf's anything we have accomplished in the past. The size of the task is amplified by the limited time we have to accomplish it.

While population control may be the single most difficult problem we must face in the immediate future, there are others not far behind it in magnitude and complexity. Some problems, such as war and poverty, are very old, and may not at first glance appear to be environmentally relevant. But we are beginning to see such social phenomena in a new context, as contributing to and being affected by ecological factors. Conceivably, this new way of viewing old problems could lead us to solutions not apparent before. For one thing, the ecological view does emphasize the inescapable relatedness to all of us with each other and of man and his works as a whole with the biophysical environment that produces and sustains life. In this statement, obviously, there are echoes of the great religious and philosophical concepts that form the heart of our cultural heritage. We are not discovering new truths about the require-

ments of our existence, except perhaps in a technological sense. But we are rediscovering that application of the old truths to the realities of our environmental situation may quite literally be the price of our survival.

To turn from general philosophy to specific example, consider what we are trying to do at the University of Wisconsin–Green Bay (UWGB). Our mission is to create a new kind of educational institution, a university designed specifically to respond to the needs of an era which has as its dominant concern the preservation and improvement of environmental quality for all men.

UWGB may be the only university in the country to be planned from its inception as an institution consciously focusing in all of its parts on problems of the environment. Although our academic plan with its pervasive ecological emphasis became operative only last fall, its formulation began 3 years earlier, long before the public at large had awakened to the seriousness of the ecological crisis. This fact is cited to emphasize that our plan is not a patchwork strategy thrown together in hasty response to a popular outcry for "doing something about the environment." Naturally we welcome the outcry and the concern that motivates it, but, had it not occurred at this particular time, we would still have been embarked on precisely the course we are now following.

Obviously there was a certain amount of foresight involved in our planning, but it was foresight for which no single individual or small group of individuals can take credit. Our plan, which is still evolving, represents the collective contribution of hundreds of persons, including not only educators and scholars from throughout the country, but many of the business and professional men, political leaders, and other citizens of Wisconsin and its neighboring states–and, of course, our students as well. Full credit must go, also, to former University of Wisconsin President Fred Harvey Harrington and his staff at Madison, to the Board of Regents of The University of Wisconsin, to the state's Coordinating Council for Higher Education, and to the Legislature, for their collective

---

Dr. Weidner is Chancellor of The University of Wisconsin - Green Bay.

willingness to consider, approve, and fund a new institution that departs radically from the established patterns of public higher education.

Ours is a university with all its curriculums designed "to encourage preserving and enhancing environmental quality and ecological balance." Our objective is not to train narrow specialists, but to extend a broad general education focused on environmental quality to all students, regardless of their fields of specialization or their professions. To attain this end, certain requisites are evident.

First, fundamental to our program at UWGB is the conviction that our mission can be accomplished only in concert with the people of our region as they act through their business and industrial enterprises, professional organizations, and governmental and voluntary agencies. We have already established a variety of community advisory committees that regularly provide counsel and stimulation for our several colleges and campuses and for the university as a whole. The community joins us on the campus and we of the campus join the rest of the community off the campus in mutual learning experiences.

Second, environmental problems do not recognize political boundaries. Most such problems may be local in origin, but they affect entire regions that are defined in part by natural features and in part by man-made features. Our region is the Upper Great Lakes area. We see ourselves as being in a position to play a unique role in focusing the attention and the efforts of students, professors, and other citizens on environmental problems that are regional, and even extra-regional, in extent. In developing this regional role, we could be establishing a prototype for other institutions.

Third, the ecological crisis is not one that has been brought on primarily by lack of scientific and technological knowledge. The crisis is rooted in attitudes that have allowed all of us, in our business, industrial, domestic, and recreational activities, to do things that have had a cumulative and massive degrading effect on our environment. The great need is for a new set of attitudes that will enable us cooperatively to apply to the improvement of the environment the scientific and technological knowledge that is available to us. This is the objective of the general education element of our university work.

Fourth, there is widespread recognition today that the traditional organization of educational institutions into narrow disciplinary departments is not well suited for mounting an educational effort directed to the solution of environmental problems. Is is much easier, however, to recognize these organizational defects than to change them. There is a relearning process

involved for virtually all faculty members, most of whom have themselves been trained rigorously within particular disciplines and have become accustomed to functioning within traditional departments. We believe that this relearning process can best be carried out in a new institution that has deliberately structured itself along lines that encourage the intermingling of disciplines within relatively broad environmental problem areas. At UWGB disciplines and professions are secondary—ecological problems are primary. In faculty hiring and faculty organization, there is little concern with the field of a professor's PhD. There is much concern with the kinds of ecological problems on which he wishes to focus, along with students and members of the community. Both the primary mode of faculty organization and the primary contours of a student's program are determined along pan-disciplinary and ecological problem lines.

At UWGB a student selects an environmental problem that forms the center of his intellectual interests. It may be a problem of the biophysical environment such as environmental control in regard to air, water, land, natural resources, or environmental engineering; it may be a problem associated with the social environment such as urban decay, regional planning, or the modernity process; it may be a focus on population dynamics, nutrition, and the resource-population ratio, or the effect of environment on human development; and it may be an emphasis on human identity and its many diverse aspects as human beings are propelled into communication and action. If none of the formally stated ecological problems satisfy a student, he is invited to formulate his own environmental problem on which to concentrate.

The environmental problem then becomes the central point of relevance for the student's problem. He chooses courses in the various disciplines and the various professions that contribute to thinking, problem-solving, and decision-making in regard to the particular environmental problem. Thus chemistry, art, secondary school teaching, and psychology all of a sudden come alive. They are means to a social end. They relate one to another, as well as to the environmental problem. The world outside the university is just as relevant to a student's learning objectives as the world of books and classroom materials inside the university. Choices of off-campus experiences and on-campus community lecturers are consequently made with this test of relevance in mind.

The theme of man and his environment must not become just a fad, not just a fancy "add-on" to permit a university to appear contemporary or to assist it in attracting outside funds. Rather, this theme must take its place as a fundamental aspect of the curriculum of every university that seriously concerns itself with the future of mankind.∎

A pioneer college instrumentality for environmental teaching, research, and extension.

THE WILLIAMS CENTER FOR ENVIRONMENTAL STUDIES

Andrew J. W. Scheffey

THE CENTER for Environmental Studies was established at Williams College in October 1967 as an interdepartmental research and educational facility with three central objectives:

To provide a focal point for undergraduate teaching and faculty research in the environmental field.

To relate the academic resources of Williams College to planning and development needs of surrounding regions.

To build a body of factual knowledge and professional understanding of environmental issues developing in the metropolitan hinterland regions of the Nation-those areas extending 50 to 150 miles beyond major urban concentrations, now experiencing profound changes in land use, population distribution, and institutional relationships.

STRUCTURE AND ADMINISTRATION

Since its inception, the Center has operated under policy guidance provided by the Provost's Coordinating Committee for Environmental Studies. In addition to the Provost of the College, this committee includes department heads representing each of the three major Divisions of the College, the Director of the Center, and several Faculty Associates of the Center. The present Director of the Center holds a joint appointment in the Departments of Political Science and Economics. The Assistant Director holds an appointment in Political Science, and faculty members from the Departments of Economics, Biology, and Art have part-time appointments as Faculty Associates of the Center. These positions are funded in part through the Center's budget, and this pattern will be expanded in the future to include additional departmental representation.

One full-time Research Associate is attached to the Center staff, with major responsibility for administration of the Berkshire Panel for the Public Environment. Consultants have been engaged from time to time for special projects.

FUNDING

In November 1967 the Center received an 18-month planning grant from the Rockefeller Foundation to assist in formulating long-term program goals and in defining research and educational projects. A subsequent Rockefeller Foundation grant of $200,000 in 1969 will permit fuller development of these activities over the next 3-5 years. Williams College provides support for staff, secretarial services, and office facilities. In October 1968 the Center received a $75,000

matching grant under Title I of the Higher Education Facilities Act of 1965 to expand the pilot program of continuing education sponsored by the Berkshire Panel for the Public Environment. Additional funds are now being sought to sustain this phase of the Center's off-campus activity.

ACTIVITIES

Substantial progress has been made toward each of the three program areas identified above: environmental education at the undergraduate level; environmental research and education focused on problems of the surrounding region; hinterland study and analysis.

Undergraduate Education

In February 1970 faculty approval was received for a coordinate program of environmental studies at Williams College, to become operative in 1970-71. Under this new program, students majoring in regular departmental disciplines will have the option of selecting environmental studies as a field of special emphasis. The program is structured around a core of six courses. Three newly-designed courses in introductory ecology, economics, and planning will be required of all students. Non-science majors will elect one additional course dealing with either the geological or physical science aspects of environment, while science majors will elect a comparable course dealing with environmental issues within the framework of one of the social sciences.

These four courses will be prerequisite to a junior-level seminar coordinated through the Center and conducted jointly by faculty representatives from the departments of biology, economics, political science, art, and psychology. Entitled Perspectives on Environmental Analysis, the seminar will approach the topic of environment as an area of synthesis, examining the contributions and limitations of various modes of analysis. During the senior year each student will elect one additional course in his own department directly related to his particular interests in environmental studies. All students will then participate in a senior-level seminar, Environmental Planning and Policy, focusing on current planning and decision-making alternatives at the regional, national, and international levels.

The coordinate program in environmental studies is not designed to train specialists, or even to provide pre-professional education. It's purpose is to give each student a common basis of understanding for perceiving environmental issues, and for appreciating the interrelationships among different environmentally-related disciplines and professions. The

Dr. Scheffey is Director of the Center for Environmental Studies, Williams College, Williamstown, Massachusetts.

flexibility inherent in the program will enable each individual to follow his own interests through additional elective courses, and through the Winter Study Program, a month of independent student research and field study offered between semesters.

The coordinate program will be directed by an Advisory Committee attached to the Center and consisting of student and faculty representatives. Additional opportunities for relating this program to special interests of individuals, including participation in research projects of the Center, will become available in the future. An experimental "Williams in the City" course, involving a semester and summer-long off-campus period of study, will provide another educational opportunity for exploring related environmental interests. Library resources and reference files are being established to support these programs.

The Berkshire Panel

In the spring of 1968 the Center, working with the Office of the County Commissioners, took steps to establish the Berkshire Panel for the Public Environment, an environmental research and educational venture sponsored cooperatively with three county-wide organizations: the Berkshire Development Commission, the Berkshire Regional Planning Commission, and the Berkshire Natural Resources Council. For 2 years the Panel has functioned as a forum for discussion and analysis of selected planning and development issues affecting the quality of environment in Berkshire County.

An original membership of 40 citizens has recently been expanded to 75, representing a spread of interests and professional areas: utilities, housing development, banking, industry and trade, preservation and conservation, governmental agencies, and private landowners. Policies are established by a steering committee representing agency, governmental, and private interests. The Panel has operated largely through 1-day seminars based upon background papers and research reports prepared by Center associates and task force groups appointed for special projects. Various environmental issues have been selected by the Panel for consideration: open land taxation policies; highway planning procedures; solid waste disposal; vacation home development; water resource planning; conservation education; public attitudes toward the environment. An 18-month Title I matching grant of $75,000 has enabled the Panel to expand its research program in cooperation with faculty members from Williams College, North Adams State College, and Berkshire Community College.

The Panel concept is still in a formative stage. Although it has functioned essentially in an educational capacity, stimulating communication and regional awareness among diverse and frequently conflicting environmental interests, some of its membership believes that it should pursue a more activist role. This could mean developing the Panel as a sounding board for development proposals and planning alternatives; as an instrument for regional policy review and coordination; as a legislative watchdog; as a model for a new form of regional environmental authority. While the Berkshire Panel has been a pilot operation, most would agree that it is fulfilling an important need within the region. Efforts are now being made to provide greater outreach throughout the county, to broaden and

diversify its membership, and to involve greater citizen participation in policy formulation through a restructuring of the Steering Committee. The source of financing to date has kept the Panel in close linkage with the Williams Center. Outside funding, both public and private, would help to widen the base of public support, and to integrate the Panel concept more fully into the Berkshire environment.

Hinterland Research

The countryside research interests of the Williams Center reflect its geographical location. Northwestern Massachusetts, like much of New England, is experiencing the environmental pressures and trends taking shape in metropolitan hinterland areas throughout the Nation. Therefore we have looked upon Berkshire County not only as a region toward which the College has a compelling corporate responsibility, but as a laboratory for education, teaching, and research. Various activities have been initiated in recognition of these needs and opportunities.

●In October 1968 the Center sponsored a major regional conference on The Corporation and the Environment, designed to highlight ways in which corporate decisions are affecting the landscape of New England. The conference was sponsored in cooperation with the New England Governor's Conference, the New England River Basins Commission, and the New England Regional Commission. It was attended by corporate executives, government officials, professional planners, environmentalists, and academic representatives. A report published by the Center summarizes the conclusions of the conference and its recommendations for followup activity. These recommendations are now being considered by the Center.

● A proposal for a Williams College Summer Institute on the Countryside has been drawn up and circulated for comment and criticism. This would involve a consortium of academic institutions in this country, Canada, and Europe, and would provide a formal educational opportunity for planners in private practice and with public planning agencies.

●A preliminary consideration is being given to the format and funding of a graduate-level liberal arts program designed for senior government officials seeking broadened understanding of environmental policy and planning issues, especially those of a non-urban nature.

● A study is being made of the feasibility of a quasi-public development corporation capable of assembling small tracts of property for development under strict environmental standards, planned in cooperation with regional planning authorities, private financial interests, and academic consulting teams.

●The Center is cooperating with the New England Center for Continuing Education and the Conservation Foundation in a comprehensive survey of environmental programs in New England colleges and universities, particularly those geared to problems of the rural or hinterland landscape.

●In the Fall of 1970 the Center for Environmental Studies and the Center for Development Economics at Williams College cosponsored a working conference, Economic Development and Environmental Problems, dealing explicitly with the ecological implications of international development. ∎

Preparing teachers to deal with environmental factors.

OUTDOOR EDUCATION, DAYTON STYLE

Simon J. Chavez

AMERICANS seem to go from one massive movement to another. Today the call to action is environmental factors. As is usual with any crisis, there is a demand that something must immediately be done to repair overnight those conditions that have deteriorated for decades.

Those who have worked for conservation are obviously elated with this sudden awakening. Immediate action is called for. Yet there should be a realization that scotch tape or bailing wire is inadequate to correct the problem. Pollution is too complex to be solved by incantations or governmental edicts. Pollution has been an element in the American way of life. To reverse this trend requires modification in our way of living, in our way of thinking, in our sense of values.

This is a problem for education. It is a problem that requires observation, diagnosis, interpretation, experimentation, and evaluation. It requires programs in the slow and tedious process of modification of behavior. It requires that individuals give reflective thought to redefining who they are and how they became the type of person they are.

The problem of environmental factors is not one in which the environment is a problem. On the contrary, it is the person that has become a problem to the environment, and consequently a problem to himself. It is essential that the learner be helped to see what effect he has on the environment that surrounds him and to understand his role in the balance of nature.

But education is not presently equipped to deal with this problem. School has become an escape from reality. Because of increasing industrialization, the experiences offered by the school have become more vicarious and more abstract. More of the child's time is devoted to verbalism, the talking, reading, or listening experiences that for the child exist only in books. It must also be noted that their teachers are prepared to deal only with these verbalistic types of verbalization. If this is the way they are prepared, we can consequently expect that the problem of environmental pollution will be handled through dis-

cussions, reports, poems, letters, or committee meetings. Any behavioral modification that will result from this approach is dubious.

What is needed is a closer association with reality—the reality that cannot be found inside the school building. Education must make room for outdoor education. This calls for provisions for children to learn from reality itself. It calls for a system of learning that is based on experience, on inquiry, on discovery, and on analysis. It is a system that involves the whole child; his affective, physical, cognitive, and aesthetic nature. It calls for teaching outdoors.

How do you teach outdoors? How do you maintain discipline? How do you prescribe what the child needs to repeat in order to pass a test? How do you make sure he covers the right things? These questions reveal the need for preparation since a teacher is likely to need help to teach outdoors. It is doubtful that he received such help in preservice preparation.

To provide this type of preparation an exploratory program was conducted in the 1969-70 school year by the University of Dayton and the Outdoor Education Center of Antioch College in Yellow Springs. A total of 20 elementary education students volunteered for this program. They spent 5 weeks of their student-teaching experience at the Outdoor Education Center. The success of their involvement is best reflected in the fact that there were six volunteers in September. The number soared to 13 for the term beginning in January. Surprisingly, none of the volunteers deserted on that first morning in January when the thermometer skidded to 9 below with a chill factor of 35 below. In all fairness to the women's liberation movement, it must be stated that all of the first 20 volunteers were women.

These students devoted the entire semester to student teaching. The first 5 weeks were spent at Glen Helen Outdoor Education Center, and the remaining 10 weeks were spent in a classroom in the city of Dayton.

The first week at Glen Helen was devoted to in-service education. The director of the center, Harry

Dr. Chavez is Chairman, Department of Elementary Education, School of Education, University of Dayton, Ohio.

Feldman; the educational leader, Steve Kress; and the staff of teacher-naturalists introduced the students to the world of outdoor science and inquiry. In each of the succeeding weeks the student teachers assumed increasing responsibility for teaching some of the elementary school pupils.

It should be pointed out, by way of clarification, that Glen Helen is a 1,000-acre tract of land that has reverted to its primitive stage. The center, bequethed to Antioch College, by a donor, is dedicated to use as a land laboratory. Each week a group of approximately 60 children from one of the nearby schools comes to live and learn at the center. There is a different group each week, rain or shine, for the entire school year. Usually there are two classes of sixth graders, each accompanied by their homeroom teacher.

At the center the children are divided into groups of 10 or less for small group instruction. Each small group is assigned to one of the teacher-naturalists. Instruction begins with teacher-pupil planning, as each group decides what is to be done to explore the topic chosen. There is a wide range of choices dealing with different biotic communities, geological factors, balance of nature, social factors, and astronomy.

Having made their plans, the groups proceed to different parts of the Glen for unstructured inquiry. It could be the pine forest, thicket, deciduous forest, meadow, pond, river bank, cascades, or the old Indian mound. In any case, children are given the opportunity to experience, sense, and inquire. The teacher-naturalist is trained to encourage questioning, hypothesizing, verifying. He is by no means a walking encyclopedia that answers pupils' questions. On the contrary, he will usually answer a question by asking another question, forcing the pupil to probe further, to make "hunches."

An example of this is the study of soil. Teacher-pupil planning begins when the teacher asks what is soil? Is all earth soil? Are there differences in soil? How can we discover differences? Armed with dixie cups, the group proceeds to various locations where comparisons are made, by feeling, smelling, seeing, and even tasting. It includes observing and making hunches about the relationships of soil to plants and animals. It becomes an experience in "reading" reality, discovering its nature, and in making interpretations.

The behavior of the pupils changes noticeably from day to day. They become more scientific by being scientific. Their sense perception sharpens as they detect the distinctive sounds of the forest, chattering of the squirrel, warning sound of the different birds, distant call of the turtle dove, or hooting of an owl. They begin to notice the change of the land from meadow to thicket to forest. They study the evidence of the web of life as they see the plants become food for mice and rabbits, which in turn become food for hawks, owls, and foxes. They begin to examine the effects of detergents and wastes in the river. You can sense their beginning recognition of the interdependence of plants and animals. You begin to see in their eyes an emerging respect for the sanctity of life.

As the children work and live together, changes in their social behavior become evident. The program facilitates sharing of hunches, suggestions for procedures, and pooling of findings and interpretations. Inquiries that begin outdoors are extended to searches in books back at the lodge, all in order to share findings with the group. Even the teacher is perceived in a new light. For example, one group was heard to observe, "I didn't know our teacher could smile."

This is the setting that awaited the student-teachers. Each one joined a group with a teacher-naturalist. Since the children changed every week, the student-teacher was able to try out different techniques, to notice their effectiveness, and to make refinements with the next group. A common remark was, "If I made a mistake with one group, I could change for the next group and nobody remembered how I had 'goofed' before."

Another significant advantage felt by the student-teachers was the freedom of social interaction. In the free unstructured atmosphere, they got to know each child by noon of the first day. And they knew each one as a person!

The student-teachers were unanimous in evaluating the outdoor education experience as invaluable in initiating them into teaching. When they reported to the city classroom, they brought with them knowledge and skills in science that had immediate application. These skills provided them with a status that was far above that of "student-teacher." In most instances, they were able to apply the same techniques of inquiry that they had used at Glen Helen.

Another outstanding benefit that the student-teachers enjoyed was the opportunity to associate and work with students and graduates of other colleges.

The group of university students that were in this program are among the most dedicated to the study of environmental factors. They have acquired the attitudes, insights, and inquiry skills that are needed to deal with environmental problems scientifically. In addition, they have gained the competence to alert school youngsters to study the problems and to gain a desirable outlook for their environment. The participating students felt that this was an answer to their demand for relevance in their education. All of a sudden, they were dealing with reality. They could see and feel behavioral modification. It was far more than making a poster or carrying a banner. They were involved in the very basic elements of a life problem. ∎

Translating legislation into action on the land.

REGIONAL ENVIRONMENTAL EDUCATION CENTERS

The Editor

THE APPEARANCE in the halls of Congress of various bills providing for federal funding for environmental education affords an opportunity for the development of new concepts and new facilities aimed at inculcating that mass conservation literacy necessary to energize the public and private quest for ecological survival.

One such approach would establish on appropriate university campuses Environmental Education Centers that will focus on the problem of translating resource management policies and plans into action on the landscape through (a) the collation of information about, and the preparation of practical materials on, restoring the quality of the environment, (b) informal instruction and technical assistance carried out directly to local governments, regional instrumentalities, and citizen groups, (c) the refresher education of key practitioners brought back to the campus for work in natural resource policy implementation, and (d) research in adult education theory and practice. Growing national programs of environmental management depend increasingly on state and local initiative and responsibility. "The problem of the states" as Life magazine said in a recent editorial, "is not lack of power or opportunity or even solely of money; it is a shortage of competent public servants." The proposed Environmental Education Centers would tackle the problem directly by upgrading such key community leaders as planners, lawyers, resource specialists, adult educators, communicators, teachers, and public administrators, and by reinforcing them with improved educational materials and professional consultation. The Centers would also be concerned with adult-education-and-communications research.

THE PROBLEM

The degradation of our surroundings and the resulting need to protect and enhance the quality of our environment is increasingly entering the consciousness of Americans. Legislative bodies at all levels of government, public agencies, and private groups are seeking to halt pervasive pollutions brought about by multiplying man and disappearing land. New federal and state agencies have come into existence, and significant federal and state funds have been made available for attacks on water pollution, air pollution,

open space acquisition, wildlife conservation, highway beautification, urban sprawl, and so on. But substantial areas of our choicest landscapes continue to approach a state of perturbation which will be difficult if not impossible to correct at reasonable cost and within reasonable time limits.

We are figuratively and literally sick and tired of what Eric Sevareid has called "t h e mis-development of America," a degradation of our environment that diminishes daily the quality of the human experience: water pollution; air pollution; soil erosion; forest, range, and wetland deterioration; waning wildlife; urban sprawl; preempted open spaces; vanishing wilderness; landscapes scarred by highways, litter, noise, and blight—a not-so-quiet crisis of decreasing beauty and increasing contamination that threatens not only the pursuit of happiness but life itself.

To do something about environmental quality conservation, redevelopment, and maintenance requires a sense of husbandry, a sense of responsibility on the part of every American citizen—that man-land ethic or "ecological conscience" about which Aldo Leopold bespoke. It is unthinking people who pollute the environment; it is thinking people who can effect a "new conservation": in the words of former President Johnson, to restore as well as to protect, to bring beauty to the cities as well as to keep it in the countryside, to handle the waste products of technology as well as the waste of natural resources, to halt the massive deterioration in the American environment, to husband those resources and amenities which are inextricably linked not only to economic prosperity but to the inner prosperity of the human spirit.

THE LIMITING FACTOR

What is the bottleneck? Why do we continue to have serious trouble translating federal intentions and state plans into timely, sound action on the land? One answer would certainly seem to be that it is only at the local and regional level that public policies can be translated into public and private practices, and it is at the intrastate level where the forces of wise resource management continue to be ill-equipped to deal with the forces of exploitation. The

Prof. Schoenfeld is Chairman, The Center for Environmental Communication and Education Studies, Director of Summer Sessions, and Professor of Journalism and Wildlife Ecology, The University of Wisconsin, Madison.

inefficiency with which public agencies and private
citizens go about performing the socially essential
tasks of environmental housekeeping s t e m largely
from the fact that the technical and organizational
skills available to the land conserver o r rational
planner are normally inferior to those available to
the land exploiter.

While we do not, of course, yet understand all the
scientific facts and societal values attendant to environmental quality control, what we do know is not
being applied on a scale commensurate with the present pace of environmental pollution. At the local and
regional level, where most of the decisions affecting
the quality of the environment are made, we must address ourselves firmly to laying a basis for action by
elucidating the choices in land and water use, relating them to general values and social objectives, instilling in people a desire for constructive change,
and providing practical guidelines that encompass integrated rather than unilateral approaches.

AN APPROACH

The urgency of need will not be met through educational processes of normal pace a n d dispersion.
What is needed now, and for some time to come, is
a steady stream of specific skills and resources rifl-
ed to the local and regional firing line. We need local leaders equipped with an understanding of the interrelationships involved between their callings and
total environmental management, and with a knowledge of the "tools of the trade" in energizing l a n d
and water use controls.

To begin to develop and equip a cadre of local resource management leaders, it will be helpful to concentrate on those individuals at the local and regional
level who typically do or can play the role of "change
agents" in conservation. Four such categories o f
key personnel can be identified: (a) layers, (b) planners and administrators, (c) field resource technicians, and (d) communicators and educators.

There is an acute shortage of competent personnel with legal skills related to land and water use.
There is an acute shortage of planners and administrators with a grasp of natural resource policy implementation. There is an acute shortage of f i e l d
biologists, foresters, hydrologists, park managers,
agricultural agents, and so on with other than a narrow approach to the ecological and economic resources over which they preside. And there is an acute
shortage of media communicators, educators, and
public relations men equipped to interpret resource
problems in such a way as to achieve consensus rather than conflict.

To train all such change agents and to equip them
and their clientele with effective education-for-action materials and services would be a role of t h e
Environmental Education Centers. The Centers would
also perform related research focused on improving
their concepts and techniques.

A PLAN

Initially an Environmental Education Center would
assemble from the university and elsewhere as necessary a staff representing overall competence i n
environmental problems, to include people trained

in biology, design, soils, economics, geology, engineering, ecology, sociology, public administration, journalism, education, law, and other environmental disciplines applicable to land-use issues.
Their extension function would be the collection and
collation of what is known, what has been done, what
is being done, and what might be done; the preparation of educational materials, utilizing a variety of
media; and the dissemination of information a n d
technical counsel to local governments and citizen
groups through institutes, audio and visual media,
and consultation. The team will be encouraged t o
work with maximum speed and practicality, yet with
intellectual breadth so that the environmental care-
takers on the receiving end develop a sound view of
the interrelatedness of decisions affecting the environment and of the immense complexity of h u m a n
needs that must be reconciled and met.

At the same time, the Center would provide fellowships for practicing change agents to come to the
campus for a year of study focused on the practical
problems faced by those trying to plan, a c q u i r e,
maintain, and manage lands and waters for public
purpose. These professionals would take regular
courses and special interdisciplinary seminars, and
would also perform research duties in the Center.
Appropriate degrees could be awarded to qualified
personnel.

A PROGRAM

The specific program of a Center would be organized under the following major thrusts:

1. Development of Educational Materials.
Assembling available knowledge and know-
how, feeding in the latest knowledge, and
preparing manuals, brochures, film strips,
case studies, technical guidelines, articles,
slides, syllabi, and other communications
devices.

2. Informal Education and Technical Services
    in the Field.
Local and regional conferences and institutes,
cadres of consultants, use of the mass media,
short courses, public forums, study by mail.

3. Resident Instruction.
Refresher postgraduate education on campus
of selected environmental management practitioners.

4. Research.
Such studies as: What is the nature of leadership in conservation, the nature of the
conservationist, the nature of those w h o
vandalize the environment? What is the key
that makes individuals feel and act as they
do vis-'a-vis the environment? the spark?
the environment? What is the force which
motivates individuals? How best can w e
employ what modes and methods of adult
education, formal and informal? How can
we enhance the role of such mass media
as press, radio, television, bulletins, and
displays?

5. Demonstration Sites and Model Programs.
In this role each regional Center w o u l d

serve the surrounding area as interpretive and teaching facilities.

All aspects of the program would be mutually supporting. For example, as a part of their educational regimen the environmental management fellows
would be expected to assist in the preparation of
utilitarian manuals and guides to community action;
in turn, the university specialists going afield as environmental management consultants would be expected to feed back to the instructional program
the dimensions of practical problems and emerging solutions. Both would engage in related
research.

A RATIONALE

Today issues of natural resource policy range
from the more traditional concern of resource scarcity to questions of preserving and enhancing the
qualitative aspects of life. Conflicts among competing resource demands are frequent and intense, and
the choice of alternatives involves legal, economic,
social, administrative, technological, aesthetic, ecological, and ethical considerations which must be
encompassed in the decision-making process. At the
local and regional level, where conservation problems
find their ultimate focus, there is a great need for
leaders who can deal effectively and creatively with
policy issues in all of their complexity, who are familiar with the tools of the trade in land and water
use control, and who are reasonably adept at the engineering of public consent for translating plans into
action. While there is always the danger of super-
ficiality masquerading under the title of breadth, the
essential role of this "change agent" at the local
level cannot be denied in the presence of massive extension of federal and state policy into new areas of
environmental planning and management. The implications for the nation's institutions of higher learning are obvious. They must supply the technical assistance and trained personnel with which to overcome
the current conservation gap occurring between gross
policies, no matter how enlightened, and timely action on the ground.

Those contending for environmental quality need
data to show that economically we can afford such
surroundings and that biologically we cannot afford
anything less. That information needs to be made
applicable and available in localities where the problems exist and where the issues are fought. We have
need of not just more research but of bringing existing techniques and existing skills to the service of
communities on the front lines. Local leadership
needs a point of focus for coordinated action. Local leadership needs a fund of counsel and special
talents on which to draw, including the effective stimulus that would come from knowing the experience of
other leaders in other communities who have met
and overcome some of the common problems. Local leadership needs an infusion of new talent.

The proposed Environmental Education Centers
would put together interdisciplinary teams of experts
in environmental management and charge them with

collecting, collating, and disseminating practical
guidelines to community organization and action in
resource conservation. Each Center would also
bring to the campus for a year of advanced study
and practical work promising "change agents" from
community and regional levels in such specialities as
law, planning, public administration, resource management, education, and communications. Further,
each Center would engage in research in adult education and communications as they relate to the quest
for environmental quality.

IN SUMMARY

Under emerging federal funding, then, what might
be envisaged is a series of University Environmental
Education Centers that will focus an interdisciplinary
thrust on educational research and the training of researchers, on professional management education of
several types, on citizenship education, and on extension counseling and services—in the classic manner of the land-grant college. Whether we should con-
template such a Center in each state is a question
fraught with academic, fiscal, and political considerations. Certainly we will need upwards of a score if
we are to generate sufficient varied skills and resources. Each Center need not be identical. It would be
well if each reflected the particular strengths and
slants of its institution and the needs of its region.

Within the flexibility assured by installing Environmental Quality Education Centers at universities
which differ somewhat in ethos and structure, it will
be important that certain national priorities be achieved.
Among the key determinants of success in environmental education, it is essential that each Center be
multidisciplinary in its posture and multi-process in
its programs; unilateral approaches to environmental management have caused many of our present
problems.

By multi-process, we mean a university program
concerned with the production of new knowledge and
new knowledge-seekers, of more and better resource
managers, of citizenship education, and of technical
counseling and services. What do we mean by multidisciplinary? We mean we are concerned with the
total environment of man: its social, cultural, economic, and esthetic, as well as its physical and biological, aspects. To seek environmental quality requires both an understanding of human needs and the
needs of a healthy natural environment. The development and management of environmental quality requires contributions by all the arts, sciences, and
professions. The end is to bring conflicting forces
into functional relationships in an order in which human impact does not needlessly destroy environmental quality and where environmental quality contributes to more fruitful human life, liberty, and the pursuit
of happiness. While we recognize the essential importance of strengthening existing disciplines, the
essential nature of environmental education looks toward research, teaching, and extension configurations that transcend traditional lines of endeavor and
are concerned with the wholeness of the relationship
between man and his surroundings.■

V New Learning Laboratories
in Field and Factory

IS THE OUTOFDOORS the optimum setting for environmental education? Many of us assume so, but Gerald Schneider presented a different point of view at a recent conference on *Man and Nature in the City*: "The naturalist may try to project his values on the urban child only to find those values rejected because the child lacks the experiences on which to base transcendental values." Certainly, in a heaving and tossing, lavender-plumbing world, some may very well seriously question, I suppose, the relevancy of the outofdoors. Faced with an "environmental crisis" in every headline, can we continue to practice in good heart such cherished diversions as bird-watching and bass fishing? Do the voice of a meadowlark or the tug of a trout impart any message worthy of the hour? Are we simply engaged in a heedless escape from stress? Or is there in fact some significant meaning hidden in a summer day afield?

I personally believe there are at least three valid reasons for the pursuit of outdoor experiences even in the face of the population-pollution syndrome. One is simply that outdoor recreation is indeed a re-creating experience. We have always felt instinctively that we need "fresh air," literally and figuratively. That the human animal demands an occasional change of pace and change of scene there is increasing scientific evidence. Arnold Toynbee has documented the phenomenon of withdrawal and return that has enriched the course of history. Biochemists have discovered alternating cycles of activity and quiescence in cellular affairs that are to be denied only at the risk of health. Psychiatrists are using outdoor activities to calm and cure their patients. The teacher need make no apologies, then, if he takes to field and stream now and then. He returns a better man, and his students with him. Exposure to the outofdoors can take on an inspirational dimension as well. Just as there are no atheists in foxholes, so are there no pessimists on spring hikes or fall drives. The resurrection of the April earth or the fire-dance of autumn impart a compelling recognition that change is a law of nature. True, a carpet of shooting stars, a congregation of warblers, a big moon over Blue Mound, even all of them together speak in a very still, small voice. What, indeed, is a June sunset in a day of space ships? And yet don't we really need, today as seldom before, something of the serenity and detachment that the outofdoors has to offer? We can use this intimation of eternity to route our jitters and clear our vision.

But the real ecological justification for an occasional retreat to woods and waters is the opportunity it provides to acquire a perception of the oneness of our world. To partake of the natural processes by which the land and the living things upon it have achieved their characteristic forms and by which they maintain their existence, to become aware of the incredible intricacies of plant and animal communities, to sense the intrinsic beauty and the creeping degradation of the organism called America—to do these things is to learn the great lesson: that there are no country problems that are not city problems, no problems of the inner core that are not problems of the open spaces, no local problems that are not world problems, no world problems that are not local problems, no problems of poverty that are not problems of affluence, no problems of crime in the streets that are not problems of conduct in the home; that insects, birds, fish, mammals, water, soil, wilderness, trees, plants, man, Washington, Vietnam, Harlem, and Weyewega are all part of the same scheme—a sort of intricately woven fabric. Snip one thread and the entire cloth begins to unravel; stitch up one tear and you begin to repair the whole. Joseph Wood Krutch said it so well:

We need some contact with the thing we spring from. We need nature at least as a part of the context of our lives. Without nature we renounce an important part of our heritage. On some summer vacation or country weekend, we realize that what we are experiencing is more than merely a relief from the pressures of city life: that we have not merely escaped from something but also into something; that we have joined the greatest of all communities, which is not that of man alone but of everything which shares with us the great adventure of being alive.

I am not so naive as to suggest that every lathe operator with a spinning rod is a potential Thoreau, that every member of the Audubon Society is an Aldo Leopold in disguise, or that every delegate to a state conservation congress is a homespun Albert Schweitzer. But I do proceed here on the assumption that exposure to the outofdoors, however casual or however intense, directly or vicariously, can be a doorway to the ecological understanding of our utter interdependence with our environment and with life everywhere, to the development of a culture that will secure the future of an environment fit for life and fit for living, and to an appreciation of those American amenities that are inexorably linked not only to economic prosperity but to the inner prosperity of the human spirit.

How to bring about the same engendering of a broad ecological conscience *sans* wide open spaces is one of the more intriguing aspects of environmental education. In this chapter we read of new learning experiences being developed in city jungles as well as in bucolic settings. ∎

FULL DISCLOSURE IN ENVIRONMENTAL USE

Michael   F.   Brewer

THE NATURAL environment embraces us all. Each of us is a component part of it; yet in our proprietary aspirations each one of us often claims the environment for himself. These claims frequently clash, as the use to which one individual puts his environment creates a nuisance or becomes preemptive to another potential user. Because of these common claims to the environment, and because in the long run the environment supports all of mankind, its management is everybody's business. Privacy, secrecy, and exclusiveness play little role in this theatre of human endeavor, notwithstanding the heavy reliance placed on them for other types of management activities.

This public character of the environment poses problems but also creates opportunities for management. Traditional notions of "efficient resource use" assume that individuals can acquire some degree of exclusive claims to resources (defensible under law), which provides adequate security to the entrepreneur to elicit from him commitments of capital and labor. This tradition and the legal fictions involved in modern concepts of property often are not in accord with the inherent "public-ness" of our natural environment.

At an operational level, the public dimension of the environment means that a viable management program cannot proceed until it can muster broad public support. It also means that governmental agencies with environmental management responsibilities can be forced to consider new management options if they enjoy broad grass root support. This is especially true when such support is institutionalized; and private citizens are rapidly learning the procedures for institutionalization.

All of this suggests that the citizenry at large plays an integral role in managing the environment, and accordingly must be informed about its problems. It must perceive not only opportunities for the environment to contribute to human welfare, but also must clarify for itself social objectives for environmental use and understand the consequences of man's activities on the environment in light of those objectives.

Casual observation suggests that the public at large is indeed more sensitive to and informed about environmental problems than in previous times. Earlier concerns with natural resources management frequently were tied to particular types of environmental use–with emphasis upon its potential contribution to national or regional economic growth. Questions about the adequacy of raw materials endowments, and potential bottlenecks to economic growth which a "deficient" environment might pose have in the past been accorded high national priority. Contemporary concern now focuses upon issues of environmental preservation and restoration. Thus one now finds problems of environmental pollution cited more frequently and vehemently than problems associated with the adequacy of the environment to sustain economic growth.

I believe this shift in outlook toward environmental matters has coupled with it significant overtones relating to strategies for public action. Our earlier concerns with environmental issues frequently were debated and discussed by "experts" who, the general public assumed without serious question, were able to speak with authority about environmental deficiencies and their implications to society and its economy. Our contemporary concern with environmental quality opens the field to everybody. Consensus on the social objectives for environmental management must emerge from debate by an informed public. To be sure technical information of a rather complex nature still must be dealt with, but dealt with now in ways in which the public at large can understand and through processes in which the public at large can participate. The recent effort to understand and pose solutions to chemical contamination of the environment through organizations such as the Environmental Defense Fund, provides an illustration of such public participation. The now popular topics of the "new conservation"–which places primary emphasis on environmental quality–poses major challenges to the processes of public education, information, and communication.

Dr. Brewer is Vice President, Resources for the Future, Inc., Washington, D.C. This paper is a transcript of his remarks to the Institute in Communications for Environmental Management, The University of Wisconsin, Madison, August 6, 1969.

NEED FOR AND NATURE OF INTERPRETATION

Rational assessment and critical choice on the part of today's public is often conspicuous by its absence. These are emotional times for the citizens of our country. Today's stage holds a new cast of characters who assemble and articulate their views and emotions through different and very formidable techniques of group organization and confrontations. Their script reflects the veiled prospects of annihilation inherent in our technology, along with uninhibited demands for individual fulfillment. It is hardly surprising that the public at large (which I take to have an over-30 outlook on things) is confused, often gullible, and frequently disorganized in its thinking about the major challenges of our times.

I think this is true for questions involving the quality of the environment along with other items on the national agenda. Our perceptions tend to be dominated by limited amounts of information, often conveyed amid high emotion. Our concern lurches from the excitement of sensing a problem's importance to the self-satisfaction of becoming advocates for particular programs of change, without the intellectual exercise of exploring the problem's dimensions and identifying an array of possible solutions. This chaotic way in which the average citizen finds himself involved with many public matters may yield useful therapeutic fallout, but I doubt that it is the most effective way of helping our society get on with the task of moderating its affairs so that our natural environment can continue to yield a satisfying existence for its human inhabitants.

The concept of interpretation can help bring order out of this chaos. Let's dwell for a moment on the meaning of the term. As I use it in these remarks, "interpretation" signifies three different things: (1) the identification of activities and processes which significantly affect the environment; (2) obtaining and analyzing information about these to ascertain cause-and-effect relationships which either degradate or enhance environmental quality; and (3) communicating this information to the public and presenting a set of alternative actions which can modify those processes or their enviromental consequences.

Interpretation thus plays a basic role in coming to grips with environmental quality problems, although it in itself cannot do the entire job. It stresses problem identification, diagnosis, and the presentation of alternatives for improving the situation. It does not include an evaluation of these alternatives and the selection from among them of the particular course of action to be pursued. This must be accomplished through activities, organizations, and techniques for reaching consensus that lie outside the domain of interpretation.

Clearly any resolution of environmental difficulties involves ascertaining, measuring, and comparing values that may be entailed in the several management options available. Modification of existing environmental use may entail positive values to one group and negative values to another. Under these circumstances it is necessary to obtain some reading of how these disparate values relate to each other. When the market fails to embrace these trade-offs, as often is the case, it must be done through transactions of a "political" nature. Only when net values

have been established, is it possible to assess various alternatives for purposive management on a comparable basis. Finally, desired alternatives provide a rallying point for public support and become candidates for action by governmental bodies. This entire chain of events, however, depends upon an effective job having been done in what we have defined as interpretation—that is, identifying problems, analyzing them, and communicating the results to the relevant public.

CRITERIA FOR AN INTERPRETIVE PROGRAM

The job of interpretation requires an array of skills in the form of staff and vehicles so the staff can communicate with the public. All of this costs money This economic reality forces us to ask whether the dollars involved in interpretive activities are efficiently utilized. If the benefits secured are less than the costs incurred, we are confronted with a net loss.

To be more specific, as assessment of interpretive programs must ascertain the following:
1. whether the interpretative effort has an appropriate problem focus;
2. whether the program involves the correct mix of skills to efficiently carry out the full range of interpretive activities; and
3. whether the level of interpretive program (the aggregate amount of dollars spent) is appropriate.

FOCAL POINTS FOR INTERPRETIVE PROGRAMS

Upon what aspects of the environment should interpretation focus? One way to respond to this question is to indicate types of environmental problems for which there is a need for interpretation. I would suggest that problems characterized by confusion or conflict regarding environmental quality objectives merit high priority for interpretation. This is a potentially powerful way to clarify the spectrum of possible objectives to narrow the range of disagreement by providing the public a common basis of fact in terms of which perception of the environment can be clarified and goals can thereby be seen with greater precision. As indicated above, the political process still may have to be relied upon to precipitate explicit management targets, but this process is greatly enhanced by removing spurious contentions and providing factual information.

In actuality, the interpretative focus of a public agency will not be without constraint. Individual agencies will require that the environmental problems their interpretive programs address are consistent with their overall mission. In illuminating these problems with fact, and presenting alternative possibilities for action, a reasonably full range of options should be identified. Too frequently in the past interpretive programs of public agencies have been little more than public relations efforts designed to secure public support for particular action programs.

I would like to consider for a moment three general categories of environmental problems, each of which I believe is important and deserves attention some place within our interpretive effort. The first of these relates to the management of waste materials which are generated by production and consumption activities. These waste materials give rise to the familiar pollution problems which have claimed national attention in recent years. The public needs to understand that while waste materials are inevitably generated by production and consumption activities, we have the technical capacity to reduce the net amounts generated from particular activities, to alter the form in which waste materials are introduced to the environment (liquid, gaseous, solid form), to shift the location and timing of waste material discharge, and to alter the environment in ways that increase its assimilative capacity. Thus, although waste materials necessarily are a part of social and economic enterprise, we have a variety of mechanisms through which we can manage these wastes. These management options should be explored in defining and diagnosing a particular local pollution problem. Basically these are management problems, and the types of information and analysis which relate to them—and which eventually must be communicated to the public—are reasonably straightforward.

A second set of environmental problems which needs to be illuminated through interpretive efforts pertains to the patterns in which we occupy our natural environment. On the one hand excessive concentration of production consumption activities produces problems of pollution, whereas a more dispersed pattern may avoid them. Uncontrolled growth of urban areas creates visual blight and economic loss through irrational and haphazard patterns of land development. On the other hand, residents in sparsely populated areas—especially those rural areas which are losing population—often are provided public services through a large number of small local communities which are hard pressed fiscally and often outmoded technically. The result is frequently inefficient (economics of scale are not realized) and frequently causes environmental degradation by deficient sewer services, antiquated water systems, etc. The cause-and-effect relationships involved in these problems are not quite so familiar, nor are the various ways in which we may cope with them. Ultimately we must cope with them. Communities may find if awkward and difficult to pose questions relating to their maximum size, and individuals accustomed to a local town or village may find the prospects of its elimination extraordinarily uncomfortable. Nevertheless, these are questions that call for public debate, and the values entailed in alternative lines of action need to be established.

The third category of environmental problems relates to environmental preservation. How do we assess the scarcity and social value of scenic amenities, of rare species of wildlife, and of wild areas which are not scarred by access roads, and by the same token, are not readily available to a general population which appears less and less ambulatory? For this type of problem, the interpretive job is one of sensitizing the public to the existence of amenities of various sorts, and providing information on how amenities afford meaningful insights into the physical and life processes of natural history and into human history. Amenities are valuable to man both in terms of services they provide, such as recreation, and also in terms of what we can learn from them as natural laboratories or historical benchmarks. Let's move on from questions of focus and consider what combination of interpretive skills are required.

WHAT COMBINATION OF INTERPRETIVE SKILLS ARE REQUIRED?

Although each of the three categories of environ-

mental problems mentioned above entails rather different issues and must deal with different types of information, we can generalize in some degree about the type of interpretive skills which are required. First of all, there must be access to individuals well grounded in the empirical nature of the human activities and processes which have substantial environmental effects. This is critical if the basic cause-and-effect relationships are to be uncovered, and especially if alternatives to the present practices are to be identified.

Next, there must be some analytical capability within the interpretation unit. Special information must be collected and analyzed in order to ascertain the nature of environmental effects that ensue from present practices, and to analyze the extent of those consequences, their susceptibility to change, and their relative significance.

Finally, one must have in the interpretive program individuals who are capable of discerning the kinds of values that are relevant in assessing alternative ways of interacting with the environment, as well as individuals skilled in the techniques which can be employed to reveal those values. As indicated earlier, the market mechanism frequently does not provide reliable indicators of important values that ultimately will decide the way we go about managing our environment. Under these circumstances, there must be skill and sensitivity on the part of the interpretive program in using group meetings, debates, and public confrontation so that these values are indeed revealed.

This may seem like a tall order to an agency recruiter who is anxious to establish an interpretive program. Indeed, it is a tall order. However, we cannot get by with mediocrity if we are to effectively mobilize an informed public to actions which can establish and maintain a high quality environment for ourselves and our descendants.

IS THE LEVEL OF PUBLIC INVESTMENT IN INTERPRETATION ADEQUATE?

I have not made any tabulation of the investment by local, state, and federal agencies in interpretive programs. Clearly the total—whatever it is—has been growing over recent years. My personal judgment is that probably the social returns to such investment still warrant additional expenditures for interpretive efforts.

Although I cannot cite the marginal productivity of interpretive efforts, there are several trends which suggest to me that increased budgets are warranted. One of these is the increasing frequency with which planning efforts are confronted with problems involving disparate goals and conflicting values. For these types of problems, objectives must be considered as "variables" rather than given or fixed. They become established, and often subsequently transformed, through social learning. Interpretation can be taken to signify this very process. Thus, the very nature of environmental problems which our affluent society will increasingly confront—those involving conflicting values—suggests that interpretive efforts likewise will be increasingly needed.

One may ask, however, whether this is an

appropriate activity for a public entity. Mightn't it be done within the private sector? I would agree that when the problem is likely to call for public redress, interpretation is an appropriate public activity.

The basis for this contention lies in a rationale similar to that which argues that pollution problems resulting from private production activities should be the responsibility of the private producers; that they should bear the costs of preventing environmental degradation; and that these costs appropriately represent costs of "doing business" and should be reflected in product prices. By parallel reasoning, I would argue that public agencies undertaking environmental activities should be held responsible for identifying to the public their consequences–some of which may well be negative. Thus, if an agency's budget must be extended in order to cover interpretive activities necessary to discuss the environmental consequences of its line activities, this increment to the agency budget should be considered its cost of "doing business."

I recognize that this may appear to be opening the door for fattened budgets–an eventuality which many economists are loath to endorse. To those of the brotherhood who take this view, I would argue that public projects which affect the environment are not completely described until they contain measures that will assure maintenance of a reasonable quality environment. If we do not have an adequate interpretive program, we may indeed fund public agency activities which will require excessively expensive corrective measures later on in the game.

Let me reinforce this point by an analogy. A project for interbasin water transfer may lead to a deterioration of water quality within the service area which subsequently requires a major drainage canal. Unless the need for the canal is seen at the outset, when the interbasin transfer is under public debate, we are likely to get trapped into approving an incomplete project–namely just the interbasin delivery system on the strength of benefits produced, and subsequently find ourselves confronted with a follow-on investment which, if considered originally may have made the venture clearly undesirable. In the same fashion, I believe our interpretive programs can help us perceive the full dimensions of certain public activities that impinge upon the environment by pointing out adverse environmental consequences and the programs we must initiate in order to prevent them. This still leaves the rather knotty question of when is an interpretive program too large? I frankly think there is no very precise gauge by which one can answer this question, and my only caveat would be to examine the interpretive activity and see whether it is efficiently organized and adequately staffed in terms of the several criteria suggested above.

CONCLUSIONS

As Proust noted, there is nothing more terrifying than ignorance in action. There are few things more expensive to society at large than ignorance in environmental action. We must understand the consequences of our acts, and figure out ways in which those which are adverse to the environment can be reduced or eliminated. The role of interpretation is critical if we are to expand ignorance into knowledge. The job is a serious one, and a sophisticated one. No longer can the interpretive program simply be addressed to extending the enjoyment of a park visitor, nor can we tolerate "interpretive" programs which in reality are little more than promotional efforts to gain public support for an agency's mainline activities. Public agencies have a responsibility to serve the public through education and promoting those types of dialogues and organizational arrangements which can reveal social preferences and values that pertain to the environment. These values change as our circumstances change: as a society becomes affluent, it places different values on different environmental attributes; as a society becomes mobile, it places new values on remote aspects of the environment– an urban society places high values on amenities that may have been of little importance to a rural society. In short, our environmental values do change as the structure of our society changes and the technology through which it interacts with its environment is expanded. Just as we must recognize that the natural environment is indeed our fundamental public resource, we must find common cause in deciphering social preferences and true values to serve as guides as we interact with it. This is the task which environmental interpretation programs must ultimately address. If we fail in this effort, the quality of our environment will deteriorate and will not be able to support the life of variety, enrichment, and dignity to which all mankind aspires. ■

"The uniqueness of all interpretation is that things are made meaningful; here is a scarce commodity in our modern world of men—the meaningful."

INTERPRETATION—SOMETHING NEW

R. Yorke Edwards

SOME AGENCIES managing wild lands have been communicating with the public for half a century and have perfected impressively effective techniques. The U.S. National Park Service and now a host of smaller park organizations reach millions of people annually with attractive methods for helping people understand the landscape. An important feature about these programs is that they take place right outdoors on the land and that the message is about something real and right there as you stand in the landscape, and not about something unreal or imagined. We need more of this approach. People are beginning to think that nature and its preservation, its use, its conservation, its many popular aspects live only in slick magazines, in books, and on picture screens. They know this really is not so, but they behave as if it were, and this is as bad as believing it. Public ignorance and the lack of public involvement is a major land-use crisis facing land managers today. We simply must get more people understanding their surroundings, and as a result, people able to comprehend land-use problems.

It would be beyond the scope of this paper to dwell on the problems, aside from the recreation ones, that our soaring numbers of citified citizens, out of touch with the countryside, are going to cause in all resource management. Let me say, however, that these investors, these consumers, these voters, can be terrifyingly ignorant of national needs.

I am going to devote some time to the need for informing people as a major contribution toward alleviating the recreation crisis.

The difficulty seems to be people, and people would be no problem if they did the right things. The interpretation method that has evolved in our parks, and which is now sweeping through our museums, is the surest, most effective method known for informing people about the outdoors, and for doing it so people enjoy it. Much of North American man, it seems, roams our highways every summer seeking new experiences, and some of us wonder how to reach him.

All the while nearby park interpretation programs are groaning under the load of too many people. Their conducted walks are so crowded that the naturalists cannot keep in touch with their audiences, and most people cannot see what is being talked about. Campfire talks have standing room only. Nature centers are jammed like sale day in a department store. The public thirst for new experiences involving new information is proven by these conditions. I must add that you do not have to be a park naturalist long to learn that interpretation actually does what it is designed to do. Its message reaches people. Results are easily seen in any good program that has been operating for a few years.

North Americans are wasteful of the land and its products. Visitors from Europe and Asia are astounded at our partial uses of resources. The recreation resource is no exception. A hugely increased number of people could use the recreation lands used now, and used properly there could be more enjoyment to the individual, less wrecking of the resource base, and large reductions of maintenance costs.

Interpretation holds the key to this better use of our recreation lands, and better use is a partial solution to the coming crisis. We note that other resource fields are beginning to talk of better use too. A well-known example concerns the water resources of the United States. Here Stewart Udall has pointed out that there is really no shortage there; the problem is one of improper use creating an apparent shortage.

Interpretation is a ponderous term with, as yet, no popular synonym, but do not let the word mislead you. Interpretation deals with people's knowledge, and their attitudes, and their enthusiasms. It attracts them with its helpful, entertaining approach. The star that it reaches for is to inspire people. It is not just education. It is not just an information service. It is not just demonstrations, or showmanship, or a guiding service, or an outlet for propaganda. It is all of these things at once. Its aim is to send

Mr. Edwards is Staff Specialist, Canadian Wildlife Service, Ottawa, Ontario. This statement is excerpted from his paper on "The Future of Recreation on Wild Lands" which appeared in the June, 1968, Forestry Chronicle.

people forth inspired by new understanding, and enthused about more involvement with the facinating new world revealed to them. Interpretation, when well done, has the light touch. It cannot afford to be ponderous, and anyway the realm of the ponderous is already crowded in the communications field. Interpretation sows seeds, skillfully chosen, imaginatively treated, that will grow into inspiration, revelation, involvement, and in some cases a new life-long passion. And it works, not always, but often enough to be impressive. It works often enough that staff members working in good interpretation programs are usually fulfilled types with well-groomed egos.

Interpretation has the solutions to most of recreation's challenges through the next three decades.

We need a populace more interested and informed on the natural things that together form the wild landscape. Interpretation is highly successful at doing this.

We need a populace that understands land use problems so it will support measures to preserve its resources while using them intelligently. Interpretation does this, properly, for it begins with building interest and respect in the fundamental parts of the landscape.

We need a populace that does not spread its garbage across the land while avoiding paths and hacking at the vegetation as if no other man would pass that way. Interpretation by creating delight and understanding, creates respect. We could use more of it in our time.

We need a populace with vandalism scarce, and strongly regarded as a crime against society. Interpretation builds public opinion by creating involvement, and it does this by opening the minds of people to understanding leading to appreciation and respect.

Park interpretation is widespread today, and requires little modification to interpret the other uses of land. In interpreting recreation use, or range management, or forestry, or any other land use, the great strength of park interpretation remains intact, and that strength is the strength of truth. Our lives have become full of fakes—pictures, substitutes for the real thing, even real things that have been put into meaningless situations. Interpretation operates on the spot with real things that are in meaningful surroundings. This is the strength of nature interpretation, and this is why inspiration and revelation can so often be its result, and this is why a life touched by interpretation may never be quite the same again because of the new interest that makes it fuller, and happier.

Land use, as well as the land itself, is open to interpretation. There is a meaningful story in the worn out vegetation of an overused campground, or in the soil erosion caused by human activity, or in the too many people jamming a beach. These are ecological situations that can be made fascinating, revealing, and meaningful. I can think of nothing easier to interpret than a managed forest, whether recreation is involved or not, with its beautifully rounded picture of land, plants, animals, and man in harmonious interrelationships.

The uniqueness of all interpretation, anywhere, is that things are made meaningful. People thirst for meaningful things in their lives. Interpretation caters to this need. If we do not use it lavishly to help solve our recreation problems, and our other land use problems too, we deserve to be swamped by the tide.

Interpretation is not just a good cure, it is so far about the only cure available to us. Most other measures are merely treatments of symptoms.

When we are dealing with the ills of public wealth, diseases cured are surely preferable to symptoms masked—especially when the cure is cheaper.

Land: The unwritten textbook.

NATURE CENTER PURPOSES AND VALUES

Byron L. Ashbaugh

OVER THE past 3 decades concern with the impact of people on the land has increased dramatically. New programs have been undertaken to protect natural resources or to correct resource misuse. Today with the push of population growth and technological advance, the crucial question is no longer simply, " What is man doing to his environment?" but also " What is the present environment doing to man himself?"

The quality of the environment and the relationship of life to it will play major roles in determining the future of society. Surely the cost of a deteriorating environment will be measured in terms of physical and mental decay and social maladjustments.

Conservation means not only the protection and management of natural resources but also the maintenance of life-supporting qualities and sanity in the human environment. Air and water pollution, siltation, blemished landscapes, noise, and meaningless urban sprawl, all are disturbing signs of our times. Thus, if solutions are to come, regional and urban planning, wise land and water use, effective zoning, protection of open space and scenic beauty, control of population diversity and density, all should be in the modern citizen's thoughts and plans.

But it is not enough to be merely interested in problems of environmental well-being. Citizen action is needed. How can this be done? Education provides part of the answer. An informed and concerned citizenry is the key to effective action. The challenge is clear: interpretive and educational programs must be advanced to effect a greater understanding of our environmental problems and what must be done to correct them. A nature center program opens windows to the outdoor world: interprets, inspires, motivates. When citizen action calls for more and better outdoor interpretive programs more and better outdoor educational facilities and activities, then and only then will the integrity of the natural environment be assured. The need for outdoor interpretive programs, nature centers, laboratories, and outdoor training for teachers and youth leaders is urgent.

Due to the size of this challenge the need for leadership is great. Each nature center to be opened should be innovative, exemplary, and demonstrative for its region. A well-planned and carefully-developed nature center will not only serve a very useful community purpose but will also stimulate interest and support for similar facilities in other regions.

A first-rate land base is paramount in any outdoor interpretation program. A good piece of characteristic geography cannot be chosen too carefully. Site selection should:

—provide good land and not leftover space that cannot be used for anything else

—consider size as an important characteristic— the larger the area, the better it will serve the community. Where possible, a buffer zone should be obtained around the key site. The smaller the area, the tighter the human use controls; similarly, the more sensitive the natural resources present, the more intensive the controls.

PURPOSE OF A NATURE CENTER

The basic purpose of a nature center is to provide an area of undeveloped land where facilities and services make possible outdoor programs in nature and environmental education. The land should be a spacious piece of terrain with varied geological features and the flora and fauna which are indigenous. A nature center and its program provide:

Education: the communication of information about our natural environment by skilled teachers and leaders through personal experience with nature. As John Burroughs once said, " It is not so much what we see in nature but how we interpret what we see. "

Research: the search for information about our environment through organized scientific observation and experimentation.

Conservation: the practical application of information about natural resources in an attempt to discover the wisest ways to manage the human environment for the long-term benefit of people.

Culture: a place to bring about human enlightenment and refinement through esthetic experiences. Such experiences stimulate thought, in turn stimulating creative expression. This is equally true for the resident as it is for the tourist who wants to see what any locality has to offer.

The author is Chief, Outdoor Education Services, Genesee County Parks and Recreation Commission, Flint, Michigan. This paper was presented to the Michigan Division of the Women's National Farm and Garden Association in June 1970.

A nature center is designed to serve everyone in a community. It seeks to acquaint young children with the mysteries and wonders of nature, a task that is becoming more difficult with the relentless destruction of native habitats. It affords teenagers an opportunity to engage in wholesome activities that are both constructive and educational. It also provides a training ground for youths who wish to become scientists. The land can be a significant outdoor laboratory for college students. Adults can utilize the center facilities and resources for serious study and the pursuit of hobby interests. A nature center is also a place where a man can take his family for a walk to see a meadow, a swamp, a stand of native trees, or to explore the shores of a secluded lake.

For all people the nature center can aid in maintaining a sense of balance in life, particularly in an age when many sound values are being eroded by the impact of material comforts, the complexities, strains, and dangers of a rapidly changing world. A nature center program can be a stimulating and pleasant activity for young children, a coordinated and complementary cog in the wheels of organized education, a refuge from the clattering confusion of mechanical existence in everyday life. For some, the study of nature has emotional and esthetic values, for others it has scientific importance. For all it can reveal a broader, more interesting world.

Many educators have pointed out the values of a continuing contact with nature for students. Here is what two authorities have said:

> We have failed to develop the understanding of the interrelatedness and the interdependence of all things in their environment. We have spent hours in the schoolroom with books, but we have spent very little of our school time to show them where . . . things, about which they read, really are, and where and how they fit in the program of living. - F. J. Schmeeckle

> Authors of textbooks pass on second-hand information they have found by observation and discovery. It is always the person who sees, discovers, or explores a situation who gets the most out of it. This, in short, is the whole theses of outdoor education. Such learning is faster, is more deeply appreciated, and is retained longer. - L. B. Sharp

The 1967 annual report to the President by the Citizens Advisory Committee on Recreation and Natural Beauty strongly emphasized the need for environmental education. This top-level advisory committee states that:

> There is a risk that lessons learned so far in this century will be lost and that tomorrow's adults will have to learn all over again the hard way. To prevent this, it is imperative that environmental education be made a basic component of. . . school programs.

> We also believe that no book, indoor laboratory, or audio-visual production can ever replace the land as a teaching vehicle for environmental education.

This concisely states the need for nature centers as educational facilities where environmental education uses the land for learning.

NATURE CENTER ROLE FOR SCHOOLS

A nature center is a community institution, just as are the museum and the public library. In this role the nature center can have a positive impact on many facets of community life. But perhaps nowhere is its impact more vital than in the work of the schools.

In terms of the school mission, the nature center may be thought of as a teaching laboratory. Like any other kind of laboratory, it is provided to teach those concepts which it can deal with more effectively than the indoor classroom. The role of the nature center is defined by the fact that certain subject matters can be more effectively taught in the natural environment than in the regular classroom. The key to effectiveness of the nature center as a teaching laboratory is the natural setting it provides. Here children can engage in firsthand discovery and exploration. Here, all the eager, inquiring senses of youth can be applied in direct experience with the natural environment.

The use of the nature center begins with explicit objectives and a carefully delineated teaching plan. In the classroom the students are prepared for the outdoor experience and introduced to the concepts to be taught. Then the experience moves out-of-doors where the individual child can be brought into direct and meaningful contact with these new concepts. The class returns from the outdoors to the classroom for an evaluation of their experience and expansion of the newly mastered ideas. In this fashion the outdoor experience grows out of the classroom and, having taken advantage of the outdoor laboratory, leads back to the classroom again. It is thus an integral part of the school curriculum.

NATURE CENTER ROLE FOR PARKS

People will not safeguard what they do not know, let alone what they do not understand. They will not protect and treat kindly what they do not appreciate. A nature center is designed to help park visitors understand and appreciate the natural environment, to help them become good stewards of public lands and all related natural resources. A well-planned nature center program will keep people from destroying the very open space and natural resources they hope to preserve and enjoy. Mr. Walter A. Tucker, director-secretary, Columbus Metropolitan Park System, Columbus, Ohio, has commented on the values of educational programs in parks as follows:

> The success of interpretive programs in our parks is reflected by increased public participation. The benefits are evident in the improved public behavior as shown by the orderliness of visitors, the absence of litter, and freedom from willful destruction of property.

> We believe that interpretive programs more than justify the expense involved. We are convinced that our park nature program more than pays its way on a dollar and cents basis.

The keys to effectiveness in a nature center are careful planning, training of youth leaders and teachers for the effective and best use of park land, and the assistance of specialized naturalist-interpreters. The needs of park users—and the needs of other facets of the community—will be best served if, in the initial phases of implementation, care is taken to involve all segments of the community in the process of planning the nature center services. Through such a procedure the nature center will be individualized to the unique needs of its community and will thus be solidly grounded to reach its full potential. ∎

Meeting the need of the city child for environmental education.

TOWARD AN URBAN ECOLOGICAL STRUCTURE

Thomas J. Rillo

THROUGHOUT the time line of his development man has been attempting to comprehend the vastness and complexity of the world he lives in. In contemporary times man's problem still remains the same. How can he assimilate with understanding all of the aspects of his external environment, all of the events that take place in that environment and his relationship to them?

Perhaps the most simplified way is to view the external surroundings through direct experience and then it may be probable that man can begin to understand and plan for a more hospitable world. Education can and should assume responsibility for the provision of those environmental experiences that it is best qualified for. Environmental education is then defined as that part of the total educational process which attempts to convey those values, concepts,and knowledges associated with the external environment. It concerns itself with the development of an enlightened citizenry, both existential and potential, which because of involvement in an experiential program will be able to make wise and judicious decisions with reference to environmental problems and situations.

IN THE BEGINNING

Mankind is a species known to science as Homo sapiens. Man stands on two feet and as a species has the unique ability to look at himself objectively. The basic human nature of man is civilized and barbaric, generous and greedy, courteous and cruel, courageous and cowardly, hardworking and lazy, sensible and stupid. But mankind exists and as a social animal represents one of nature's most recent experiments.

Looking back with pride at his evolution he was astonished at the rapid rate his ancient predecessors overcame their vulnerability through the ability to invent and use tools. He then proceeded to build the beginnings of civilization in less time than it took his earliest predecessors to invent the stone ax. This new civilization ultimately required habitation in large groups for security reasons. Thus the encampment, the village, and finally the town were born.

Usually a body of water such as a lake, river, or ocean was selected because of the accessibility of food and also because it provided a mode of travel. As increased leisure time became prevalent the proximity near water also provided a site for recreation.

For a multitude of reasons there was a strong centripetal movement to the cities. The urban environment became the center of commerce and industrialization. The pagan concept of exploitation of the land and moving on to new fertile soils was continued into the early and middle Christian eras of time. However, the structure of the family unit changed when the inheritance of all land was passed on to the eldest son and the younger males received very little or none at all. This change in social patterns caused Western society to take a new look at the agricultural structure. In addition, rural folk became tired of the rigorous routine of a primitive agricultural life and this provided another motive for the migration to urban centers.

The new world offered different opportunities to those not first born and to other relatives. The words of Horace Greeley were sung long before he actually lived and phrased them. This was demonstrated from the very earliest days of the colonial settlements. The cry echoed, "go west young man" for opportunities. The land for taking changed the social structure into equality in lieu of autocratic rulers, and town councils became the governing bodies of these new small settlements.

In a relatively short period of time the American industrial revolution came into being and became the catalyst for a large migratory movement to the urbanized areas. Great changes happened to the American modus vivendi.

Until a few decades ago America was still a rural land with an endless span of open space, deep rivers, of limitless fresh water, and air swept clean by the flow of westerly winds. In the early part of this scene a frontier wife washed clothes with lye soap rendered from hog fat and wood ashes. When the washing chores were done she simply cast the water out the

Dr. Rillo is Professor of Outdoor Education, Glassboro State College, New Jersey.

door where it sank into the soil. If the soil nutrients were impaired it did not matter for it was soon rejuvenated by the droppings of foraging farm animals. There were few cases of water contamination because sun, fresh air, and some bacteria were enough to decompose the human sewage. Animal manure was spread on the fields as fertilizers and any other accumulated material waste was simply placed in a gully or ditch and became an erosion control.

There were no tin containers in great quantity since the farm wife did her own canning. There were no plastic containers, disposable bottles, cellophane wrappings, or aluminum foil, for individual packaging of food products was not yet a supermarket fetish. Woodsmoke coming from a house chimney was only prevalent to any great degree during the cold months and did not represent a threat to the biosphere.

THE PENDULUM SWINGS

The situation changed as the years passed. Small towns became bigger and the problem of what to do with waste products became bigger. There were more people and this represented increased human and material waste. Inventive engineers created the central sewer system which drained into a river where moving water, sunlight, oxygen, and bacteria could break down the contamination. The smell and pollutants of smoke from the city dump was an accepted thing and served as a directional indicator for all residential and commercial development to move in the opposite direction.

Life killing chemicals moving into a river became the symbol of prosperity which meant more jobs and more money for more people. Housewives could hurry to the city's stores to buy more and more material things which in itself became another hallmark of prosperity. The waste from this activity continued to grow and become a serious problem.

As young men and women moved to the city they served their urban bondage until accumulated affluency enabled them to move out into the cleaner suburban countryside. Now the suburban areas are becoming sicker with many of the same problems which plagued the city. In some areas of the country there is limited direction in which to run from the rivers man has converted to sewers, the land he has saturated with material waste, the air he has polluted with smoke as well as poisonous gases from the automobile.

Because of this movement to the urban areas for greater prosperity the city and town are rapidly becoming unpleasant places to live and the land, water, and aerial wastes are accumulating faster than they can be removed.

THE HERE AND THE NOW

The biggest problem with man's environment is the fact that too many of his kind live in too limited an area at the same time. This statement may be self-evident and contradictory to people who have worked hard to solve some of the prevailing environmental problems. An individual can grow very pessimistic about the situation and although apparently justified in some situations, it is not the condition which will instigate change. Nothing constructive

has ever emanated from a pessimistic viewpoint. What is needed is an enlightened citizenry equipped with an adequate framework of reference sufficient enough to motivate participation in action programs leading to the alleviation or modification of our environmental problems.

The development of this enlightened and informed citizenry is represented by two approaches. One approach is immediate action so vitally needed in contemporary society. This avenue would concern itself with those individuals who constitute our adult population and would concentrate its program of information dissemination through all the medias of communication including newspapers, radio, television, and films. It would also avail itself to conferences, workshops, forums, conservation commissions, legislative involvement, community planning boards, local, state, and federal involvement and support. Immediate results are going to mean vast amounts of monetary support. The profit motive of many enterprises is going to have to be challenged by the powerful impact of pressure groups who are able to underwrite their activities for as long as it takes to effect change. These activities will involve many groups and the problem of coordination will represent one of the largest hurdles to be encountered.

The second approach is of longer range in perspective. It involves the children and youth of our nation. The largest segment of our population in one place at one given time is the private and public school group. Of this specific population, the largest segment concentrated in more limited areas are those who attend schools in urban areas. It is recommended that an experiential program in environmental education be provided for students rather than a program of indoctrination via the lecture method. This experience program should be related to the subjects students study in their regular school curriculum.

Basic concepts and understandings of the environment should not only be an integral part of every subject matter area at each grade level, but should also spiral upward through the grades. A concept or basic understanding can be introduced at the primary level and continue upward through the grades attaining sophistication and refinement with each succeeding step. The program of environmental experiences need not mean the allocation of more time, space, and equipment.

CASES IN POINT

An example of integration with the existing broad curriculum is illustrated by the following example. A sixth grade class is studying mathematics, social studies, science, language arts, and health as part of their everyday routine. A concern for the pollutants in the environment is motivated as a social problem by the teacher in a social studies class. It emanates from a discussion of how people choose an area to live and work.

An introduction to the environmental conditions hostile to man's continued existence arises. Reading the literature in magazines and newspapers, viewing filmstrips and television broadcasts, the class is motivated to participate in some type of action research. The class decides to investigate the pollutant contributions to the atmosphere by jet aircraft. They learn that one jet aircraft emits 88 pounds of pollutants per take-off. The class decides that a field trip to the local city jetport is imperative.

Upon arrival at the airport they proceed to count the number of planes taking off each hour. The students multiply the average of planes taking off per hour by the poundage of pollutants emitted by one plane. They next multiply the number of hours that the airport is operative by the average number of jet aircraft taking off per hour by the poundage of pollutants per plane. The total figure is astonishing to the students. The data is so astronomical in proportion that the class decides to continue their investigations and disseminate their information.

The mathematics class is utilized for the data treatment and analysis. The science class is utilized in developing equipment for collecting and measuring pollutants at the jetport. The language arts class becomes the center for written material concerning the students' findings and is submitted for publication. Oral presentations are prepared by the students for delivery on local radio and television stations. The art class becomes the scene for the preparation of an exhibit illustrating the pollution of jet aircraft with suggested proposals for its modification or removal. The class decides that it will continue its investigation of pollutants in the atmosphere when they learn that one automobile emits 500 pounds of pollutants per year. Plans are formulated for the conduction of field trips, similar to the jetport trip, to strategic intersections in the city.

A secondary school biology class in a city is studying ecology. They have explored vacant lots, sidewalks, railroad track right of ways, roadsides, and the city park as part of their field experience. The teacher suggests that they might try to do an ecological study of an abandoned apartment building. They decide that they will embark on a study of the habitation of a deserted city apartment house for evidence of life other than that of man.

The ecological investigation entails the constructing and setting of coffee-can live traps for rodents. Sweet traps are then placed throughout the building and baited with honey or sugared water for the study of existing insect life. Scat boards are placed throughout the building for the determination of rodent populations by analysis of the incidence of droppings on each board. Peanut butter is placed on each of the boards as an attraction for various types of rodents and small mammals.

The class was able to identify several ecological niches complete with all sources of food supply to each niche. The class also explored the immediate exterior environment of the old building including the rooftops. The interdependency of living things is firmly established despite the apparent lifeless look of the old building.

An elementary class is also interested in air pollution. They decide to conduct their investigation with kites in order to ascertain gypsum dust particles saturating the air in their neighborhood. The students utilize gauze material covered with a grease substance and attach the gauze strip to each kite. The kites are then flown from various positions in the neighborhood in order to ascertain the amount of

dissipation of the dust particles at succeeding distances from the source. They decide to replicate this experiment by utilizing microscope slides covered with a petroleum grease substance and attached to the line with clothes pins. Additional information is then added to the data previously obtained and the class next concerns itself with dissemination of the data.

The above described activities as well as many more can contribute a great deal to the development of an environmental awareness . . . for these same students will become adult citizens. They will seldom view the environment with apathy because their experiences were direct, firsthand, and their active involvement precipitated retention. It is this retention of concepts and values that conservation and environmental educators are concerned about with reference to attitudinal changes. This in itself is motivation enough for firsthand investigation of the environmental urban climate. It is a learning climate that should be a part of the indoor-outdoor-indoor approach to environmental understanding.

There are many opportunities at various grade levels for environmental explorations of the city environment. Through the eyes of the ecologist, man in an agricultural and/or urban setting is always viewed as a part of the total ecosystem. Any imbalance or disturbance in the supportive ecosystem can cause serious setbacks and deterioration or demise if adaptation is not fast enough or does not occur at all.

URBAN MAN'S NEED FOR ENVIRONMENTAL PERCEPTION

A beautiful and delightful city environment is not commonplace and some individuals would say an impossible thing to achieve. Not many American cities larger than 10,000 inhabitants are of consistent fine quality, although a few have some pleasant fragmented features. Very few Americans can ascertain what it means to live in such an environment. They are cognizant of the ugliness of the environment in which they live, and they can verbalize about the dirt, smoke, congestion, chaotic conditions, and even the monotonous routine of daily living. Seldom are citizens aware of the potential value of harmonious surroundings.

The late Aldo Leopold, (1887-1948) Professor of Game Management, University of Wisconsin, has defined conservation as being, "harmony between man and land" (1). This simple definition has been adhered to by some architects, planners, conservationists, and others who are concerned with environmental problems.

Most Americans lack basic knowledge of what a high quality environment can mean in terms of daily enjoyment or as a continuous framework of reference for their lives. The use of this knowledge can produce deeper insights into the meaningfulness and richness of the exciting journey of life. The ability to structure or identify the environment is common among those animals who are capable of agile movement. Many kinds of perceptions are utilized: the senses of touch, smell, hearing, sight, gravity, and balance, the visual sensations of color, shape, rhythm, and motion are all biological techniques of orientation to the environment.

Social scientists, ecologists, anthropologists, philosophers, and other disciplinarians have observed the ability of the general body sensorium to organize from simple to complex patterns. The professional literature emanating from the activities of the above-mentioned professional people indicated that this organization is basic to the efficiency and survival of mankind.

A keen perception of one's environment can give the individual the element of choice and a point of departure for the acquisition of additional information. A clear and distinct perception of both the internal and external environments is thus an essential ingredient for the total growth of an individual. It can also establish a degree of emotional security and the individual can begin to perceive a harmonious relationship between himself and the immediate external surroundings. A distinctive and identifiable perception can also serve to vitalize the potential of life as the gap between man and the external environment narrows.

The need for environmental education for the urban scene is very apparent. The environment when perceived through the various academic vehicles can give distinction and relationships and the observer can with his ability of adaptation and in keeping with his aspirations begin to select, organize, and support with greater meaning that which he perceives. As a major manipulator of his external environment man must maintain his constant interest in qualitative changes and to continued existence.

Man has had no constraints either moral, philosophical, or otherwise except those which physically limited his freedom to exploit, manage, or conserve his environment. This freedom has meant latitude to progress but at the same time has also provided the freedom to retrogress.

Mankind now has the opportunities and abilities to achieve a maximum-yield environment and human life or to destroy both in a manner previously unparalleled. He has destroyed many times without the knowledge or ability to foresee the consequences of his acts. With long traditions of these attitudes, he never felt his responsibility for these consequences. Early man was forced to improve his perception of the environment by adapting to the immediate landscape. He made minor changes in this environment with primitive edifices, religious and trail cairns, but significant modifications were not within his frame of reference. Only those civilizations who have mastered some technology and science can change or modify their environment on a large scale.

The rehabilitation or remolding of the large scale environment has been only recently made possible and consequently the techniques and modus operandi involved in creating environmental awareness are new. The need for an informed and aware citizenry is now. Our present youth and the next several generations must act as a guiding force for the world that they want to live in successfully. They have to enter the present and future world as educated citizenry capable of making global, intelligent, universal decisions.

It is not the intention of this paper to infer a return to a primeval nature system which is no longer available even if we desired it. What is inferred is that parallel to the natural ecological scene we must create a new system, that of an urban ecological structure.

The need for environmental education for the megalopolite is an integral part of the total struggle for survival. We can survive if as a species our planning is in complete balance and harmony with those ecological conditions that sustain life. It is that vital—it is that simple.

REFERENCE

1. Leopold, Aldo, A Sand County Almanac, Oxford Press, New York, 1966, p. 222. ▪

Is the naturalist a slave and a serf to his own value system?

WHITHER URBAN ENVIRONMENTAL EDUCATION?

Barbara   J.   Reid

ENVIRONMENTALLY, the cities of North America may be the products of man's worst failure to date in dealing with his surroundings. In terms of both natural resources and the quality of life, our cities are deteriorating. Seventy percent of Americans now live in metropolitan areas, and it is estimated that 90 percent will do so in 20 years.

The overpowering results of man's technology are polluting the air through the factory, the automobile, and the private furnace; and polluting the streams to such an extent that during last year's drought in Northeastern America the residents of New York City could not drink the water of the mighty Hudson which flows next to it. In 1966 ten million families in America were estimated to be living in deteriorated or substandard housing (4). Urban sprawl continues unabated with little or no attempt at city or regional planning. Our population growth is taking place at the fastest rate in those urban areas that can least afford it. Transportation systems are clogged by commuters, and freeways through the cities continue to be built without considerations of either their effect upon the residents of the area or the land itself.

Growth rates that are projected by planners, etc. are taken as fact, and systems are designed to accommodate such growth in population, automobiles, housing needs, and other areas without ever questioning the assumption that such growth may not be desired. For example, it is no surprise to those within the city that the transportation systems are incredibly clogged at the present time. Yet, we continue to build functional and aesthetically displeasing freeways to accommodate even more traffic jams. This need not have to occur, and citizens are beginning to realize this. In sum, the most basic questions about the use of natural and man-made resources are not being asked on a broad scale. [1]

Educationally, the inner city can also be deemed a failure in many ways. The urban deprived are of course the most obvious example of this failure. In New York City alone 65 percent of all Black People and Puerto Ricans drop out of high school (3). In some school districts in Chicago the rate is the same, if not worse. This amounts to about one thousand students a month (3). Children in metropolitan areas are not all deprived economically and socially, but many if not most are deprived educationally in the sense that they are not aware of the basic ecological relationships of the world around them. They are not in most cases aware of nature in the wilderness sense or of the ecology of the city—both in terms of people and nature. The traditional educational curricula of the U.S. does not include questions that deal with the environment—man's relationship to it and the results of the relationship in the past. Because of the failure of the urban schools in many of the most rudimentary concerns, educational innovation is becoming a concern for most urban educators. This innovation is taking place in terms of curriculum, educational techniques, teacher training, classroom organization, and a restructuring of the schools in relation to parents and to other community organizations across a broad spectrum.

It is hoped that the growing student and citizen environmental action will encourage the development of environmental education on the part of students, teachers, and all citizens. Future international conferences such as the 1972 United Nations Conference on the Environment will also provide forums for educational concerns. It is hoped that those involved in educational innovation and those concerned with environmental education can come together to forge a new program for the urban child.

It is often assumed that taking the city child out of the city and into nature will suffice. The following comment by Gerald Schneider of the Audubon Naturalist Society of Washington, D.C., gives a different point of view:

> The strength and the backbone of the conservation movement and love of nature have come

Miss Reid has served with the Conservation Foundation and with Environmental Action, Inc., Washington, D.C. This article is adapted from a paper appearing in the Winter 1969 Commission on Education Newsletter of the International Union for Conservation of Nature and Natural Resources.

from naturalists, and still do. But the naturalist, to paraphrase the philosopher Rousseau, may be a slave and a serf to his own pretensions, unable to separate that which is his value from that which may be someone else's value. As such, he may try to project his values on the urban child and find his values rejected because the child lacks the experience to base nature values on (2).

The question must be asked whether an urban child, in learning about trees and the natural food chain, takes this knowledge back into the city as something relevant for his everyday life of concrete, ghetto (or suburbia), air pollution, over-crowding, and museum-protected open space.

The answer may be to focus the attention of t h e city child on his most common experience—neighborhood planning in the city, waste disposal, water supply, man's growth within the city, and how the city came to exist in the first place. A sense of partnership with the world of nature and human beings that surrounds the city child may have to be established before he can feel a partnership with nature "o u t there." Partnership can be defined in many ways, but it may be that a sense of continuity with the development of both man and the structures he has created is more specific. [2] For the city is a man-made environment and it may be preferable to deal with the resource base on which it depends and the functionally pleasing improvements that can be made in terms of the city itself. "Since nature as it exists now is largely a creation of man, and in turn shapes him and his societies, its quality must be evaluated

in terms not of primeval wilderness, but of its relation to civilized life (1). Aesthetics become extremely important in a man-made environment. Nature left to its own devices may be aesthetically satisfying, but the same can scarcely be said of the cities.

FOOTNOTES

1. For a good discussion of this see Marine, Gene, America the Raped, Simon and Schuster, New York, 1969.

2. For a good discussion of the new biological and anthropological discoveries and its justification of the sense of continuity see Ardrey, Robert, The Territorial Imperative, Dell Publishing Company, New York, 1966.

REFERENCES

1. Dubos, Rene, So Human an Animal, Charles Schribner, New York, 1968.

2. Conference, Man and Nature in the City, Bureau of Sport Fisheries and Wildlife, U.S. Department of the Interior, Government Printing Office, Washington, D.C., 1969, p. 68.

3. New York Times, December 29, 1968, page E11.

4. Schussheim, Morton J., Toward a New Housing Policy, Committee for Economic Development Supplementary Paper No. 29, 1969, p. 9. ∎

Taking a "man-centered" approach to conservation communications.

THE NATIONAL PARK SYSTEM
AND ENVIRONMENTAL EDUCATION

Boyd   Evison

THE NATIONAL Park System embraces an array of natural and cultural treasures which are, for the most part, exemplars of environmental quality. They are outstanding bases on which to build a communications effort aimed at engendering in Americans the understanding of, and respect for, environmental interrelationships on which the quality of human life depends. An American public possessing that understanding and respect is unlikely to continue the incremental process of befouling and shredding those resource complexes which afford us sustenance and options for diverse pleasurable experience. So the National Park Service is necessarily in the environmental education "business"–both in defense of the resources for which it is directly responsible and in the valid interest of using those resources to convey the broader message of environmental quality as an essential to worthwhile life.

In its environmental education efforts, the Service is taking the "man-centered" approach to communications. Unlike the more common resource-centered approach, with its emphasis on taxonomy, soil profiles, and tree rings, this one puts man in the middle–where, in fact, he instinctively "knows" himself to be. The key lies in attention to the inevitable question, "So, what does it mean to me?" The NEED, ESA, and NEEL programs are addressed to that question.

NEED (National Environmental Education Development) seeks to foster an appreciative and critical environmental awareness among Americans through an understanding of the natural and cultural interactions illustrated in the areas administered by the Service. It is a curriculum-integrated program built around specially developed teaching materials and experiences. We are producing materials and ideas that will help teachers make ecological principles a central part of what they teach, whether the "subject" is math, history, art, music, science, or social studies.

ESA's (Environmental Study Areas) are natural and cultural "laboratories" within Service-adminis-

tered areas, designated primarily for day use in interpreting the areas through the on-going educational programs of nearby schools. Through experiences and materials developed specifically for each ESA, we try to reveal the story of man's personal, inextricable involvement with every aspect of his environment. The NEED materials should provide excellent base materials for these programs; but no group's participation will be contingent on their adoption of NEED. Application of the ESA approach to education beyond the National Park System is to be encouraged through the NEEL (National Environmental Education Landmarks) program. NEEL areas would enjoy status on a National Registry by virtue of the programs conducted on them, rather than on the basis of outstanding physical resources.

NEED, NEEL, and ESA are aimed at preschool through high school youngsters in and beyond the parks. To date, most of the Service's efforts at adult education have been incidental to the conveyance of information through the mass media, and interpretation programs in and near the parks. The urgency of environmental problems indicates a need for greater effort in supporting the development of environmental literacy among adult Americans. We expect soon to be producing environmental communications "packages" which will respond effectively to that need, for use in interpretive programs and through the mass media. The Division of Environmental Projects, Harpers Ferry Center, is planning and developing those communications packages, in cooperation with the Divisions of Audiovisual Arts, Interpretive Planning, Museums, and Publications, and with the assistance of other units in, and outside of, the National Park Service.

An Environmental Education Task Force, established in January, has evaluated existing environmental education programs and policies of the National Park Service and recommended modifications and innovations to insure an effective environmental education effort by the Service. At the same time, the Task Force has continued to work on the development of the programs now in progress. Briefly summarized, the status of those programs is listed on the next page.

Mr. Evison, a Consulting Editor of this journal, is Chief, Division of Environmental Affairs, The National Park Service, Harpers Ferry, West Virginia.

NEED. Materials for use with fifth or sixth graders before, during, and after 1-week camp experiences in the outdoors are now in final revision. Over a 2-year period, these have been tested, revised, retested, and further revised. About 11,000 students have used them, in the testing process, which has been conducted primarily by Educational Consulting Service. Mario Menesini, Director of ECS, has guided the development of these materials. A committee of National Education Association leaders, representing a wide assortment of disciplines and geographic regions, has evaluated the materials.

Third-fourth and seventh-eighth grade materials, for use with 1-day (or shorter) excursions near the schools, have gone through their first large-scale testing in twelve schools across the country.

Negotiations are now under way with several prospective developers and publishers for revision of the third- through eighth-grade materials, development of the balance of the kindergarten through twelfth-grade package, and final publication and dissemination. This work will be done through the use of funds provided by the National Park Foundation—the non-profit organization whose financial support has brought NEED to its present status. A modified version of the current fifth/sixth grade materials is to be published on an interim basis, for use starting with the fall term of 1970.

ESA. ESA sites have now been established in sixty-three areas of the National Park System; twenty-five more are planned for establishment in 1970.

The NEEL program will encourage local programs of environmental education, and help make such landmark areas available for use as outdoor classrooms. The ESA and NEED materials will give guidance and support to many of those who will want to establish NEEL's. The means by which the NEEL's may be identified, encouraged, and monitored, will be recommended by the Environmental Education Task Force.

ECS has produced a manual to guide teachers and service personnel in setting up ESA and NEEL activities. This is a "how-to" manual, covering the logistics and the myriad details that should not be overlooked in making an ESA program function effectively. The NEA has reviewed the manual and plans to modify and publish it by early summer, in cooperation with the National Park Service and the National Recreation and Parks Association. With specific area manuals and the NEED materials, interpreters, and teachers will then have the kind of tangible support that it takes to make them comfortable with school groups in an outdoor "classroom." ▪

Some educational impacts of outdoor education on school grounds.

OUTDOOR LEARNING LABORATORIES

Norman F. Marsh

SOMEDAY, at some school, somebody is going to come up with a communique that here—in the out of doors—is an unique opportunity to make a worthy contribution to education. Here, in a natural setting, the child's mind can be unshackled from the bonds of enforced conformity. Emergent therefrom will be not only new learnings but especially a fresh new approach to other learnings which will be processed by the child and the teacher working and experiencing together.

As we broaden the opportunities to explore—to discover and investigate, to question, hypothesize and put to the test, we increase the likelihood that creativity will be nurtured, resourcefulness encouraged, and ingenuity accepted and praised.

Outdoor education on school grounds could well be a major breakthrough in education curricula—breaking through the artificial barriers so many educators have erected or perpetuated in uncasing the learners' minds.

When, "What book is he in?" and "What page is he on?" seem to be the predominating criteria for determining a child's learning and progress, then this pressure for mass conformity dulls the curiosity, stifles the initiative, and results in the "lockstep" methods of the mediocre indoctrinators.

If history teaches us anything, it is that the greatest advancements in music, art, science, technology, and industry have not resulted from everybody thinking, saying, planning, and doing the same thing at the same time. The conformists and lock-steppers merely solidify the gains of the rebels—until new processes and approaches are again presented for mankind's next forward step.

Throughout history it has been the rebel, the nonconformist, who has had the initiative, the inquisitiveness, the _feeling_ for something different who has broken through the barriers imposed upon him by less imaginative, less progressive, and less visionary associates.

The rebel recognizes and accepts the differences as well as the similarities he encounters, realizing that both contribute to change.

In outdoor education, teacher and pupil have a chance to reorient themselves by direct experiences interrelating the natural and man-made environments. Thus each person can "find himself" and realize his own value and place in the scheme of things. This regaining of personal identity can well lead to one's adapting to his changing environment in a more productive and humanistic manner.

The creating, developing, and utilization of these outdoor learning laboratories are often excellent examples of community action. The pooling of school and community resources unifies and adds purpose and vitality to the programs—a "we-ness" that many schools are losing.

Boys and girls at schools with outdoor learning sites will for many years to come experience untold and unforeseen involvements that sharpen their powers of observation and deepen their understandings of the real, live, ongoing lessons continuously presented by nature. It could well be that these kinds of experiences may turn out to be the most cherished and longest remembered of their school experiences.

It is always a distinct pleasure to associate with persons who make possible school outdoor learning laboratories. In the years to come it can be said that here, in these green oases, some adults cared enough to see that going to school really meant something . . . a chance to adjust and grow mentally and spiritually while serving apprenticeships in the educational institutions of the times.

In leaving things better than we found them maybe we partially justify our existence on earth and can reasonably expect an extension of time. ∎

Mr. Marsh is the author of Outdoor Education on Your School Grounds. He is a classroom teacher in Sacramento and part-time consultant for planning school arboreta in northern California.

Nature Centers can help urban dwellers develop a conservation conscience.

NATURE CENTERS--

ONE APPROACH TO URBAN ENVIRONMENTAL EDUCATION

Joseph J. Shomon

ONE HEARS a great deal today about our deteriorating environment and our need for more environmental education. There is much talk of developing a conservation conscience—a conservation ethic, if you please. It is good talk and we need more of it.

But the practical question arises: How do you develop a conservation conscience? How does an individual, for example, or group or even a nation, develop an ethic, or, if you prefer, a philosophy? These are questions not too easy to answer. However, I believe that common sense gives us a clue— that an ethic is an attitude and as such is really a belief and beliefs transmit themselves into behavior. An attitude or belief is something a person acquires or builds up, something one learns. A dolphin in an aquarium or a man in a pluralistic society is not born to behave in a certain manner. Disciplined behavior must be learned.

It seems to me that if we in America are to have a conservation ethic (and we surely need one in our country and in the rest of the world), then correct behavioral patterns must be learned and practiced by all men, everywhere; they must be learned. And just as a teacher learns a profession by practice teaching or a plumber learns his trade in apprenticeship plumbing, so too the average man, woman, and child can learn a conservation discipline.

One can, of course, gain knowledge from books but better judgment tells us that personalized experience is still the best teacher. Knowledge of philosophy can be obtained by reading the writings of great philosophers but the development of a philosophy, which is something else, must arise out of the synthesis of experience.

If we want a land ethic, alone, then surely the richest source for it lies in the Creator's earth. If we wish to go a step further and make it a geo-biotic ethic (land-life ethic), then we must go not only to the land but also its life. Here I am firmly convinced that when a man gets close to nature, he gets close to God, or, the Cosmic Creator; and when one gets close to Divine Providence, he surely approaches the life of Divine Right.

Through these philosophic overtones we are reminded that it was St. Bernard who said, "You will find something far greater in the woods than you will find in books. Stones and trees will teach you that which you will never learn from masters." Here is profound wisdom and I dare say that much of it is applicable to modern life.

Today our affluence is turning our good ol' earth into alarming "effluence." More and more man is divorcing himself from the naturalistic world and, in many incredible ways, waging actual hostility toward it. Instead of seeking to restore a healthy balance between man and nature, the tendency nowadays is toward a greater rift.

Outside of preventing a holocaustic nuclear war and containing our very numbers, the greatest challenge facing us today is making our world more habitable—more habitable for man and all other living things that share this planet with us.

How can we make our planet more habitable? Surely the answer lies not in more runaway science and technology or in escaping to new planets. Nor does the mere pursuit of political systems offer much hope, or the passage of more unenforceable laws. And money alone cannot do it. Neither can manpower alone. What rational choice then do we have?

The answer, if there is one, I perceive, must

Dr. Shomon is director of the Nature Center Planning Division, National Audubon Society, 1130 Fifth Avenue, New York, New York 10028.

The new Aullwood Nature Center at Dayton, Ohio.

somehow, in some way, arise out of the spirit of man and out of a developing awareness of his rightful role on earth. And this can come only through the proper disciplining of man's actions and through such long, well-established formats as careful upbringing and sound education.

What seems most needed in the world today is a new perspective of man's relationship to his environment—an emerging land-life awareness of man's place on earth and his responsibilities toward it. Man as an individual as well as a group species must accept a stewardship role on earth, working for its betterment, its improved habitation, or he will not have it for long. A rock or mossbed not fit to support a lichen in an air polluted megalopolis may soon not be fit for the germination of a tree seedling, and an ever larger ecosystem not fit for certain forms of life may eventually not be fit for man. The answer again comes back to awareness.

The quality of awareness in man obviously is a developmental trait, and the power of awareness like perception, we are told, lies dormant in the individual. It must be awakened to be useful. Common sense tells us again that the development of awareness must start with the young. An infant soon learns the danger of fire. A child of loving but discipline-minded parents soon becomes aware of right or wrong. In a similar way the growing child can be made aware of things in nature, or, if we so choose, we can neglect the child and allow this awareness to be stifled. Moreover, with regard to nature and the child today, the more a child is removed from natural things, the more he needs them. City children and adults need this exposure to nature particularly nowadays or they may easily become so desensitized to natural living things as not to know one tree from another or one bird from the next, and may take the attitude of "couldn't care less." But let's not fool ourselves. Country people need this exposure to nature, too. All mankind needs it.

These are among some of the valid reasons why

the nature center idea is such a wholly worthy concept. If as the individual goes through life he is able to receive training and guidance and education in nature appreciation in the normal sense, then well and good. However, if this is not possible, then the next best thing might be to have special nature centers developed where attitudes of stewardship toward land and its life can be stressed and learned. Perhaps in this way much of the present-day divorcement of man from nature can be stopped and the unfortunate trend reversed.

Awareness and appreciation seem basic to a conservation philosophy. If we want a habitable world, we first must learn to appreciate what a habitable environment is like, what the dangers to it are, and what action is needed by all of us to make the change for the better.

The nature center concept is aimed at the urban dweller and hopes to do just this. It is in a sense a new approach to the development of environmental awareness for millions of urban people everywhere.

A nature center, it should be explained, is an area of undeveloped land (at least 50 acres) within a city or town or near it with the facilities and services planned to conduct community outdoor programs in natural sciences, nature appreciation, and conservation education. In essence, it is an outdoor focal point, a facility, an institution, where community citizens (especially the young) can enjoy a segment of the natural world and learn about the interrelationship of living and non-living things, including man's place in the ecological community. Thus the nature center can become a viable tool for the development of environmental awareness and perhaps lead to the development of a land-life ethic. Surely, it offers us a hope and seems worth trying. But like all new ideas, the process of getting full acceptance of this concept has not quite arrived, although nature centers are now developing rapidly in many areas of the United States and Canada.

HISTORY

The nature centers movement began somewhat obscurely after World War II. No one knows for sure where the first nature center began. Stamford, Connecticut, and Bear Mountain Park, New York, led off in the late forties with some good nature center facilities in outdoor interpretive education. People like William Carr, Dan Beard, and Freeman Tilden were in the forefront of the outdoor interpretive movement.

The National Audubon Society began its interest in nature education back in the thirties. In the fifties it started a number of successful nature centers where nature education and ecological conservation were stressed. Centers were developed at Greenwich and Sharon, Connecticut; El Monte, California; and Dayton, Ohio. Also at the Aullwood Audubon Center, near Dayton, the Society developed a 120-acre popular children's farm. During the past decade, close to a half-million young people have received instruction and no small measure of inspiration at these Audubon facilities.

However, the Society had long realized that it could not do the entire job of nature education alone and so in 1961 it launched a new and vigorous program of stimulating interest in community nature centers. It merged with the relatively new Nature Centers for Young America, Inc. to throw new and combined weight behind this program—a nationwide effort of encouraging communities (government agencies and private groups) to set up nature centers of their own. And so the broad effort went ahead. For several years the program was nip and tuck, but then the effort began paying off. Nature centers began emerging everywhere. Today the Society's Nature Center Planning Division, although less than a decade old, can point with pride to the planning help given over 100 separate communities in more than 25 states and provinces. In this effort local communities as well as government agencies have set aside more than 100,000 acres of natural land for interpretive education and have spent in capital outlay alone (land, building, and equipment) more than $30,000,000. The value of this nationwide program in arousing a nationwide ecological consciousness is beginning to show and the future impact on growing numbers of urban people is bound to be great indeed.

THE PICTURE TODAY

The broad picture with Audubon centers and nature centers in general today is this:

1. The National Audubon Society is not in a position to establish any more new nature centers of its own, unless the conditions are so unusual and the site so unique and fully endowed that an exception to an established policy can be made. What the Society is more interested in is support for the concept and the successful development of local community nature centers everywhere.

2. Support for community nature centers is growing but many conservationists and community leaders still need to give strong backing to the concept. Great gaps remain in geographic areas where there are no nature centers whatsoever.

This is especially true in the South, Southwest, and Rocky Mountain states.

3. There is a dire need for the setting up of standards in nature center development and programming. It is in this area of planning and guidance where the Nature Center Planning Division is trying to be of service.

4. And finally, there is today too much worship of bigness—structures and machines—and gadgetry and not enough on effective personnel. There must be a swing toward the more simple approaches to development and programs, and to more personalized operations.

Most needed in nature centers development is support for the value of master teacher-naturalists. The best results in programming being obtained today point to personalized activities rather than to elaborate buildings, exhibits, and expensive dioramas. It seems a little ironic that it is easy to get support for structures and so hard to get authorization for needed and talented personnel. Also we seem to have money for equipment but very little for personnel to perform good maintenance. These weaknesses must be corrected.

REQUIREMENTS FOR A NATURE CENTER

To get a community nature center established is not an easy or simple thing thing to do. Some real effort must go into it. Several conditions or requirements are needed if a center is to become a reality:

1. There must be local interest and leadership.

2. There must be land available.

3. There must be a good plan and a sound organization structure behind the plan.

4. There must be funds.

5. There must be implementation.

Each of these merits brief treatment.

Generating interest and finding dynamic leadership at the local level are key factors in getting things moving in any community. Experience has shown that where private citizens and government groups are sufficiently aware of local conservation problems and are already organized in groups for possible action, the chances of getting something going are excellent. In other words, community readiness for a nature center is absolutely essential if a project is to succeed. Here is where national and state agencies and private conservation groups can help so much by providing the necessary communications and conservation education leadership that lies at the base of any good action program.

To spark a community into action, some one or two individuals must become the prime movers. The Kalamazoo Nature Center, the Lynchburg Walton Conservation Park, the Carver Park Nature Center outside of Minneapolis, are but a few examples of successful conservation education projects pushed through by one or two leaders. The point is, first

A naturalist
orients a
school group
before starting
down a nature
trail at the
Cincinnati
Nature Center.

create the interest, then find the leaders, and then
wade into battle.

AVAILABILITY OF LAND

Second in importance to local interest and leadership is availability of natural land for a nature center. As cities expand and engulf the countryside, as
roads, highways, and subdivisions take over, choice
natural areas for nature centers become available less
and less. This points up the need for long-range planning in urban development, for zoning, and the setting
aside of open space—park lands and other recreational areas, outdoor areas, and nature centers.

Lands for nature centers can be acquired in several ways: 1. gift; 2. outright purchase; 3. condemnation and purchase; 4. easement; 5. lease. At
the present time some federal aid is available to local and state governing bodies wishing to acquire land
for open space. This is handled by the Federal Housing
and Urban Development Administration, Washington,
D.C. Applications for grants, amounting up to 30
percent of the appraised value of the land, should be
sent to the regional office of HUD. Not to be overlooked, too, are some state aid monies to communities for park lands and open space handled by the
Bureau of Outdoor Recreation, Washington, D.C.

Available open space and natural lands near most
cities are getting so critical today that unless communities move quickly, both the available land and its
price may be such that a nature center may be out of
the question. As an example, some 10 years ago
sites for schools in Long Island and New Jersey could
have been bought for as little as a few thousand dollars an acre. Now, prices in at least two areas have
shot up to $75,000 and $35,000 an acre, respectively.

PLANS AND ORGANIZATION

No nature center can enjoy success without good
planning and effective organization. To sell a project to a community, a plan must be available; it must
then be presented to an action group for support and
approval. Nature centers which are foundering today—and there are some—can put the blame on poor
planning or hardly any planning at all; also on structural and personnel weaknesses in their organization.
Those that are succeeding—and there are many—have
carefully planned and organized their efforts.

Where a center is planned by a private group, it
is necessary to form a legal organization and gain
tax-exempt status. Usually an organization must
have an educational program under way for at least
a year before the tax exemption is granted.

FINANCES

The subject of financing is complex and the situations so varied that no attempt can be made to go
into details here. It must suffice to say that a good
nature center, like any other worthwhile facility
costs money, and adequate financing must be faced
squarely and boldly by the sponsoring organization.
Initial capital expenditures may range from $50,000
or $75,000 for a small center to as much as
$1,000,000 for a large one. Similarly, annual op-
erating expenses may range from $25,000 for a
modest center to $200,000 for a sizeable facility.

To date nature center projects have been financed in three general ways:

1. All private funds.

2. Combination of private and public funds.

3. All public funds.

Some of the more successful private community
nature centers, other than the four operated by the
National Audubon Society, are located at Stamford,
Connecticut; Kalamazoo and Dryden, Michigan; Cincinnati, Ohio; and Peoria, Illinois, to name a few.

Some typical center run by government agencies are Rock Creek Park Nature Center, Washington, D.C.; Brookside Nature Center, Wheaton, Maryland; Carver Park Nature Center, near Minneapolis, Minnesota, and the Rogers Conservation Education Center, Sherbourne, New York.

IMPLEMENTATION

The final phase of nature center development is full-scale program implementation. This stage is reached when the center has a full complement of trained people and is open all year around.

To help communities get over some of the hurdles mentioned above, the Nature Center Planning Division, National Audubon Society, has prepared a series of how-to-do guidebooks which are available to groups and individuals at cost. In addition, the Division has available a staff of trained specialists to give communities actual planning expertise.

A new concept, like that of a nature center, always requires a period of pioneering and trial and error before a breakthrough is possible. A real breakthrough is possible if all conservationists and educators will put their shoulders to the wheel and help back this movement. When 2,000 community nature centers across America will have become established, think what the effect could be in terms of moral and spiritual re-creation? Think of what the effect could be in terms of nature awareness, personal self-reliance, discipline, and individual responsibility?

This we know: all that is great in science, all that is good in technology, all that is noble in literature, music, philosophy, and religion has come about by the individual's striving to realize himself and his worth. If personal responsibility, courage,

vigor, rugged individualism, the pioneering spirit, and love of land and nature seep out of our people, America will be dead.

The countdown is near zero, the hour close to midnight. If all conservation-dedicated groups—local, state, national, government, and private—will close ranks and meet the challenge that faces us in resource use education, particularly in our growing urban social order, we will have developed the kind of conservation conscience we need and justifiably deserve.

SELECTED BIBLIOGRAPHY

Ashbaugh, Byron L. Planning a Nature Center (National Audubon Society, 1963).

Ashbaugh, Byron L., illustrated by Robert F. Holmes, Trail Planning and Layout (National Audubon Society, 1965).

Shomon, Joseph J. A Nature Center for Your Community (National Audubon Society, 1962).

Shomon, Joseph J. Manual of Outdoor Conservation Education (National Audubon Society, 1964).

Shomon, Joseph J., editor. Manual of Outdoor Interpretation (National Audubon Society, 1968).

Shomon, Joseph J., Ashbaugh, Byron L., Tolman, C.D., sketches by Ned Smith, diagrams by Robert F. Holmes. Wildlife Habitat Improvement (National Audubon Society, 1966).

Tilden, Freeman. Interpreting Our Heritage (North Carolina, University of North Carolina Press, Chapel Hill, 1957).

How to use an outdoor learning laboratory.

THE ECOLOGICAL STUDY PLOT

Gordon J. Swearingen

CONSERVATION Education is not another subject or separate area of study, but rather a program designed to enrich, vitalize, and complement the content of existing school curriculum. In conservation education, pupil experiences should involve learning more about the environment in which we live and how man can properly use and live in his environment. An effective approach to injecting this into the curriculum is the use of an outdoor classroom, or—if you will—an ecological study plot.

A designated area of land, 1 or 2 acres in s i z e, and including as many of the natural resources as possible, would provide students with firsthand observations and direct learning experiences relative to environmental study. Use of such a plot could r a n g e from a single field trip to a resident outdoor living experience. It is usable at any grade level.

Seldom would school ownership of the designated area be necessary. In some instances, t h e school ground itself offers possibilities, a n d many public parks contain a suitable area. In other situations, privately owned woodlands or land areas may be used with the owner's consent.

Preferably, the ecological study plot would include a live stream or water frontage where students would measure stream flow, test water, collect and identify aquatic life, and study the dependence of adjacent plant and animal life upon the stream. Students would also determine the depth, structure, texture, a n d chemical composition of the soil, recording this information together with samples of each layer or horizon of the soil. They could also determine water holding capacities, erodibility factors, and soil-plant relationships.

A study of the plant community in the designated plot would lead students from collection of p l a n t specimens to projects in determining effects of plant competition for survival, effects on forest influences, effects of soil erosion on plant life, and the interdependence between plant and animal life—how each sustains the other. A study of wildlife resources on the plot would involve evaluating the habitat available for different species, carrying capacity of the land, evidence of overuse or under-use of the food, and species counts. Students should be lead to search f o r and observe all available evidence of the food chain phenomenon, as well as the naturally provided d e - fense mechanisms employed by plants and animals. They should interpret how these factors contribute to maintaining the balance of nature and to the natural principle of survival of the fittest.

Each student should maintain a plot-study notebook consisting of problems and activities in e a c h resource study area, so designed t h a t the student must actually do the projects and experiments to complete the notebook. The objective of each plot-study session is to lead the students to their own observations and conclusions through actual involvement with the natural environment. If this i s achieved, there is a minimum of telling and a maximum of participation.

The outdoor learning experience provided by a n ecological study plot can be both challenging and motivating. Each student is involved in conducting investigations and experiments and recording his findings. Students are also provided opportunities t o make practical application of many classroom learnings in science, mathematics, social sciences, and creative arts. More importantly, each student i s lead to a better understanding of his own relationship to the ecosystem of which he is a part, and how this ecosystem is effected by its environment. ∎

The author is a conservationist, Arkansas Soil and Conservation Commission, Little Rock.

Stepping-stones to an environmental ethic.

NEW INTERPRETIVE METHODS AND TECHNIQUES

Byron L. Ashbaugh

NEWS REPORTS of the day confirm that most of us face an environment that is becoming increasingly crowded, noisy, poisoned, soiled, trashy, and ugly. Evidence points to the way people conduct their lives and pursue their jobs as the major cause of the dangerous and unsatisfactory condition of our surroundings. In fact, many authorities have concluded that man himself is a planetary disease, and unless there is a reversal of trends in natural resource use and environmental care, human beings will indeed have to be considered as a threatened species. It seems strikingly clear that we have failed to convince people that as individuals they must take strong, personal action to achieve a pleasant and life-supporting place in which to live.

The persistent problem before us is one of how to reach people so as to influence the way they treat natural resources and their environment. What people do today and how they live are patterns that will be seen in resource use and environmental control in the future. To create environmental-mindedness, it is necessary to stress personal experiences and develop perception through all the senses. This is not just a matter of perceiving things that are pleasant but the survival of the human race.

Today, ever-expanding populations, natural resources depletion and mismanagement, environmental pollution, droughts, floods, shrinking open space, dust storms, construction of huge and not necessarily useful projects, all are matters of which our citizens must have informed opinions. The basis for such opinions can be built by our interpretive programs through an understanding of fundamental ecological principles illustrated in the familiar context of one's surroundings. A person can learn to appreciate and know the ecological setting in which he lives through direct, firsthand experiences in a living environment. It is our challenge to find creative and innovative interpretive facilities and effective methods of teaching so as to actually involve our citizens, be they old or young.

VISITOR GOALS

The approach to follow in outdoor interpretation must be focused on people. The program should help each visitor to see himself as part of his surroundings and to recognize his importance and individual responsibilities. The whole interpretive offering should be centered on people and where they live. The program aided by the resources of park lands should be designed to provide a wide variety of opportunities for inspiration, knowledge, and skills so as to assist each visitor with the following general goals:

- Appreciation for the immediate surroundings.
- An understanding of his place in the broad environmental picture.
- Activities in which he can participate to keep his community attractive and the environment life supporting.

An innovative interpretive program should be a change agent for park visitors and cause them to move toward the following specific achievements:

- Realization that man is destroying the environment that supports him.
- Improved learning through use of real objects and demonstrations.
- Appreciation of natural beauty.
- A chance to compare the park with his neighborhood.
- An opportunity to contrast a park vista with the Monday-at-work scene.
- An understanding of the need to preserve adequate open space in the community.
- Understanding of natural resources and their preservation.
- Awareness of man's history on park lands.
- Development of an environmental conscience or ethic.
- A personal commitment to a strong individual effort to oppose vigorously through political and legal means the pollution of air, land, and water.

Mr. Ashbaugh is Chief, Outdoor Education Services, Genesee County Parks and Recreation Commission, Flint, Michigan. This paper was presented at the 1970 Great Lakes Park Training Institute, Pokagon Park, Indiana.

- Training as professional or lay managers of the environment.
- Enjoyment of being outdoors.
- Finding solitude which enhances the human spirit.

VISITOR PERCEPTION

In planning and operating an interpretive program we should remember that park visitors have at least six senses: hearing, seeing, touching, tasting, smelling, and muscular tension. Educational research has shown that efficiency of learning varies directly with the number of these senses that are exercised in an interpretive situation. When we have something to interpret, we usually speak and expect others to listen, hear, and understand. We are using mostly one sense—hearing. Even for this category, we are inclined not to allow the sounds of nature to "speak" for themselves. But consider for a moment how the other senses can contribute to firsthand experiences, and relate their use to some commonplace, everyday actions—probably without conscious effort to the visitor. For example:

- seeing··as in perceiving the colors and design in a flower or rainbow.
- touching··as in deciding on the difference between the "feel" of a block of ice and a piece of stone, or the difference between the bark of birch and oak.
- tasting··as in finding the flavor of maple syrup or a persimmon.
- smelling··as in identifying peppermint, spearmint, pennyroyal, or catnip.
- muscular tension··as in determining how difficult it is to break a hickory stick.

COMMUNITY AREAS

There are usually areas available in a community that will lend themselves to innovative interpretive techniques. A few of these are:

- Mill pond··sometimes with the old mill.
- Cemetery··has significant information for historical interpretation and research.
- Power line right-of-way··electric companies will often permit the use of space under power lines for trails, wildlife food plantings, soil and water demonstrations.
- Abandoned railroad right-of-way··nothing better for cross country bicycling and hiking trails.
- Old canal··can be restored for canoeing and paddle boating. Towpaths are ideal for trails.
- Natural areas - owners are often willing to permit access for controlled use as school laboratory or research areas.
- Water supply and power reservoirs are commonly used for interpretation and recreation.

ZONING

We should zone sufficient acreage within our parks for exclusive educational and cultural use such as the Genesee County Parks and Recreation Commission has done at the For-Mar Nature Preserve and Arboretum

at Flint, Michigan. The tract which is 355 acres in extent and one mile from the eastern edge of the city has been divided into four areas to facilitate planning and development to meet community needs:

- Nature Preserve··205 acres.
- Arboretum··100 acres.
- Special Education Area··27 acres.
- Land Laboratory··13 acres.

The Nature Preserve will be used year around for environmental education and research by schools, colleges, and the general public through use of trails, trail-side exhibits, demonstrations, observation points, labels, and other devices. Some facilities planned for the preserve are:

- Run-off pond.
- Woodland pond.
- Stump fence.
- Hedgerows.
- Weather station.
- Wild meadow trail.
- Foot bridges.
- Soil pits.
- Springs.
- Upland hardwoods.
- Pine plantations.
- Ground water ponds.
- Perched marsh.
- Old country lane.
- Observation blinds.
- Bluebird trail.
- Mowed meadow.
- Elevated walkway.
- Council rings.
- Brush piles for wildlife.
- Bottomland hardwoods.
- Oxbow ponds.
- Restored tall-grass prairie.
- Michigan shrub and tree trail.
- Overlooks at edge of flood plain.
- Spruce and white birch plantations.

The Arboretum will be a living collection of plants made up largely of trees and shrubs grown for study and popular interest. The Arboretum at For-Mar will feature the following:

- Shrubs, trees, and woody vines native to Michigan.
- Landscaped-demonstration lawns.
- Groupings of miniature evergreens.
- Flowering shrubs.

The Special Education Area will be land and facilities for visually, mentally, and physically handicapped persons and those in special education classes of schools or institutions. Facilities planned for the area are:

- Touch and see trail.
- Trimmed tree trunk, placed on ground.
- Herb garden.
- Shelter with fireplace.
- Windmill.
- Garden.
- Bee tree.
- Aromatic shrubs and trees.

The Land Laboratory is conceived as an area to be used by school children for first-hand experiences related to working with soil and measuring land as well as activities dealing with geology and wood study. Features to be included are:

- Garden plots.
- Shrub and tree nursery.
- Land measurement Laboratory (a square-acre lawn).

- Rock hounds haven—a plot for supplies of gravel and rocks, mineral specimens, geology wall; a place to select and prepare rock samples for a collection.
- Wood yard—an area in which to study tree, stump, and log sections; to see a cord of wood; to compare rough-cut with finished lumber; to use a cross-cut saw to cut a section from a log; to move a log with a cant hook or peavey; to see forest-fire and grass-fire fighting tools.
- Observation mound.

ENVIRONMENTAL ATTITUDES

People are not born with attitudes. Correct attitudes toward the environment and natural resources in general are created over a person's lifetime. An outdoor center can be a significant place where proper attitudes toward one's surroundings and those things which sustain a person are built. Unless we shape good attitudes, especially in young people, all of the current talk about the environment will be meaningless. The shaping of proper attitudes into an environmental ethic might well be the greatest value of outdoor education. Unless people have the right understanding and appreciation for the environment and open space, the will to protect and use wisely cannot be created and those concerned stand to lose the very things they hope to maintain.

Constructive and wise use of the environment becomes a way of life through the building of attitudes in the hearts and minds of people. These attitudes are action tendencies within each person that determine what he will do under certain circumstances. The building of an environmental ethic is like following a flagstone path where the stepping-stones are delineated as follows:

- Knowledge··"acquaintance with facts, truths, principles"
- Understanding··"being thoroughly familiar with, apprehend clearly the character or nature of"
- Interest··"feeling of one whose attention is particularly engaged by something"
- Appreciation··"act of estimating the qualities of things and giving them their true value"
- Respect··"esteem felt or shown"
- Reverence··"a feeling of profound respect mingled with awe and affection"
- Responsibility··"the state of being accountable for something within one's power"
- Action··"something done, a deed" ■

A regional approach to environmental education in New York.

PROJECT R.A.C.E.

Jerry Passer

THE MAJOR challenge to any regional program, regardless of the type, is that it be designed for maximum participation by numerous individuals and groups representing a variety of interests and age levels. Project R. A. C. E., a Federally-funded Title III conservation program sponsored by the Ilion School District, has met this challenge successfully.

Now beginning its third year of operation, R. A. C. E. has instituted innovative activities for young folks in nearly 60 school districts and 20 parochial schools. The counties served by Project R. A. C. E. include Chenango, Madison, Herkimer, and Oneida.

A key to the success of the program has been the continuing cooperation between R. A. C. E. and the State Department of Environmental Conservation. The Department's new Rogers Conservation Education Center at Sherburne (The Conservationist April-May 1968) is an invaluable asset to conservation education efforts both locally and statewide.

Through a unique facet of the R. A. C. E. funding agreement, monies were made available for the renovation of a large building at the Rogers Center site. The building (formerly a brooding house for pheasants), has been converted into a modern dormitory facility that will accommodate 60 students and at least, six adults. The building is complete with kitchen, dining room, separate sleeping quarters for boy and girl students and their adult chaperones. A nurse's office and nature/craft room on the upper floor are also available to visiting groups.

SCHOOL GROUPS USE ROGERS CENTER

Many school districts, encouraged by the enthusiasm of their teachers, are now utilizing the dormitory during the school year. Overnight visitations are arranged through R. A. C. E. and Rogers Center staff. Due to the recent installation of a heating system, the dormitory has become available for year around visitations and is being used regularly during the winter months.

Use of the dormitory and participation in the over-night program is not restricted to area groups. For anyone, who is interested in this type of experience, a packet of materials describing the program is available from the Project R. A. C. E. office.

Snowshoeing, introduced by R. A. C. E., has become an extremely popular wintertime activity with area teachers and students. Following a classroom discussion on the history of snowshoeing, the construction, and scientific principles involved in their use, the snowshoes are distributed to the students for an exhilarating outdoor experience. School yards, nearby parks, and other snow-covered areas are used. Resulting from the experience are letters, poems, drawings, and follow-up field trips to areas that have been surveyed and catalogued by Project R. A. C. E. staff. Last winter over 200 children a week were participating in this activity. Thus, conservation and environmental education can be introduced in the winter.

NEW COURSES

New courses in "Backyard Ecology and School Site Utilization" and "Environmental Education—A Multidiscipline Approach" have been introduced by R. A. C. E. These courses, conducted each semester in area schools, are made possible with the cooperation of such agencies as the Soil Conservation Service, Cooperative Extension—4-H, New York State Department of Environmental Conservation, State Education Department, State Outdoor Education Association, area colleges, and a host of others.

Workshops are frequently conducted for teachers using local sites that appear in the "Environmental Resource and Study Area Catalog," completed by Dick Kaskoun of the Project R. A. C. E. staff. For each workshop a special booklet is prepared and used throughout the lesson. A teacher, using the booklet, is then able to return to the site with her class on a self-guided basis. The value of this plan lies in the fact that as a direct result, demands upon the staff decrease at areas visited. Thus, the visiting teacher often receives greater cooperation and latitude with respect to the

Mr. Passer was Director of Project R. A. C. E. and is now Assistant Director of Conservation Education for the New York State Department of Environmental Conservation at Albany. This report first appeared in the June-July 1970 issue of The Conservationist.

hours that she may visit the site with her class. Sample workshop booklets are available from R. A. C. E.

Summertime is a busy time, too, as 240 eager youngsters will participate in a resident environmental education program at Rogers Center. Each week for 4 weeks, 60 children arrive at the Center bright and early Monday morning to begin 4 full days of new and exciting experiences in the out-of-doors. Again, cooperation is the key to success as the staff of R. A. C. E. and the staff of the Rogers Center work together in the week-long program. The entire summer program is funded by Title III, E. S. E. A., and there are no costs to the participants. Interestingly, the most common problem encountered each week is blisters on children's feet.

During the past 2 years R. A. C. E. has built an impressive audio-visual library with nearly 70 titles. Films, film strips, study prints, and records help teachers reduce the level of abstraction when discussing environmental problems or unique structural adaptations of certain forms of life. Soon, we will add to this library a 16mm. color and sound film of the 1969 Summer Resident Program held at Rogers Center. Noted wildlife photographer Earl Hilfiker of Rochester and Bob Rehbaum with the staff of The Conservationist have prepared the film which tells the story of a typical week at the Center as experienced by the youngsters. Additional copies of the film will be available from the film library of the New York State Department of Environmental Conservation.

Project R. A. C. E., after funding for a third and final year under Title III, must be continued through the sponsorship of local educational institutions. Presentations are frequently made to area teachers and administrators as well as the Boards of Cooperative Educational Services of the region to discuss this question. Hopefully, when Federal funding terminates on February 28, 1971, definite arrangements will have been made to continue the project. At a time when environmental education has become so vitally important, Project R. A. C. E. seems to be filling the bill. ∎

The regional effects of a college environmental education program.

ANTIOCH'S GLEN HELEN

Kenneth W. Hunt

SINCE 1946, Antioch College has been engaged in environmental education through the activities conducted in its nature reserve, Glen Helen. I report here what these activities have been, and will suggest how they may have influenced environmental relationships in southwestern Ohio.

Glen Helen is adjacent to Yellow Springs in the upper Little Miami Valley. It has 1,000 acres of which about one-quarter are of old-growth forest, relatively undisturbed, where one can glimpse the biota as it originally existed in southwestern Ohio. Other parts of Glen Helen are former farm fields, and pastures where the process of biotic succession can be observed or manipulated. In some 170 acres we have prevented the process of succession by continuing farming operations, thus keeping some options open for the future. Recently 10 acres were subtracted from the farm and seeded to an experimental prairie, and another 15 acres are being converted to a wildlife study area for our Outdoor Education Center. Following is a chronological review of the environmental services of Glen Helen, with comments about possible regional effects.

NATURE TRAILS

Since 1946 trails in Glen Helen have been open to the public. A census taken over the 2-month period of April—May 1967 showed over 17,000 visits. Over two-thirds of our visitors came from outside Antioch College and Yellow Springs. It is likely that many of these people would welcome more open space resources for their own communities.

YELLOW SPRINGS SCHOOL FOREST

In 1947 we arranged for the Yellow Springs High School to have the use of 100 acres of former farm land in Glen Helen as a School Forest. The school began a n annual program of Christmas tree plantings. This led to the popular Christmas Tree Festival, when families select and cut their own trees and pay the school. This was the first School Forest to be recognized and was awarded a sign by the Ohio Forestry Association in 1949. On several occasions workshops for teachers were sponsored here. Now there are about 110 School

Forests and Land Laboratories developed in O h i o. Of course the School Forest in Glen Helen is not the whole reason for all this, but we know it has helped.

OUTDOOR EDUCATION CONFERENCE

In May 1949, an enthusiastic group of students organized a weekend Outdoor Education Conference for teachers and youth leaders in southwestern Ohio. This has become an annual event, and altogether over 1,000 persons have attended the 20 conferences to date. These people have carried back to their communities the result of their discussions and experiences about nature interpretation, conservation, and environmental problems.

TRAILSIDE MUSEUM

In 1951 we built the Trailside Museum, to serve as the gateway to the Glen. The students who work here create seasonal exhibits to show visitors what to look for, and to make clear the responsibility of every visitor: that he must in no way deplete the biota or the beauty of a natural area; that the only way we can each hope to share these scarce remnants is to be scrupulous about this. Local children attend Junior Naturalists clubs here. School buses come daily during spring and fall for field trips guided by our students. A variety of activities are scheduled—from evening shows to a maple syrup breakfast.

Nature Centers were new when we built the Trailside Museum. We were preceded in southwestern Ohio by the Burnett Woods Museum in Cincinnati and were parelleled by the development of the present Dayton Museum of Natural History. We are indebted to both of these for ideas and inspiration. In 1956 the National Audubon Society asked if it would seem competitive if they set up a Nature Center at Aullwood. I told them we needed it—that each Nature Center would stimulate more. The newest now is the Cincinnati Nature Center. Not that we can say who caused it—but for years some of the sponsors of the Cincinnati Nature Center have been visiting the facilities of their predecessors!

OUTDOOR EDUCATION CENTER

It is good if children can spend a few hours in the

Mr. Hunt is Director of Glen Helen, Antioch College, Yellow Springs, Ohio.

woods, but it is better if they can come for a few days. After years of struggling for ways and means, in 1956 we finally built the Outdoor Education Center in Glen Helen. This is a residential facility for school classes, teacher education, workshops, and conferences. It receives around 2,000 school children annually, from Cincinnati and Columbus and points between. In addition, many church and other youth groups schedule weekend retreats and workshops here. Our staff conducts a thorough-going program of environmental education for the children. The conferences that have been scheduled here include the Outdoor Science Section of the Ohio Education Association, the Nature School of the Ohio Association of Garden Clubs, the Intercollegiate Outdoor Education Conference, and many others. In the summers it has hosted the Ohio Conservation Lab and the Miami–Antioch Outdoor Education Workshop for Teachers.

The real payoff comes when some of the teachers and some of the schools that have used our Outdoor Education Center create outdoor schools of their own. Several suburban Cincinnati schools, which used to come to Glen Helen, now operate their own program at Camp Kern. The Centerville Board of Education has designed and built outdoor education facilities on their own property. The Tri-District schools, north of Columbus, do school camping at the 4-H Camp Ohio. Both Centerville and Tri-District teachers had attended Glen Helen workshops.

The credit for this vigorous growth of our outdoor education service for schools belongs to Mrs. Jean Sanford Replinger, who developed and directed the Center for 10 years until her marriage.

RIDING CENTRE

In 1957, 80 acres of former farm land in Glen Helen were leased for a program of horseback training called the Riding Centre, and a bridle trail was routed through a second-growth region of the Glen. Now there are three riding academies in the vicinity of Yellow Springs, and the Village's Open Space Plan envisions bridle paths ringing the town.

FIGHTING OF ENCROACHMENT THREATS

During 1958 and 1959 Glen Helen was more severely tested than at any other time to date. Land that is underdeveloped is vulnerable to engineering projects, such as highways, utilities, municipal services, or dams. The nearer the land is to an undisturbed natural condition the more vulnerable it becomes. On the economist's totem pole of "the highest and best use," the wilderness occupies the very bottom. Ten years ago the fact that biologists rated such resources as the most valuable of all was generally regarded as ludicrous. Today we are in a significantly better position. New rules by the Federal Highway Administration require State Highway Departments to allow citizens to participate more fully in the process of choosing highway locations. Furthermore, the highway departments must maintain a list upon which any public agency or advisory group may enroll to receive notification of new projects proposed.

This altered bureaucratic attitude has been forced by public pressure. The pressure has mounted as a result of struggles all across the country against the powers of the economic-engineering complex. These struggles have made news, and have had a powerful educational effect on the general public. Today we have a strong measure of citizen and voter support.

Glen Helen's struggle began in September 1958, when a highway representative informed us of a plan to relocate U.S. 68 through a portion of Glen Helen, including the Yellow Springs School Forest. The Glen's Advisory Council, a statewide group of conservationists and educators, said we should fight. And we did. We appealed to all the schools and organizations that had used the Outdoor Education Center, to all the visitors that had signed the Trailside guest register, to all the people that had attended our conferences, and to biological, conservation, and nature societies. Finally Gov. O'Neill, and then his successor, Gov. DiSalle, each wrote assurance that another route would be found.

Nor was this our only struggle. Overlapping this, in 1959 and 1960 we had to contend with engineering recommendations that a sewer trunk line and disposal plant be located in the forested valley of the Glen. Finally an alternative location was found outside.

THE GLEN HELEN ASSOCIATION

These successes were hard-won, but they accomplished a great amount of publicity and education about the values of natural areas. Moreover, they left us with a large and enthusiastic body of supporters, who in 1960 organized themselves into the Glen Helen Association. The purposes of the Association are to protect Glen Helen, to promote the idea of community natural areas, and to generally advance ecological education. It raises funds to strengthen the educational services in Glen Helen, and it sponsors an annual public lecture which has featured such conservationists as Karl Maslowski, Stanley Cain, Harry Caudill, and Charles Mohr.

THE COUNTRY COMMON

We are fortunate that adjacent to Glen Helen is John Bryan State Park. Together we preserve 1800 acres in the upper Little Miami Valley, and this has attracted other outdoor agencies to our region. Within the park now are a 4-H camp and a State orphan's home camp. The Boy Scouts and Girl Scouts bought land for camps adjacent to the Park. The Nature Conservancy raised the money to buy Clifton Gorge and then gave that splendid scenic and scientific preserve to the State. The Village of Yellow Springs has acquired land north and south of Glen Helen as increments toward a future green belt encircling the community. All these open space landowners have since 1962 been associated as a Committee for a Country Common, committed to the purpose of doubling the permanent open space reserve from what they started with, and of cooperating to help each other achieve the best protection and the best use of this beautiful region. A recent film produced by the U.S. Department of Housing and Urban Development includes the Country Commons as one of the methods of saving open space before urbanization takes over.

GATHERING MOMENTUM

To speak of a "trigger factor" that may be altering environmental relationships in southwestern Ohio is a rather ambitious metaphor. It suggests an explosive impact. These various endeavors at environmental education which I have been reporting have seemed to us at Antioch to be painfully slow in their development and always short of the mark. Yet as we review them we find a cumulative effect and a gathering momentum. I expect that others who have been engaged in environmental education have noted similar encouraging evidence. What is more, our several efforts have reinforced each other and tended to merge.

When Jean Sanford was struggling to attract teachers to her Miami-Antioch Outdoor Education Workshop, most teachers saw more future in taking summer sessions in chemistry or math. Now Jean's successor, J. Douglas Dickinson, is again arranging instruction for teachers in outdoor education, through the auspices of the Dayton Miami Valley Consortium of Colleges. Already the response is most encouraging. The educational climate is changing.

In 1962 the fledgling Association of Interpretive Naturalists held one of their first meetings at our Outdoor Education Center, with 98 persons attending. Last year this organization returned to Ohio for a national meeting at Hueston Woods, with a registration of 350.

In 1959 the young Ohio Chapter of the Nature Conservancy undertook the effort to preserve Clifton Gorge.

As I have said, this has been achieved, and so have 12 other such projects across Ohio. But the Ohio Chapter has created more than nature reserves. It has created public understanding such that legislation is now enacted to create a National Areas System to be administrated by the State of Ohio.

One final example in testimony of this gathering momentum is the announcement by the Ohio Department of Natural Resources of its plan to designate the Little Miami as a scenic river. Many conservation interests have cooperated through Little Miami, Inc., to support this purpose. I think this means that two very significant principles are becoming recognized. One is aesthetic: that government has a responsibility to safeguard important scenic resources; the other is practical: that flood plains are excellent and low-cost sties for nature and recreation, and on the other hand are dangerous and extravagantly costly sites for development, after all the expenses of protection are reckoned.

We have made environmental education our business in Glen Helen, and are greatly relieved to realize that at long last we are but one of many centers of environmental education. ▪

A novel Montana venture in environmental education.

THE FALLS CREEK PROJECT

Meridan Bennett

THE FALLS Creek (Montana) Project is an attempt to create new concepts and methods for environmental education. Like many another new venture today, it is an alternative to the existing education system. Its threefold objective is to challenge students to discover themselves, to create an ecological conscience in them, and to build skills for action.

By the end of 1970, the Project's first year, it had involved high school students and teachers from all parts of the United States. In environments ranging from the pristine Bob Marshall Wilderness in Montana to the inner-city ghetto, participants learn to measure and understand specific environmental conditions and to become skilled in presenting the evidence to other people. They also move directly into exploration of the conflicts between their own attitudes and the needs of a healthy environment. The Falls Creek Project also trains its participants to create a human community in order to inaugurate action. Under the sponsorship of the Falls Creek Environmental Education Foundation, the Project sees itself not only as a way to change behavior and attitudes in students, but also a kind of research and development for the public schools.

NEEDED: LIVING WITH LEARNING

Man's stewardship over the environment (which we must accept as our only real choice in 1970) has increasingly produced uniformity rather than diversity. Monocultures, including the educational monoculture of the Dick and Jane reader, have become the standard. Thus, when the concept "environment" penetrates the educational system, it becomes "conservation" and then, too frequently, it is made an elective course and forgotten altogether along with a lot of other nice, nostalgic things like Latin and good manners in children. Eduaction, which tends to hallow the past at the expense of adapting to survival needs, has failed to create in us an awareness of our vulnerability in the ecosystem. Where once such vulnerability was well understood, modern man has become easy prey to schooling which separates intellect from value, thinking from feeling, living from learning, and work from study. Education badly needs new models for reversing this process—for reintegrating living and learning so as to create an ecological conscience in man.

On top of the foregoing challenges to education is the fact that in our country the most vital environmental decisions are being made increasingly by city people. It is terrifying to realize that tomorrow's stewards of the environment in the United States (and therefore the world, since we grandiosely out-consume and out-pollute our nearest competitors) will have little native experience of the whole ring of life, of which we humans are only one highly vulnerable part.

A city politician with whom I once discussed zoning believed that he should work to make his city into a collection of special-use areas (banks here, low-income housing there, rich people on the hill, and so forth). I was arguing for a revision of zoning practices so the system of rewards and punishment would create maximum diversity in all areas of the city. "You mean," he stammered, shocked, "you'd let a $10,000 house be built next to my $40,000 one? Never !

This same penchant for creating monocultures has resulted in clear-cut forests, King Cotton, and sugar cane colonies—and much human misery and destruction of life. In short, the much—touted crisis of relevance in education appears to be in part, at least, a lack of environmental concern in our formal learning systems.Thus, kicking the war habit and rewriting corporate tax law are just as much environmental concerns as saving grizzly bears and cleaning up the Mississippi. Clearly, we need to discover that "the environment" begins within us, not at the edge of the forest.

It goes without saying that traditional education has failed to create an ecological conscience inWesternman; however, some non-school structures of traditional education (such as boy scouts, church, student conservation, role-modeling, and exhortation by parents) can be changed to accomodate the new need.Likewise, higher education, and particularly research, are very slowly being changed to make the fruits of cerebration avail-

Meridan Bennett, of Missoula, Montana, writes and lectures on social change. He is a member of the Board of Directors of the Falls Creek Project, and is the author with David Hapgood, of Agents of Change.

able to the task of survival. There is an immense need, however, for people who know how to make the needed changes within traditional structures.

Lack of emotional content in education has caused a rapid explosion of new learning methods: the old-fashioned student bull session became a T-group, which spawned encounters, sensitivity training, and "feelie" groups. Today even staid corporations nervously experiment with OD (organization development) methods, including ways to make their executives more sensitive to each other. However, from these innovations, the moral responsibility to act—conscience—seldom springs directly forth to aid the badly beleaguered environment.

Finally, somewhere at the root of the relevance crisis in education is that disturbing, unmanageable grounds well from the young (and the poor and the ethnic minorities) demanding participation in running their own affairs. Self determination, it is called, a concept absurdly contradictory yet fundamental to the life process. The professionals are inclined to say, "You can't put the inmates in charge of the asylum. Leave running the schools to people who know how." The clients of the system, however, are pointing the finger back at the educators and saying, "It's you who are crazy"

THE ALTERNATIVE

On the theory that the best portion of education is nothing more than some planned experiences, the Falls Creek Project set about devising as many such experiences as it could, leaving it to the people involved to choose. Out of a number or programs being projected for the next 5 years by the Falls Creek Environmental Education Foundation, the one getting the most attention in the first year was a basic environmental awareness program, a $4\frac{1}{2}$—week course being offered twice during the summer to high school age students.

Each environmental awareness program takes fifteen students from all over the country. It starts with a mixture of hikes and rap sessions. The staff presents the students with a statement of the project's purposes and asks them to become a responsible community dedicated to achieving that purpose. At the same time, the goals of the students themselves are discovered, often confronting those of the project, in an intensive encounter training session, called attitudinal skills training.

The place is the Swan River Valley of western Montana. Most of the students have never been on the edge of wilderness before. Basic needs of plants and animals (including the students) come to the forefront quickly: air, water, food, shelter, space, reproduction, sex. They soon discover that fundamental to becoming aware of one's self and one's environs is the ability to perceive: touch, taste, see, or hear, or some combination of these. Studying deer and birds and plants, and themselves as well, helps them come to value a wide variety of perceptual aids, which they learn to use. The second week they are offered increasingly far-ranging experiences during which they can discover the natural laws that limit or perpetuate natural biotic communities as well as their own. The third week sees participants pushing outward into settled rural areas to discover how the same natural laws influence larger human populations; at the same time, judicial law is contrasted with natural law to illuminate

where conflict lies. In the fourth week the group moves down through the Columbia River drainage to the urban centers of Portland and Seattle, where students conduct action research to determine what people think about their own problems and what steps they are going to take to solve them. After this intensive urban plunge, the students return to the Swan River valley for the final 4 days of the program to reexamine their own attitudes toward the environment, and to plan an action program for themselves once they get back to their home communities. They are helped by a communications seminar to find alternative ways of presenting themselves to parents, teachers, and friends.

Out of the tension of making group decisions (involving both students and staff) on how to meet the challenge of the foregoing structure, a community begins to form. The new community must meet outside challenges as well—having to do with acceptance by the people who live in the Swan Valley. In this process of building a social group, outsiders are welcome provided they are willing to be participants as well as observers. Thus, everyone begins to assume responsibility for both successes and failures. The process is made intentional by periodic encounters involving both staff and students.

As this is written, only one cycle of the environmental awareness program has been completed. Already, however, it is evident that students are capable of rising to a high level of concern for their actions in a community of religious, rural people who have little experience of ethnic minorities and urban behavior. The group which has just finished voluntarily cleaned itself of drugs. The action came shortly after the staff described how the whole future of the project would be endangered by drug use.

Other programs are planned by the Falls Creek Project: an 8-week action learning experience in ongoing action projects (open to graduates of the environmental awareness program); 2 to 3 day seminars to be incorporated in regular school curriculum presenting concepts of wildlife and human ecology. There will also be wilderness survival courses, an oceanographic project, an Indian reservation project, and travel projects designed to build environmental awareness in such diverse locations as Alaska, Africa, and the prairies of the American west.

The Falls Creek Project was devised and put together by Geoffrey Foote, a wildlife researcher and former high school teacher, his wife, Kathie, Todd Schlapfer, an ecology student, Penny Thompson, a skilled group trainer, and a somewhat heterodox board of directors (scientists, professional people, educators, and businessmen) who put themselves through many of the steps described above before students were selected for the first cycle.

PUTTING IT ALL TOGETHER

The funding program of the Project (entirely nongovernmental so far) is aimed at making the various activities of the Foundation open to any student or teacher who qualifies, regardless of ability to pay. During the next 2 years 560 students and teachers will attend the programs, according to present plans. Of this number, 60 will have completed the basic $4\frac{1}{2}$—week environmental awareness program.

The Project's staff and directors have concentrated on eight regions of the United States for initial selection of students; the purpose of broad geographical representation is consistent with the principle of diversity. Students from north, south, east, and west —from the urban ghettoes and the golden ghettoes in the suburbs, high achievers and drop-outs—were chosen to attend. Selection for the first year was done by interview alone, with a personal fact sheet being kept on each potential participant but no formal application blank or letter of recommendation. The directors of the Foundation felt that diversity of outlook and skills would be a crucial factor in creating a learning environment in which participants take responsibility for teaching each other as well as for learning. Staff and board members did all the selection interviews. They also presented informational programs in different parts of the country to explain the project. Beyond this contact, it is expected that the nucleus of students who have been through the first summer's awareness program will create an "induction" system to help select the second year's participants — a process which will develop and test, over the course of a whole school year, students' motivation in advance of their involvement with Falls Creek.

There is another dimension to the Falls Creek Project: a component designed to mesh this alternative educational experiment with the public schools. Whenever a staff or board member travels to a locality to interview students he deliberately searches out as many teachers and school administrators as he can, putting them on the follow-up list and taking seriously any expression of interest on their part. At the same time parents and friends of aspirants are urged to get together not only to support the Project but also, along with their children and the schools, to create environmental action projects in their own community (or to strengthen already existing ones). For example, several variants of the Falls Creek Project are already being planned in communities from which students have been selected. Thus, plugged into the system, and riding the crest of the environmental crusades popularity, the Falls Creek Project has already been able to create some joining of interests between old and young, between school and community.

MONITORING THE PROJECT

By involving state and federal school officials, as well as by seeking a heavy proportion of private funding, the Project has got a lot of people looking over its shoulder besides the local residents of the Swan Valley. It is actively seeking interested participant-observers.

The Project intends to measure its progress by frequent staff-student evaluations to determine what happened, what went wrong, how the participants felt about the experience. In addition, the following types of ongoing research will keep tabs on certain measures of change in students:

1. The growth of a communications network among former participants relating to environmental concerns;

2. The involvement of ex-students in inducting and pre-training the following year's candidates for the environmental awareness program;

3. Increased involvement of students' families and friends in environmental concerns (in other words, creating, not breaking communications links);

4. Participation of ex-students in running the Falls Creek Project or in creating and operating new environmental education centers;

5. Involvement of ex-students in further ecological action.

Staff output will also be measured in several specific ways:

1. The extent to which a community grows closely tied to a purpose, as against the mere creation of an environmental Alice's Restaurant;

2. Case studies of staff interaction with other teachers in the field;

3. Evaluations of participants passing through the environmental awareness program, and the staff's ability to create new educational experiences;

4. The depth of staff involvement with supporters of the Project in the various areas of the country from which students originate;

5. The extent to which staff challenges new groups and individuals to examine the Falls Creek Project's concept of personal involvement in environmental issues.

The question of the Project's growth has not yet been tackled. Right now there is a strong feeling that a pilot program ought not to put the pilot ashore too soon—that crash-basis expansion too frequently does just that: crash. At present the Project is looking for close personal involvement among participants and a proliferation of the concepts in regional centers rather than at Falls Creek. It will be very important to keep track of such alternative education: will it starve for funds and die—or worse, get fat and fuse into a new bureaucratic empire? Will it wither away once its value has been transferred to other schools, or to the people themselves? ■

VI *Adult Education for Ecological Action*

THE WORD *ecology* has been lying in the dictionary for some 100 years, but it has been only recently that the term has begun to flit about in everybody's vocabulary, like a bat emerging suddenly from a cave into bright sunlight. Just exactly what does the word *mean*? What *is* ecology? What does it *do*? What can *I* do with *it*? Is it one of those complex things that only a scientist can really understand and employ, or is it something within the ken of the average person? Well, there are all sorts of approaches to ecology, because e c o l o g y is a very rich word; that is, we can put it to many uses. Like the celebrated committee of blind m e n examining an e l-ephant, we can come up with all sorts of answers to our questions about ecology.

From one point of view, we can define ecology scientifically as "the study of the interrelations of organisms and their environments." This is the classic way the term is used in college catalogs, to distinguish ecology from other basic divisions of biology like physiology, embryology, and so on. In this regard, it may be helpful for us to note that ecology is a word we derived from the Greek root "oikos," meaning "house." So ecology is concerned literally with "houses," or more broadly, "surroundings," as opposed to cells or organs or individual organisms themselves. Perhaps the best synonym for this sense of the term ecology is: "the s c i e n c e of community," Odum says.

Viewed a little more broadly, ecology is not simply the study *of* something; it *is* that t h i n g. In other words, the word refers in a grander sense to the makeup and operations of the living world, to "t h e structure and function of nature," including man himself. Or we can use the term to refer to a property of a *piece* of nature, like a lake or a covey of quail. By this we mean the whole complex of living conditions of a body of water or a group of birds. So we can speak of "the ecology" of a park, or a walleyed pike, and so on. It used to be that we applied this ecology concept only to living organisms in "nature." In more recent years, w e u s e t h e term in connection with *any* structure or organization. So we can speak of the ecology of a suburb, or of a labor union, or of the conservation movement itself—meaning, still, the *relationship* between an "organism" and its environment.

And thus, we come to the more philosophical meaning of ecology. In its broadest s e n s e it is *a way of looking at things*—a viewpoint that sees not the things themselves so much as their connections with other things. So it is a concern with processes—with the myriad of mechanisms that make up the web of life of whatever it is we are looking at. In other words, in an ecological look at an oak woodlot, for example, we concentrate on the spaces *between* the trees, spaces that are actually filled with all sorts of mechanical and chemical operations, or processes. What is more, in this eyeball shift from *thing* to *process*, we recognize that the human observer himself is an integral part of the picture. So ecology really becomes a way of looking at "things" from the inside out, rather than from the outside in.

Who, then, is an ecologist? Well, obviously, a modern ecologist can be a scientist, although not all scientists are ecologists by any means, not even all those who carry "ecology cards." Some "ecological" pundits are so concerned with bits and pieces of nature that they literally do not see the forest for the trees. Other professors of ecology, on the other hand, are today's leading representatives of real ecological thinking. But so are some politicians and some English professors—those who see that everything is connected to everything else.

Prehistoric man was a superb ecologist. He could not run fast enough to escape his enemies; if caught, his teeth and claws were small protection. So he had to become a student of his relationship to the veldt. Peering from his hiding place in the bushes around a clearing or from the opening of his cave, his science w a s the practical kind. His laboratory was the place he lived; the success of his observations could be measured by the fact that he made it through the night—or didn't. So, today, an ecologist can be simply anybody who appreciates the 2-way-street relations with his environment and with all of life everywhere. He is the hunter who knows that you look for whitetails not on a prairie but along the edge of a forest. He is the fisherman who understands why DDT sprayed on a carrot patch can affect the eating quality of lake trout caught miles away. She is the housewife who sees the connection between her automobile engine and air pollution.

We give this sense of interlocking community the term *ecological awareness* —an awareness that the community to which each of us belongs includes soil, waters, plants, animals—and p e o p l e. Then, if we h a v e a n *ecological conscience* as well as ecological awareness, we know that an action is *right* only if it tends to protect the "health" of our man-land community; that is, its integrity, stability, and beauty–and we act accordingly, regardless of what may be momentarily convenient or profitable. So what we used to call "conservation" becomes *applied ecology* –the ethics that should govern the relations between humans and the living landscape, the "resistance movement" that challenges anybody's right to pollute or over-populate the environment.

In a nutshell, then, while there are a number of approaches to the use of the term *ecology*, when we "take all the feathers off of it," as the saying goes, ecology is a way of looking at our world that says to us: "I am a part of my environment, and my environment is a part of me."

Out of such ABC's of ecology has come a new set of tenets or beliefs, held increasingly by the youth of the country particularly. Grady Clay calls these new principles *eco-logic*. They can be summarized as follows:

1. Everything is connected to everything else. War in Indochina is a part of the Indiana ecosystem.

2. The earth is a delicate, closed life-support system that cannot tolerate unlimited growth and its wastes. Nothing can expand forever, and nothing ever really goes away.

3. All environments have a carrying capacity, a ceiling which, like bank credit, cannot be exceeded without dire penalty.

4. Some environments are inviolable and must not be altered by man.

5. The quality of life is more crucial than the quantity of things produced. The question is *how* we survive, not mere survival.

6. For the environment to survive, society as a whole must adopt constraints thay may seem radical. We have met the enemy and he is us.

In short, growing numbers of Americans now see their environment as a limited resource. They know that all environment is subject to man's influence, as well as the other way around. They see all land, water, and air as invested with the public interest. They believe the quality of the environment should no longer be left to whomever happens to own a piece of it. They are determined to have an increasing voice in decisions about their environment. And that voice will become increasingly strident.

This is the ultimate in ecology–the translation of esthetic feelings and scientific knowledge into political action–*eco-tactics*. It is this dimension of education-for-action that so distinguishes environmental education, particularly at the level of adult education. We conclude this book with a look at emerging principles and experimental approaches in adult education for environmental action.■

"It is correct to give adult education the first priority."

INFORMED FORCES FOR ENVIRONMENTAL QUALITY

Frederick   Sargent   II

THERE HAS been much recent attention given to the fact that man's behavior and his behavioral products have given rise to a deterioration in the quality of the environment. As a consequence man's perception of the resources of his environment has begun to change. He is coming to realize that he faces a crisis of unprecedented dimensions, unprecedented for that crisis threatens the very survival of the human species. In view of this greater ecological sensitivity, Theobold (6) emphasizes, "It is no longer sufficient to argue that a person 'meant well' when his intervention in a personal or social or ecological situation worsened rather than improved the situation. Today it is necessary to possess information, knowledge and widsom before acquiring the right to interfere."

INADVERTENT DETERIORATION

That the quality of the environment is deteriorating, few would dispute. This environmental condition has been created by man. He brought it about before he fully realized the implications of his impact. Those changes—he called them inadvertent—seem to have been motivated by a religious viewpoint which held that the bountifulness of the environment was for him to draw upon and to utilize in any way he desired (7). That the bountifulness of the environment was exhaustible or that biological productivity might be disrupted does not seem to have been a serious consideration. Rather suddenly it became evident to him that his actions were deleterious. He discovered, for example, that there was insufficient water to fulfill the diverse and heavy demands placed upon it by industrial processes, power generating facilities, sanitary systems, irrigation, and human requirements. Chemical pollution, thermal pollution, and eutrophication suddenly loomed as problems of staggering proportions. The alternative use of the atmosphere for waste disposal led to air pollution and showed him that vast as the earth's air resources were they were limited and subject to measurable

alterations. Because biological productivity could be enhanced in managed ecosystems by fertilizers and biocides, their application was expanded. Then it became clear that excessive use of fertilizers contributed to eutrophication, and that biocides had effects on the biosphere far beyond their point of application.

These uses of the resources of the environment had not been planned as part of a soundly based program of resource management. They were undertaken by particular groups whose concerns and goals were immediate and parochial. When it became clear that such schemes were leading to a depletion of resources and a deterioration of the environment, there arose the need for a strategy to conserve resources and restore the quality of environment.

CONSCIOUS INTERVENTION

When it was realized that the need for important resources such as water would exceed the naturally available supply, it occurred to some that by conscious intervention in environmental processes, they might be manipulated to increase their yield for the welfare of man. The quest for water, for example, has motivated man to explore the feasibility of extracting fresh water from the sea and to seek ways of modifying the weather. Modest success has spurred him to undertake more ambitious experiments. Plans to modify the weather, however, are being formulated at a time when it is becoming evident that atmospheric pollution from technological wastes has set in motion alterations of weather the consequences of which can now only be dimly perceived (3). That man plans to engineer his environment makes all the more compelling the need for a long range strategy for managing its resources.

Whether we deal with restoring the quality of environment or with engineering the environment, the

An MD, Dr. Sargent is Dean; Professor of Human Ecology, College of Environmental Sciences, University of Wisconsin-Green Bay, Green Bay, Wisconsin. He is a Fellow, American Public Health Association, and a Fellow, Royal Society of Health. This paper first appeared in the mimeographed <u>Proceedings</u> of a Conference on Informed Forces for Environmental Quality, Green Bay, Wisconsin, March 28-29, 1968.

fundamental issue for a strategy of resources management is environmental quality criteria. These criteria must be framed within the context of an acceptable set of concepts about the environment and the relations of organisms to that environment. For these reasons the criteria must be developed in ecological perspective.

ECOLOGICAL CONCEPTS

In the course of evolution an inseparable bond developed between organisms and environment. As the environment changed, the organisms adjusted and adapted. This bond is conceptualized in the term ecosystem. This system exhibits metabolism and regulation. The metabolism of the ecosystem appears as complex transactional flows of materials such as water, carbon, nitrogen, and so on from the environment through an hierarchy of organisms and back to the environment. The energy that drives this system is solar energy captured in photosynthesis in the green plants. By these metabolic flows the organisms condition their environment and continually recycle detritus deriving from excreta and dead bodies. For example, atmospheric carbon dioxide is maintained through its consumption in photosynthesis. Atmospheric oxygen is maintained through its release in photosynthesis. Regulation in the ecosystem is exhibited in the control of population and in the interactions among organisms and among species.

The organisms of the ecosystem are capable of making adaptations to environments. Across the long span of geological time, these plants and animals have experienced wide environmental changes. The particular organismic composition of this system has varied from epoch to epoch, and the organisms that have survived down to the present represent organisms that have made successful adaptations. It must be emphasized that these adaptations are past-oriented. They reflect the evolutionary experience of the species. They provide no assurance that novel and suddenly different environments will be successfully accommodated.

The dependence of environment on organism, the dependence of organism upon environment, the capability of organismic adaptation to environmental change, all constitute fitness of the ecosystem (5). By this concept we mean that organisms are fit for their environment and that environment is fit for supporting organisms. There is a uniqueness about this fitness. It was first lucidly described by L.J. Henderson in his classical Fitness of the Environment.

ENVIRONMENTAL QUALITY CRITERIA

These concepts provide useful bases for the formulation of environmental quality criteria. In the first place, there is need to evaluate the magnitude of the deterioration for the complex transactional flows in the ecosystem, and the consequences of this deterioration for human welfare. In the second place, there is need to develop quantitative knowledge about the dynamics of the ecosystem, to guide man's drive to engineer an environment that will fulfill his needs and requirements. The criteria would constitute baselines for comprehensive ecological analyses and investigations and guidelines for rational programs of environmental regulation by man.

Consider for a moment some of the problems of this ecological crisis in the context of the concept of fitness of the ecosystem.

ADAPTIVE CAPACITY OF ORGANISMS

First, there is the problem of organismic adaptation. The adaptive capacity of organisms must be judged in perspective of a geologic time scale. Phenotypic plasticity, within limits set by the genotype, of course, provides for adjustments to more rapid changes. However, the adaptive capacity is past oriented and does not assure success in novel environments. In the case of man, there is some evidence that he can adapt to environments never before experienced. For example, the Bantu mine gold at 12,000 feet below the surface where the prevailing temperatures are 32-34° C and the atmosphere is almost saturated with water vapor. There is also some evidence of human adaptation to air pollutants, notably carbon monoxide. Evidence such as this suggests that man may be able to endure some environmental deterioration. The perplexing question, however, is one of time. The changes that he is now effecting are proceeding at such a pace that accommodation to them may not be within his norm of reaction. To this question we simply do not know the answer. In an evolutionary sense, selection serves as an adaptive mechanism, but now there is no time for selection to act. Thus we must probe deeper into the range of man's adaptive capacity.

Within the biosphere there are some curious problems that arise from differential adaptability of organisms within a food chain (4). Several species of important fodder plants have made a successful adaptation to high concentrations of fluoride in the soil. The fluoride is bound in these plants as monofluoroacetate. When these plants are consumed by cattle, death rapidly follows. The monofluoroacetate blocks the Kreb's cycle and large amounts of fluorocitrate rapidly accumulate. Citrate intoxication is the cause of death. The accumulation of citrate under these circumstances has been called the "lethal synthesis." The ecological implications of this differential adaptability within the biosphere are clear. Such facts must be carefully noted in evaluating the dimensions and consequences of environmental deterioration.

ESSENTIAL LINKS IN ECOSYSTEM

Second, there is the question of essential links in the transactional metabolic flows of the ecosystem. The fitness of the ecosystem stems from the continuing flow of materials from environment as detritus. Energy captured in photosynthesis drives the entire system. Continuing receipt of this energy by the green plant is essential for the operation of the system for energy is finally dissipated as heat. The deterioration of the environment from air pollution has set in motion atmospheric alterations that threaten to disrupt this flow of energy (4). Man's detritus has begun to accumulate faster than it can be recycled. The concentration of particulates and aerosols in the air is mounting. At lower levels of the troposphere these derive from industrial and automotive wastes. At upper levels they derive from jet airplanes. Atmospheric turbidity is increasing. Haziness, cloudiness, and contrails evolving into cirrus clouds provide visible evidence of this trend. The consequence may be a general atmospheric cooling due to increasing reflection of solar energy. If these trends continue, there may be a critical reduction in energy input to the ecosystem. What constitutes a "critical reduction" is not known.

Another constituent of this atmospheric detritus complicates the ecological evaluation of the current condition of the environment. Atmospheric carbon dioxide is increasing. By virtue of its greenhouse effect, the carbon dioxide may cause the temperature of the atmosphere to rise. If the present discharges of carbon dioxide released from the consumption of fossil fuels continue, some authorities predict that by the year 2000 the mean global temperature will have risen 3-4° C. Such a heating would have widespread terrestrial effects. For example, one can foresee melting of glaciers, rising levels of the oceans, and inundation of cities.

To evaluate the consequences of the deterioration of the environment one must quantify the transactional flows in the ecosystem and identify the essential transactional links. Certainly the green plant is one such important link. While the direct effect of environmental pollution on human health is a matter of great concern, we cannot overlook the indirect effects. To fulfill his nutritional needs and requirements, man depends upon the biological productivity of the ecosystem. If this productivity is disrupted, man may suffer more indirectly than directly. For this reason environmental quality criteria must be formulated for all organisms of the biosphere, not just man.

MULTIPLE USES OF THE LANDSCAPE

Third, there is the problem of multiple uses of the landscape. There is a finite landscape, and the impact of human activities has been felt on most of it. To fulfill his needs and requirements he has increasingly bulldozed, stripped, and plowed the land. To set up communication networks, he has crossed the land with highways and railroads. To provide for recreation he has invaded what wild areas remain. His impact has caused the extinction of many species and has led to the confinement of other species to smaller and smaller natural areas. The movement of species from one wild area to another has been increasingly impeded by barriers—the farm, city, highway. The net result has been to reduce the space occupied by wild genes and to block the flow of wild genes. When viewed in terms of the narrow food base that man now has in the form of domesticated plants and animals, this trend has serious implications. A reserve of wild genes is a precious resource. It is a source of genes to invigorate domesticates. It is a source of entirely new domesticates that may someday be needed by man. The minimum space required to maintain wild gene pools is not known. The impact of the landscape barriers on the flow of wild genes is not known. Indeed the ecological impact of multiple uses of the landscape is not known. The study of what Odum calls landscape ecology thus becomes an important focus for the environmental sciences.

AN EDUCATIONAL PROGRAM IN ENVIRONMENTAL SCIENCES

What we have been discussing is the need to formulate a strategy for resource management. This strategy involved developing a deeper understanding of the qualities of the environment so that it may continue to provide for human needs and requirements, developing quantitative knowledge of the transactions of the ecosystem so that the system may be modeled and the consequences of particular manipulations anticipated before they are attempted, and developing rational policies for utilizing the natural biological productivity for human welfare. The formulation of such strategy requires a consortium of university, industry, government, and public. The formulation of a strategy for resource management is a central objective of the program of the College of Environmental Sciences, UW-Green Bay.

In implementing this objective the faculty of this College will engage in education, in research, and in service to the community in the field of the environmental sciences. It is the service aspects of the College program that I wish to emphasize here.

The deterioration of the environment is but one symptom of the ecological crisis. This crisis has global dimensions. It is not a local problem; it concerns all men. Indeed, the human species is the population at risk in this crisis. Consequently all men must be made to understand the problems and the implications of non-solution. The ecological awareness and perception of man must be sharpened and the ecological comprehension deepened. Nowadays there is too much public indifference and apathy on these matters. The problems do not seem to have local implications; the problems are those of someone else. Why don't "they" do something about the problems? Here "they" usually refers to some governmental agency, scientific experts, industry, and the like. It is my considered opinion that these problems will not be solved until all of us become involved, each in our own way, each having some understanding of the nature of the crisis. It is for reasons such as these that I suggest the solution of these problems involves a consortium. The implication, of course, in implementing their solution may well mean a rather considerable change in our way of life. I suggest, however, that there is no ready alternative.

What can a partnership between the university and the community accomplish in this context? Several recommendations were made by Working Group VI for "A New Agenda for the Church in Mission" (1).

"Furnish trained ecologists to interpret field biology and ecology to interested citizens, such as vacationing families at appropriate locations." To implement this recommendation demonstration units might be developed and moved among the recreational areas of northeastern Wisconsin. These units could serve to expand the ecological awareness of vacationers by showing them just how man's impact was acting on an area apparently far removed from places where environmental deterioration was most publicized. For example, how many vacationers realize that their outboard motors are most inefficient? Some 10-30 percent of the gasoline these motors consume passes directly into the lake or stream to pollute the water with raw gasoline.

"Urge mass media to introduce conservation conscience and land ethics in their programs and advertising." As a public service the mass media devote space and time to ecological problems, but the space and time are neither adequate nor prime. To be effective the presentations must be timely, continuing, and show evidence of progress at the level of the community.

"Offer short courses and clinics on ecology to conventions of service clubs, churches, banks, and insurance companies, city and county managers, and political leaders." Through these short courses and clinics the ecological awareness of local leaders could be increased. The pay-off would be more ecologically rational urban planning and legislative action.

These action programs for education aim at the adults of the community. Although the important role of the younger members must not be overlooked, the emphasis on adult education is appropriate. The pace of environmental deterioration is accelerating. There is an urgency to initiate remedial programs. The decisions made in the next two or three decades may well spell man's destiny. For these decisions to be rational and successful, it is, therefore, correct to give adult education the first priority.

The Working Group, however, made no recommendations about educational programs for young people. In spite of the urgency of the present ecological crisis, I think that it is important that ecological concepts and experience be introduced into the programs of the local grade and high schools. Here the objective should not be to begin teaching ecologists. Rather it should aim to enhance awareness and understanding of these young people regarding the concept of the ecosystem and the meaning of natural resources and their usefulness of human welfare. They should come to appreciate the variety of landscapes and the diversity of their uses, the significance of their preservation, and the consequences of their misuse. I am pleased to note that the Board of Education of Green Bay has just such a plan in mind. We at the University intend to work closely with teachers in the schools carrying out their plan.

EPILOGUE

Man is the agent of this ecological crisis. Because of it he is at risk. He must develop a strategy for coping with the crisis. The strategy involves first recognizing the nature and dimensions of the

problem and then taking decisive steps that will maximize the well being and minimize the hazards to the survival of human populations. Because the problems of the deteriorating environment are global rather than local, they must be perceived and understood by all people and the people must agree to be involved in the decision-making process. Because the problems are complex their solution will involve a working consortium of government, industry, univeristy, and public. The solution cannot be a return to an earlier stage of human history. The direction of time's arrow is irreversible. The solutions would seem to lie rather in improving the efficiency of use of energy, in learning ways to more completely recycle wastes into the dynamics and adaptability of the ecosystem so that realistic goals can be set for regulating the quality of the environment. Man indeed now holds his destiny in his own hands. Whatever the strategy he adopts, there will be profound changes in his way of life.

REFERENCES

1. Hall, C. P., Human Values and Advancing Technology (New York: Friendship Press, 1967).

2. Henderson, L. J., The Fitness of the Environment (Boston: Beacon Press, Inc., 1958).

3. Sargent, F. II, "A Dangerous Game: Taming the Weather," Bulletin, American Meteorological Society, 48:452-458, 1967a.

4. Sargent, F. II, "Adaptive Strategy for Air Pollution," Bio Science, 17:691-697, 1967b.

5. Sargent, F. II and Barr, D. M., "Health and Fitness of the Ecosystem," in The Environment and Man (Hartford, Connecticut: Travelers Research Center, Inc., 1965), pp. 28-46.

6. Theobald, R. "Compassion or Destruction: Our Immediate Choice," in Human Values and Advancing Technology, compiled by C. P. Hall, 1967.

7. White, L. Jr., "The Historical Roots of Ecological Crisis," Science, 155:1203-1207, 1967.

"A force for worldwide environmental improvement."

A CROSS—CULTURAL ENVIRONMENTAL EDUCATION MODEL

Noel P. Ralston and Ivan R. Martin

RAPIDLY SHRINKING distances between inhabitants of space ship "Earth" preclude our planning for long-run environmental improvement as one nation. Planning must include methods for developing worldwide unity of thought in regard to the importance and problems of maintaining a satisfactory habitat. A modular-type educational program devised and developed by American scientists and educators, but adaptable to all cultures and comprehension levels, can be a strong force for worldwide environmental improvement.

ENVIRONMENTAL IMPROVEMENT IN THE LONG RUN

People throughout the world are exhibiting gratifying concern over environmental quality. The U.S. Department of Agriculture has planned and held learned discussions by and between recognized experts in ecology, government, economics, planning, law, education, and other disciplines. UNESCO sponsors similar functions in recognition of worldwide aspects of problems pertaining to influences on the biosphere. Many other equally important sessions have stressed the immediate need for action to reduce the eroding of man's physiological and psychological stature which results from his fouling of his environment.

There is normal and expected resistance to such proposals for change. This comes primarily from the proponents of the status quo who fear the obvious increased dollar cost. This is understandable. To overcome this resistance in the past, some ecologists, conservationists, and preservationists joined together in the standard theme of "What is a dollar for industry compared to a diseased lung or, indeed, to a human life?" This labeled industry people as profit mongers (or worse) and tended to alienate them from the environmental improvement camp.

Recently, there is evidence of divisiveness appearing among those historically working together. The trained ecologists and conservationists (and we include "wise use" in our definition of conservation) are often accused of "infidelity to the cause" by the preservationists.

Obviously, the splintering off of one genuinely concerned group, then another, is an effective deterrent to the unity necessary for effective action. There is only one way to promote unity and, through unity, obtain an improved environment. This is through unity of thought. Each segment of our system must recognize the sincerity of purpose and the problems of the other.

The effectiveness of this approach was demonstrated recently when an irate Chicago citizen heatedly took the editor of a forest industry magazine to task for his position pertaining to the redwoods. The editor accumulated a wealth of factual information from highly regarded authorities in ecology, forest management, and conservation and presented them methodically and logically to the Chicago preservationist who, basically a logical person, then viewed the situation with more light and less heat. Large scale application of the person-to-person educational process is not, of course, feasible. More rapid diffusion processes must be adopted. Without widespread general appreciation of the problems accompanying environmental improvement, we will continue in a series of impasses while our environment deteriorates.

By standing apart and viewing the diversity of attitudes of the people involved, it is obvious that the complexity of their relationships at their present levels of ecological knowledge exceeds the complexity of ecological relationships themselves. How then can we achieve unity of purpose toward a better environment? The only avenue open to us is worldwide appreciation of the ecological system and man's position as an increasingly influential component. A wavering step in this direction would include mutual appreciation of each other's problems that arise as we progress. The theory, for example, that increased product prices will reimburse industry for expensive smoke abatement installations is obviously not sound if that industry is competing for world markets. Perhaps competing industries in other countries are not concerned about air pollution, yet they are selling to the American who refuses to pay

Dr. Ralston is Deputy Director of Science and Education, United States Department of Agriculture. Mr. Martin is Coordinator, Natural Resources Programs, Federal Extension Service, U.S. Department of Agriculture.

the higher local price he has helped create. When the smoke maker and the smoke breather can understand and calmly discuss each other's problems, progress begins, and we have taken a step toward understanding the worldwide nature of the problem. But this step only underlines the potential good that can result from a broader understanding of the interrelationship of all of the components and inhabitants of the biosphere.

A carefully designed groundwork of factual ecological information available to age groups from preschool through postdoctoral levels or the equivalent can significantly increase the general level of knowledge pertaining to this complex but easily understood subject. Understanding can replace differences and establish alliances between groups now holding opposing positions.

With this thought uppermost, a generalized model (See Figure 1) is offered which sets forth the overall concept of the natural resources of the biosphere. The model can be used to systematize and rationalize thinking about man's fundamental requirements and necessities. Man is the hope for fostering a complementary balance within the total ecological system.

This model presents a matrix with the ordinate reflecting the classical organization of study of our natural elements and ecology. It ranges from the very general and simple at the top, to the very specific and complex at the bottom. On the abscissa is a general breakout of people—cultural levels, age of people (the life cycle), and the three significant ways of reaching people of all ages and stages in their respective cultures. Contacting and influencing the minds of people occurs to a great degree through the formal educational system, the informal educational system, and general information.

The intersection of each point on the ordinate and abscissa represents specific interplays and interactions of people in their natural environment. To facilitate their phenotypic response, education is the process. A "module" or "block" of information relating to ecology and to our obvious environmental improvement needs can be designed complete with teaching aids, materials, and homework, (or mass media materials) to appeal to and be understood by people in their natural environment in any age group or comprehension level. To be effective, each module must be developed by professionals in fields with strong ecology links in collaboration with educators knowledgeable in methods effective at a predetermined level. Also, to be effective, careful determination of use of the correct modules must be made by competent local educators or officials. Each module can then contribute, along with reading, 'riting, and 'rithmatic, toward strengthening the total knowledge level of the individual.

Let us see how this system is based on fundamental educational processes. The three basic processes of education, or improvement of mental and physical powers, is to "fill," "drill," and "build." The minds of people must be filled with information, facts, etc. They must have the opportunity for repeated practice, utilizing such information and facts in order to get them set in their minds. Then they can utilize this knowledge in various conditions and

situations. To maximize the fill and drill, it is essential that we create experiences which will provide inductive mechanisms for utilization and instrumentation of systems. People can then use these to build a sequential matrix for their advancement and progress.

Cardinal to education's three basics are four functional processes to improve the mental powers of people. They are (1) absorptive—the ability to observe and apply, (2) retentive—the ability to memorize and recall, (3) reasoning—the ability to analyze, compare, and judge, (4) creative—the ability to visualize, foresee, and generate ideas. Educational experiences which proceed in sequence through all four of these stages of mental growth can lead man toward wise use of the resources of his total ecological system. He will recognize the need for equilibrium within and between the competitive-complementary cycles of nature.

Broad applicability of the model can be maximized by modification of the characteristics on the abscissa to make them apply to the cultural, educational, and economic levels of the involved country, state, parish, or other geographic or political subdivision. This requires the following:

1. Analysis of Each Country—Local educational leaders must make a thorough analysis of their culture, value systems, etc., and specific educational systems. This latter system represents the point of entrance with highest potential for gaining the understanding so much desired.

2. Cost Benefit Analyses—The components of each country's social and political systems must be determined. Appropriate information about rational use and conservation of natural resources can be introduced at that point within each of these systems that will result in the highest degree of understanding and wise use. This is required to provide the best return from the resources invested.

3. Getting Attention of Key Decision Makers—The society of each country is a large-scale organization. The three basic elements for growth of an area can be identified and developed. These three elements are (i) the people who benefit from the utilization of the knowledge taught, (ii) the people in the organizations who are working with the specific areas of knowledge, researching and teaching them, and (iii) key governmental officials at all levels. All three should be made aware of the basic idea that wise use of natural resources will permit people to devote their energies to better endeavors. Key decision makers will quickly realize that such a shift will help their people live a fuller life with greater appreciation of nature, more enjoyment from recreation, and more satisfying use of leisure time. These, in turn, can result in fewer frustrations and a reduction in the number of dissidents and revolutionaries—conditions sought by local power structures.

4. Use of Accepted Channels—Specific modules of educational materials can be developed and introduced into all phases of the educational system, as well as the general information system. It would not be feasible to substitute natural resources

FIGURE 1. GENERALIZED MODEL OF THE OVERALL CONCEPT OF NATURAL RESOURCES OF THE BIOSPHERE

	ILLUSTRATION OF MODEL FOR ADAPTATION TO A COUNTRY'S SITUATION								ILLUSTRATION OF POSSIBLE MODEL FOR U.S.A.							
	TROPICAL*				TEMPERATE*				MEGALOPOLIS				RURAL			
	Effective in Training and Influencing People			Specialized Training for Program Aides**	Effective in Training and Influencing People			Specialized Training for Program Aides**	Effective Methods			Specialized Training for Program Aides**	Effective Methods			Specialized Training for Program Aides**
Comprehension Level	Formal	Informal	General		Formal	Informal	General		Formal	Informal	General		Formal	Informal	General	
A Simple relationships and needs of plants and animals: Land, Air, Water — Preschool		X	X	X		X	X	X			X	X			X	X
B Elementary Specifics pertaining to interdependency — Primary and Intermediate	X	X	X	X	X	X	X	X	X	X	X	X	X	X	X	X
C Natural Resource Appreciation — Junior High School	X	X	X	X	X	X	X	X	X	X	X	X	X	X	X	X
D Conservation and wise use needs and practices — High School	X		X	X	X		X	X	X	X	X	X	X	X	X	X
E Specifics and Planning Conservation and wise use needs and practices — University	X		X	X	X		X	X	X	X	X	X	X	X	X	X
Other		X	X			X	X				X		X	X	X	
F Specifics and Planning Conservation and wise use needs and practices — Graduate	X		X		X		X		X		X		X		X	
Other		X	X			X	X			X	X			X	X	
G More Specifics Broader Planning Conservation — Post PhD	X		X		X		X		X		X		X		X	
Other	X	X	X		X	X	X		X	X	X		X	X	X	

* Substitute here the local conditions or hurdles (literate-nonliterate, ethnic, cultural, religious, etc.) and "X" the blocks offering the best opportunities for success under those conditions.

** "Program Aides" refers to sub-professionals, local leaders, and others who could, through special training, assist professional personnel by working in villages, communities, etc., with local groups, schools, and clubs.

EXAMPLES OF OFFERINGS BASED ON COMPREHENSION LEVELS*

A. Simplified interdependency necessary for continuing existence and enjoyment. Where we get milk and eggs, helpful bugs, cleanliness, helpfulness, pride in accomplishment, consideration, effect of actions and reactions of children's relationships as examples of ecological relationships.)

B. Eggs hatch so we can have more eggs, Oxygen-CO_2 cycles, water cycles, plants need nutrients we supply to use them for food and feed, etc. Enfilter "Dick and Jane" with conservation information. Field trips to see erosion, farms, trees, woods, fish, and wildlife.

C. Organized Clean-Up Fix-Up, identification of obvious air, water, and land pollutants and need for controls; field visits—plants, animals, habitats, needs, relationships, sewers, incinerators, land-fills.

D. Introductory Geology, Biology, Meterology, Genetics, Sociology, Anthropology, Government, etc.

(Continued on next page.)

(Figure 1 — Continued)
    Water Run-off Control, Feed Conversion Ratios, Nitrogen Cycles.

E. Microbiology, Organic and Quantitative Chemistry, production efficiency of soils, climate control. Sociology, Demography, Appreciation of contribution of other related disciplines such as Landscape Architecture and Engineering.

F. Continue specifics and add relationships i. e., Riparian rights, macro-systems, social action processes.

G. Socioeconomic relationships, natural resource planning, city planning (open space, transportation, crowding effects), city and rural zoning principles, politics of river basin development, and appreciation of contribution of all related disciplines.

*   From Figure 1.

----

subject matter for such basics as language and mathematics, but ecological relationships can be used as examples in teaching the basics. Many of the simple stories for children can relate to fundamental ecological relationships. This same process should continue throughout the total range of experiences of young people in informal and general educational programs.

5. Research and Education—Professionals in ecology and related fields can develop organizational arrangements promoting close liaison and rapport between the research and educational staff in ecology and the research and educational staff in education. Such a relationship can be most effective in developing appropriate materials and techniques for teaching ecology to each age level.

6. Formal Educational Programs—In line with items 4 and 5, appropriate educational materials and methods can be developed for enhancing the importance of environmental improvement in the minds of students in each of the grades or levels of the higher education system. This can include college, university, and postdoctoral levels.

7. Informal Educational Programs—There is a definite and growing universal need for an informal educational system (continuing education, adult education, extension, etc.) which relates to the formal educational system, to all levels of government, and to the people in their respective communities. Environmental appreciation can be an important part of such systems presently in use and others as they develop.

8. General Information—The mass media (newspapers, periodicals, books, radio, television, etc.) can most effectively bring to the attention of the people of a country the elements of their environment and the total ecological system in such a way that they can see the need for wise use of natural resources. General information programs are extremely valuable in creating the corporate image and motivating people. These can be so designed that people may not even be aware that they are being educated in wise natural resource use.

9. The Corporate Image and Wise Natural Resource Use—Competitive-complementary cycles exist among the components of the total ecological system. The existence of these cycles must be foremost in the minds of our people. Man is destructive when he devises resources which upset the balance of natural resources. Conversely, man-made resources can help maintain the equilibrium which must exist to support man and his society.

Our forward thinking ecologists, along with concerned educators, can join in developing a powerful force for environmental improvement. The broadly outlined system described here invites further development, modification or replacement by a better system. ∎

"There is need for recognizing the nature and dimensions of the problem and developing new approaches to it."

CONSERVATION THROUGH ADULT EDUCATION

Charles A. Dambach

ALTHOUGH WE have developed many mechanisms such as the free press, conferences, workshops, town meetings, meetings of organizations, public hearings, and the courts for resolving conflicts, it is apparent that many conservation problems are not resolved by these means. There is, I believe, need for improvement of all of these mechanisms and for development of nonpartisan referral systems to which the interested citizen can turn. The report prepared by a group of scholars on the Rampart Dam controversy at the request of a consortium of conservation organizations is an example. In this instance, 15 organizations acting through the Natural Resources Council of America contributed funds to conduct the study. Although all of them are primarily concerned with wildlife and aesthetic resources, there appear to have been no restraints placed upon the investigators. There are other examples. The study and report of the League of Women Voters on Lake Erie and the Citizens Potomac Planning Guide prepared by the Conservation Foundation are objective guides to resolving conservation conflicts.

I believe that scientists and the educational institutions they represent can make a notable contribution by offering their services in organizing and conducting educational programs for adults which keep them informed before controversy sets in, to offer unbiased information when it is needed, and to referee conservation conflicts when appropriate.

Increased opportunity for conducting adult education programs for communities, at least on an experimental basis, is now possible under Title I of the Adult Education Act. Through the medium of television, there is the opportunity of extending adult education from the classroom to the parlors of the nation.

I believe there is a special need for formal adult education programs in which professionals in disciplines which impinge on resource planning and management may learn enough about related fields that better understanding will result and new insights will be gained into the multidisciplinary character of resource problem-solving. The biologists, the economists, the engineers, the geographers, and others concerned are too often at odds on these matters.

The universities, I believe, can make a special contribution in this area. Several have in post-graduate programs, and there have been a number of special resource institutes or seminars offered. There is need for the resource agencies, organizations, and interested foundations to get together with the universities to establish a basis for filling this need.

I want to emphasize that while resolution of conservation conflicts through adult education generally seems to be in a confused state, there are excellent materials and excellent programs. There is need for recognizing the nature and dimensions of the problem and developing new approaches to it. Forces competing for public favor in conservation matters are not likely to alter their approaches. Thus, we need to develop better mechanisms whereby the biases are identified and the basic concepts and facts involved are made clear. Scientists and educators in speaking out on conservation issues through their professional journals, through the mass media, and through participation in formalized adult education programs can contribute significantly to the solutions because of the public respect they enjoy. They need to be encouraged in this effort through support from sources not committed to any resource bias. Support from similar sources is needed to enable unfettered adult education groups dedicated to examination of conservation conflicts to enlarge their efforts. Internal policing of what goes out to the public from "conservation organizations," government agencies, and private business, through impartial review by competent scientists, would be helpful. Finally, mass media, particularly public television, promises a mechanism through which conservation issues can be presented generally with a minimum of bias or with a balance between biases.

There are few clear-cut conflicts in conservation. Resolution of these conflicts thus necessarily involves carefully considered value judgments. There is an obligation by all concerned to give the public decision-maker such judgments. I believe we will come nearest to that goal if everyone concerned with education at all levels strives for the development of a national philosophy which in the words of Irving K. Fox, "feels an inhibition against damaging our physical and biological environment and a responsibility for leaving it better than when he arrived."

Professor Dambach is Director of the School of Natural Resources, the Ohio State University, Columbus. These remarks are taken from a longer paper by the same name which appeared in the September, 1968, BioScience.

"The weak link in our resource management effort is the information function."

NEEDED: CITIZEN CONSERVATIONISTS

Durward L. Allen

AS PROPRIETORS of North America, we have custody of a great freehold. How we handle it will identify us in times ahead. Probably the most exacting demands on our skill and conscience are in dealing with replaceable natural assets, those that can be improved in use through biological processes—soils, waters, forests, ranges, wildlife, and scenic beauties.

Historically, the management of renewable resources has been a threshold of frustration and delay. Accomplishments, often good in themselves, fitted only by chance into any reliable outlook for tomorrow. There has seemed to be no plan at work, nor even a comforting philosophy.

Despite the difficulties, we must invoke what foresight we can in resource use, and in terms of major issues I think we have much to work with. Our context is the field of human, or resource, ecology. This is a developing scientific discipline concerned with relationships of humanity to the total environment. Characteristically, it involves synthesis and generalization. Inevitably it includes conceptual trial and error.

The ecologist is aware of his limitations, but he is learning to distinguish rights from wrongs. I suspect he knows considerably more now than anyone can apply. If this is true, then a weak link in our resource management effort is the information function that should be telling the customers what they need to know. Information people strive with great diligence to sell the conservation idea. But it probably is good for anyone to have an occasional review of premises and a more critical focus on the issues.

To put first things first, what is the objective of our concern with the resource environment? What do we want for mankind now and in the future?

I suppose the only reasonable answer is this: <u>We are after the best possible living standard for every individual.</u> Such a statement identifies a worthy goal but does not define it. How could anyone describe an idealized life pattern for the future? This involves personal attitudes, and for each of us standards are likely to change with time. For my part, I cannot accept a common viewpoint: I doubt that the output and consumption of material goods is a satisfactory measure of living standard. It is a part of our well-being, but there probably are more fundamental things. Surely, good health is the greatest beneficence that modern science has to offer. No doubt a quality existence includes being well fed, well clothed, and well housed; but space and pleasant surroundings must also be high on the list. In social terms, we take for granted all the freedoms that are a part of human dignity. Freedom from work is not one of these.

Resource problems are characteristically a national concern. At local level they frequently are obscured and fragmented by provincial attitudes and politics. It seems right to expect of any government that it consider responsibly the needs of the whole public and use our unmatched technology to plan ahead for human welfare. Surely a century hence is not beyond our limits of responsibility.

Assuming that there is a science of environmental relationships, how does it go about its problem solving? Probably you could not get the same answer from any two people. However, I think there are basic aspects of the population-resources equation on which many thoughtful persons could agree:

First, we are dealing with a strictly limited quantity, the finite earth, its space and raw materials.

To this we apply our atom-age culture, a variable of bewildering complexity that includes our industry,

Dr. Allen is Professor of Wildlife Ecology, Department of Forestry and Conservation, Purdue University, Lafayette, Indiana. He was recently awarded the Wildlife Society's Aldo Leopold Medal for outstanding service in the cause of conservation. This statement is excerpted from his "Natural Resources and the Cult of Expansion" which appeared in the December-January, 1968, <u>The New York State Conservationist</u>.

science, and a l l we do to make resources useful.

Another variable is the number of people who divide the benefits, today's steeply ascending curve of population.

Finally, a living standard is resolved from relationships of the other three. The concept c a n b e represented in this way:

$$\frac{\text{Resources X Culture}}{\text{Population}} = \text{Living Standard}$$

It is common knowledge that over half the earth's inhabitants are perpetually hungry, and that on this continent we have the highest living standard of any major area. The relationships I have cited are inherent in some calculations by sociologist Philip M. Hauser, of the University of Chicago. Hauser states that all the goods and services now available in t h e world would support about half a billion people at our level of living. Yet the total population of this planet now numbers 3. 5 billions!

Since the resource professional is trying to raise living standards, and since he is working w i t h a n earth whose space and raw materials are fixed, it behooves him to consider how many people he is trying to serve. He must be concerned with what is happening to human numbers.

    *   *   *   *

It is unthinkable that we should fail to cope with the population problem in decades ahead. Our only approach is through the birth rate—it must be drastically reduced over most of the world, as we continue to promote good health and prolong life among all peoples. There is reassuring evidence that once a high level of education and material prosperity is attained, a lowered birth rate will tend to be maintained. Hence, such accomplishments will be, in a measure, self-perpetuating.

Today's challenge is to make known at home and abroad the overriding urgency of what must be done. A few far-sighted people have fought on this front for several decades. They deserve an uprising of support that can originate only in North America.

If a downward trend in population could be achieved, the imperative demands of our proliferating e-conomy should ease. This need not be a disaster in any sense. Economists are becoming increasingly interested in the mechanisms that s u c h a situation would involve. Economist-demographer Joseph J. Spengler of Duke University points out that favorable economic trends are not dependent on steadily increasing numbers of people. In effect, a limited population could stimulate demands for goods and services almost indefinitely through better living. Spengler ended an address to the Industrial Conference Board in New York this way:

"In the future, economic growth will depend mainly upon invention, innovation, technical progress. . . . Population growth will probably play an even smaller role than I have assigned it in earlier discussion. It is high time, therefore, that businessmen c e a s e

looking upon the stork as a bird of good omen. "

It goes almost without saying that the best anyone can possibly do in damping the population boom will not be soon enough. Meantime a line is to b e held; there is a program of quality control to be applied with judgment and courage to the human environment. In North America we have great possessions that will cost us little to keep but much to lose.

The most perishable amenities of this world are its open spaces and quietudes, its greenery, pure waters, natural rivers, wetlands, w i l d l i f e, and choice scenery, its dwindling modicum of true wilderness. Substantially, these are what President Johnson has characterized as "natural beauty." Nationally they are the out-of-doors we use for recreation. Locally they may be the charm of the pleasant countryside or well-groomed city.

Since pioneer times this landscaping has graced our inherited estate as a luxury we could afford. Its dollar value is difficult to pin down. It is vulnerable to attrition by piecemeal decisions, which assume that a little more of one thing or a little less on another won't really matter.

This public attitude is an honest one. Our leadership in resource affairs is largely a thin line of mercenaries, where there should be backing in depth by citizen volunteers. Most of today's universities are centers of technology, rather than philosophical thought. The vast majority of young p e o p l e g o through school with no exposure to the biological realities of human existence or the natural world. They assume the duties of citizenship with little u n d e r - standing or feel for the order among living things— a necessary basis for workable attitudes t o w a r d human and resource husbandry.

Holding or salvaging the most fragile values in our environment has become an emergency issue— first in time because the headlong impetus o f o u r makework enterprise has no built-in controls. Our history and success have fostered a certain a r r o - gance toward the native wilderness of our homeland. North Americans are commonly so bemused w i t h the charm of bringing straight lines and square corners to the chaos of nature—our bulldozerkampf— that they have no idea where it should stop. Among choices to be made, it seems essential to dissipate our wasteful momentum in doing more of everything we know how to do, useful or not. In the resolution of values, man's mastery of the earth will pay him greatest tribute when he achieves the forbearance to leave some of it alone.

    *   *   *   *

The way is opening ahead, but the vast bulk o f humanity is not informed. In fact, on this continent the best educated people in the world are bumbling ahead under an expanding economy slogan that still largely ignores space values, fails to distinguish between quantity and quality, and regards overflowing masses of human beings as a consumer base essential to "prosperity. " We still have the hang-on attitude toward land that the "highest use" f o r any acre is to make it yield dollar tribute in the form of something that can be used up and r e p l a c e d.

This is our wastrel era, which people of the future are unlikely to admire. On a different plane, and under a different rationale, it is as much a me-first, dollars-for-today program as was that of the exploiters of the late 19th century. We have conned ourselves into a state of mind whereby it is popular to dignify the "user" and deride the "preservationist." It seems a doubtful hazard that too much of anything is going to be preserved; many things could be over-used.

*   *   *   *

Inevitably we come back to the proposition that in man's future there is to be an ecosystem whose basic relationships will resemble those in the natural world. In our world too, the healthy developments will be toward stability—a state in which input equals output. It is evident that we are going to have population control. The question is how soon, and how much we will have left to work with when it becomes effective. Our science can rise to its potential as the boon and salvation of mankind only when the frantic demands of the population emergency are abated.

As a general guideline, if we are able to muster the control to preserve and improve in reasonable degree the esthetic features and recreational open space of this continent, it is likely that many other aspects of the resource management program will fall into place. As a critical reality, any major accomplishment of this kind will require support by millions of informed citizens; and on that score, the difficulties are increasing.

We have a vital problem of communication. People must be kept in touch with the out-of-doors and conscious of their privileges as owners of it. Our up-to-date conservation story tells of human numbers, quality living, quantities of resources. It describes how we monitor our status and progress by careful inspection of our range. The story will have to be told by spokesmen who know whereof they speak. I have no doubt that all of us who take on this critical information job can be most effective if we hold ourselves keenly aware of a fateful mission—that the message concerns the greatest challenge which mankind has yet had to deal.

Some citizens may be a lot smarter than we think.

EVALUATING A UNIVERSITY EXTENSION CONSERVATION PROGRAM

Bruce T. Wilkins and Richard J. McNeil

A CHANGE in behavior is a major goal of education. Such change will occur only after an individual or group gains new knowledge relating to this behavior. Cooperative Extension educational programs are largely directed toward changing people's behavior in a given situation. Recognizing this as the primary goal, it seems valid to determine if the knowledge of participants in Cooperative Extension programs increases, and, if so, to what degree.

To help answer these questions, New York's Cooperative Extension educational programs on wildlife management were evaluated. Pre- and posttests were administered to persons at three educational meetings, portions of a series held in March and April 1966 (see Table 1).

The meetings in Rochester and Buffalo were part of a series developed for persons owning land in nearby counties for recreational purposes. Each of the programs in the Binghamton series had relevance to developing lands for wildlife. In this series the pretest was administered prior to the first lesson and the posttest was taken at the concluding session, 7 weeks later.

METHODS

A pretest and identical posttest consisting of 25 true and false questions were taken by those at the Rochester and Binghamton meetings. At Buffalo, some of the group received the pretest, the remainder the posttest (four took both). Buffalo and Rochester respondents also provided information on personal characteristics.

The content of the tests included material on wildlife resources and a section on personal characteristics of the respondents.

CHARACTERISTICS OF RESPONDENTS (Buffalo and Rochester)

Occupation

Attendees responding were largely "professional," or "technical or kindred workers," with substantial

TABLE 2

PERCENT OF RESPONDENTS IN DESIGNATED OCCUPATIONAL CLASSES

Occupational Class	Buffalo (N=79)	Rochester (N=30)	Total (N=109)
Professional, technical, or kindred workers	34	47	36
Craftsmen, foremen, and kindred workers	18	10	15
Operative and kindred workers	15	0	11
Retired or student	10	7	9
Housewives	4	13	6
Clerical and kindred workers	5	7	6
Sales workers	6	3	6
Managers, officials, or proprietors	6	3	6
Farmers	1	7	3
Service workers	1	3	2
Total	100	100	100

percentages being "craftsmen, foremen, and kindred workers," or "operative and kindred workers" (see Table 2).

Cooperative Extension Membership

In New York, membership can be taken out in Cooperative Extension Associations at a fee of $5.00 or

TABLE 1

MEETINGS AT WHICH TESTS WERE ADMINISTERED, 1966

Location	Number of participants	Length of total program	Length of wildlife portion of program	Interval between pre- and posttest
Rochester	35	$1\frac{1}{2}$ hours x 4 weeks	$1\frac{1}{2}$ hours	$1\frac{1}{2}$ hours
Buffalo	89	$1\frac{1}{2}$ hours x 3 weeks	30 minutes	$1\frac{1}{2}$ hours
Binghamton	28	2 hours x twice weekly x 3 weeks	most	3 weeks

Drs. Wilkins and McNeil are Assistant Professors in the Department of Conservation, New York State College of Agriculture, Cornell University, Fernow Hall, Ithaca, New York.

TABLE 3

PERCENT OF RESPONDENTS OWNING
SPECIFIED ACREAGE

Acres owned	Buffalo (N=84)	Rochester (N=35)	Total (N=119)
0	7	14	9
1 - 24	29	9	24
25 - 49	11	3	8
50 - 99	20	28	23
100 - 149	17	20	18
150 - 199	5	9	6
200 and over	11	17	12
Total	100	100	100
Mean acres owned	88	111	95

TABLE 4

PERCENT OF RESPONDEES BY YEARS OWNING
A GIVEN PARCEL OF LAND

Years of Ownership	Buffalo (N=74)	Rochester (N=28)
Less than one	0	11
1 - 1.9	11	17
2 - 4.9	35	28
5 - 9.9	14	14
10 - 14.9	19	4
15 - 19.9	5	14
20 - 29.9	14	4
30 - 39.9	3	4
40 or more	0	4
	101	100

TABLE 5

REASONS FOR INTEREST IN GAME ANIMALS

Interest	Percent Indicating Interest	
	Buffalo (N=81)	Rochester (N=30)
Viewing	68	56
Hunting	48	56
Other	6	0

TABLE 6

PERCENT OF RESPONDENTS WHO HAD CARRIED
OUT A SPECIFIED PRACTICE

Practice	Buffalo (N=76)	Rochester (N=27)
Planted Trees	76	89
Planted Shrubs	45	59
Planted Crops	19	41
Stocked Game	9	4

less. In both counties most people in attendance were
not Cooperative Extension members. More of the
Rochester attendees were members (47%) than those
at the Buffalo meeting (18%).

Land Ownership

Those attending the Buffalo and Rochester meetings typically (over 85%) owned some land. Of those

owning land, most owned under 100 acres. The mean
acreage owned by Buffalo attendees was smaller (but
not significantly at the .025 level) than that owned by
the Rochester attendees (see Table 3).

Length of Ownership

Almost half of attendees had owned their land less
than 5 years—most had owned the property for less
than 10 years.

Interest in Wildlife

Interest in game for hunting was greater among
the Rochester group (see Table 5). We know no reason for this difference. One might have anticipated
the reverse situation, as professional, technical, and
kindred workers tend toward lower participation rates
in hunting than do craftsmen or operatives (1:38). The
greater interest in viewing wildlife among the Buffalo
group was accompanied by a greater likelihood of
having a structure on the property (Buffalo 80%,
Rochester 43%).

Management Practices for Wildlife

A higher proportion of the Rochester group had
carried out certain practices which may increase
wildlife populations (see Table 6).

Achievement on Tests

The average score in Rochester and Binghamton
was significantly higher on the posttest than on the
pretest; in Buffalo no change was noted. The changes
in mean scores are shown in Table 7.

In each of the three sessions certain topics upon
which test questions were based were not covered
during the meetings. Dropping these questions (2
in the case of Binghamton, 6 at Rochester, and 11 at
Buffalo) resulted in the scores noted in Table 8.

Performance on Test Items

The proportions responding correctly to individual questions in the tests are shown in Table 9. Three
questions (Questions 11, 16, and 20) were answered
correctly before any teaching was done by over 90
percent of those responding. This was true for each
meeting. An additional eight questions were correctly answered by over 80 percent prior to teaching (Questions 3, 5, 9, 10, 13, 17, 20, and 25). Only
two questions (4 and 19) were answered incorrectly
by more than half of those taking the pretest (except
at Buffalo, where 54 percent responded correctly to
Question 4).

Summing the pretests and posttests from the three
meetings indicated significant knowledge gains (.025
level) for eight questions (Questions 1, 2, 4, 5, 10,
17, 24, and 25). This gain held true at each of the
three meetings. A significant loss of knowledge was
indicated for Questions 7 and 14. This too was consistent at each of the three meetings.

It is difficult to explain the apparent decrease in
understanding for the two questions. We believe that
in both cases the concept was fairly complex but was
only cursorily discussed at the various meetings.
Attendees may have gained only enough knowledge to
recognize the concepts but not to evaluate details of
the questions, thus incorrectly marking "T" for
questions whose wording required an "F" answer.
If the questions had been worded so as to require a

TABLE 7

SCORES ON PRETESTS AND POSTTESTS

County	Maximum possible score	Pretest	Posttest	Percent Increase
Buffalo	25	19. 6 (n=35)	19. 6 (n=58)	0
Rochester	25	18. 8 (n=34)	21. 3 (n=29)	13*
Binghamton	25	18. 4 (n=28)	20. 7 (n=27)	12**

*Statistically significant at . 025 level using one-tail test.
**Statistically significant at . 005 level using one-tail test.

"T" answer, we might have seen a measurable increase in understanding.

DISCUSSION

The Buffalo and Rochester meetings reflect the wide variations existing today between Extension audiences and also indicate certain similarities. Professional workers were most common and few farmers were present. Extension membership was not usual although more common among Rochester attendees. Leaders in Rochester had held meetings of interest to this audience in prior years, and doubtless more of their residents could identify values in belonging to Cooperative Extension. Persons at the meetings were not normally "new" owners, but many had held their land for less than 5 years.

Planting of either crops or shrubs for wildlife had been undertaken by roughly one-half of those attending the Buffalo and Rochester meetings. The higher interest in hunting by Rochester attendees was matched by greater activity in plantings favorable to game animals, particularly planting of crops.

The portions of the three meetings at which tested information was presented varied from 30 minutes within a larger meeting to a 6-evening, 12-hour course.

In all meetings a high proportion of the audience selected correct answers to most questions before the meeting started. This indicated a higher level of knowledge by attendees than we had anticipated. All groups indicated in posttest an increased knowledge in areas to which they were exposed, but those receiving the most information (Binghamton) did not display the greatest proportionate increase in test scores. It is believed this is partially a reflection of the greater time lapse between presentation and posttesting in that instance but may also be due to the higher initial level of knowledge of the Binghamton audience.

Attendees gained knowledge from these meetings. The speakers presenting material could have assumed a higher beginning level of knowledge. Future meetings should reflect this through increased depth of coverage and more sophisticated discussion.

The very small increase in score for the Buffalo audience suggests that 30 minutes is about the minimum length of time which should be scheduled for presenting materials of this sort. A failure to retain knowledge should be guarded against, possibly through distribution of printed material.

These audiences clearly were not the traditional farmer audiences of Agricultural Extension programs. Information on plantings for wildlife, including techniques, would doubtless be well received. Actions appropriate for the early stages in planning and developing a rural property would appeal to a high proportion of future audiences.

The participants reacted favorably to being tested. None objected to the time spent, and many found the experience interesting. Since no names were requested, the respondents did not feel threatened by the possibility of achieving low scores.

The test results were useful in determining levels of knowledge of this type of audience and, therefore, in designing appropriate materials for future presentations. In addition, the results gave a good indication of the effectiveness of teaching of various aspects of the subjects considered. This simple and effective tool should be used more frequently for planning and evaluation of environmental educational programs.

REFERENCES

1. "Outdoor Recreation Resources Review Commission, National Recreation Survey," ORRRC Study Report No. 19, Washington, D. C., 1962, 394 pp.

TABLE 8

MEAN SCORE OF PRETEST AND POSTTEST INCLUDING ONLY QUESTIONS COVERED TO SOME DEGREE IN LESSONS

Location	Maximum possible score	Pretest	Posttest	Percent Increase
Buffalo	14	11. 8 (n=35)	12. 7 (n=58)	8*
Rochester	19	13. 9 (n=34)	16. 3 (n=29)	17**
Binghamton	23	17. 3 (n=28)	19. 5 (n=27)	13***

*Statistically significant at . 01 level using one-tail test.
**Statistically significant at . 005 level using one-tail test.
***Statistically significant at . 025 level using one-tail test.

ENVIRONMENTAL EDUCATION

TABLE 9

PERCENT OF ATTENDEES GIVING CORRECT RESPONSES (AVERAGE OF ALL THREE MEETINGS)

Question Number	Correct Answer	Percent Correct	
		Pretest (N=97)	Posttest (N=114)
1. Ecology expresses the idea of an interdependent group of organisms living in the same environment.	T	79	93*
2. Ecological principles may safely be ignored when solving renewable resource problems.	F	75	89*
3. The process whereby different plant species replace each other in an area until a stable stage exists is called plant succession.	T	88	91
4. It is the final stages of this process which are preferred by our most popular forms of wildlife.	F	39	73*
5. The stable stage of plant growth which finally dominates an area is called climax vegetation.	T	84	97*
6. All energy pyramids owe their existence to the presence of green plants.	T	71	78
7. In the energy flow of the food chain, a pound of clover becomes a pound of rabbit which, in turn, becomes a pound of fox.	F	76	56*
8. Prey species have a higher reproductive rate than their predators.	T	63	60
9. In conservation, "carrying capacity" refers to the number of pounds of game the average hunter kills.	F	86	92
10. Stocking more squirrels will permanently increase the carrying capacity of a woods for squirrels.	F	87	97*
11. The area within which an animal lives and moves is properly called that animal's home range.	T	97	97
12. Sustained yield is the maximum number of animals that can be harvested from a given area for a long period of time.	T	79	80
13. Wildlife numbers are increased by providing more vegetative "edges."	T	89	94
14. A renewable resource is one that will never wear out; will continue for ever.	F	61	43*
15. Wildlife is more productive on land that has rich soil.	T	59	66
16. In our State, wild animals such as rabbits and grouse belong to the landowner.	F	96	97
17. Annual stocking of game is usually not needed in good wildlife areas.	T	84	97*
18. All organisms have the capacity to increase their numbers beyond the point where their environment can support them.	T	77	85
19. Fire is generally detrimental to deer habitat.	F	31	31
20. Good deer habitat includes much brushland, with a mixture of forest, grassland, and other vegetative types.	T	98	100
21. In the usage of a wildlife technician, "wildlife" is defined as the higher, or vertebrate, animals.	T	61	63
22. Virtually everything done positively for game animals benefits other wildlife, too.	T	90	95
23. Planting wildlife shrubs always results in more pheasants.	F	66	68
24. Annual stocking of game is usually the cheapest way to good hunting.	F	76	92*
25. Game populations are best increased by management of vegetation.	T	86	97*

Effective presentation of range ecology to the layman.

A SELF-GUIDING COMMUNITIES APPROACH

Leonard R. Askham

I WILL NOT insult your intelligence by quoting abstracts of current education theory. If you are interested in education, you probably know the basics better than I. Instead, I will show you, through my experiences, a better way of developing self-guiding nature trails.

THE EDGE OF THE CONCRETE

When you design a self-guiding nature trail, you must keep two things in mind. The first is that a nature-trail-user is there to learn; nothing more and nothing less. You are not concerned about what motivated him to participate; that is the psychologist's bag. All you have to remember is that people learn because they like to learn. The second thing to keep in mind is that most of the trail-users are urban orientated recreationists whose lifestyle is firmly fixed to the television set and the automobile. For this recreationist, the edge of the concrete signifies the edge of the wilderness.

THE CHILDREN'S RECREATION SCHOOL

Over the last 2 years, I have been directing a nature study program for the University of California's Children's Recreation School. Three hundred children attend three, 1-hour activities each morning for 5 weeks. All of these children come from upper, middle-class families. In addition to these 300 middle-class children, 40 ghetto children are sponsored by the University so that they may participate in the program. Unlike the middle-class children, these children are so poor that we must find them swimming suits, shoes, and even a sweater on cold mornings. I make this distinction clear so that there will be no mistake in your mind when I make the next statement; there were no differences in the children's reactions on their first nature walk. As far as the children were concerned, they were in a wilderness. The only tie these children had with the real world was their guide, who represented a figure of authority and a symbol of security.

As the program progressed the children began to feel more at home in the woods and were able to exert more of their individual characteristics. Some adapted faster than others and some learned faster than others, but several things became clear. The children had to have a goal, a central theme, a systematic association, and a transition for learning to take place.

The goal or objective was important because the children had to know what they were going to do for the day. They had to have a theme or "big idea" to guide them because taking a walk and looking at plants was not good enough. The theme or "big idea" had to be tied with an association that the children could understand; an association with which they were familiar. The most successful association that I found was a community. The children live in a community, have a community of friends, and the community controls their lives. By starting out each session with this community approach, more progress was made than without it. For example, the children know how many people live in their house or apartment building. They know how many houses or buildings there are in their block. With a few well-placed questions, the children soon develop a concept that the people in their house are a family, that the families living in the apartment building are a community, that this apartment is part of a large community of apartments and families. From here, the transition to biotic families, communities, communities within communities, and finally, an ecosystem is not difficult. A tree easily becomes an apartment full of living families of birds, animals, and insects. A creek becomes a moving highway of life.

All of the children exhibited the same learning progress. When shown a new tree, they had to touch and smell it; they had to tell each other about it. One tree was not enough. The children had to find another tree just like the one they were just shown to see

The author is Education Coordinator for the Botanical Gardens and a graduate student in conservation education, The University of California, Berkeley.

if all of the trees with the same name looked alike. Next, several different trees were found and the process of observing, communicating, and comparing repeated until they had enough information to organize the different trees into groups or families. Sometimes the children would experiment by trying to see if they could match trees and leaves together. The children's favorite questions were "Why does this tree grow here?" and "What good is it?" And always, we tried to find ways in which the information given could be applied to their everyday lives.

RESULTS OF THE CHILDREN'S SCHOOL

Out of these 2 years of work and reflection, five things are apparent to me: (1) that all of these children showed the same, edge-of-concrete skepticism of the woods when the program began, (2) that all of these children needed a single idea or theme for learning to take place, (3) that all of these children went through the same learning stages; observing, communicating, comparing, organizing, experimenting, inferring, and applying, (4) that learning was faster when two or more previously-known facts were associated, and (5) that each child wanted to know how he was doing.

THE UNIVERSITY BOTANICAL GARDEN

The knowledge gained working with these children has been beneficial in developing new education programs for the University of California's Botanical Garden in Berkeley. The Garden's emphasis has recently changed from one of pure research to one of research and education. The Botanical Garden is no longer a museum but a teaching tool and outdoor laboratory for teacher and student. For the local school child, the Garden has become an extension of the classroom.

Drop in tours are developed for children and adults, who do not live close enough to the Garden for weekly or monthly visits. The tours last 1 hour and cover less than a quarter mile. Only a fraction of the Garden can be seen during this time, so tours are divided into sections or areas; the California section, the Australian section, the African section, etc. By knowing that the tours are divided into sections, the teacher can choose the section which best fits into the class sequence. This type of program enables the teacher to prepare the children before the Garden visit and gives her some idea what she can talk about after the visit. Each visit is tailored to fit the needs of the class.

Each tour has a theme—a simple theme which all can understand. During the tour, only four topics, related to the central theme, are discussed. In the California section of the Garden the theme is plant communities. The four topics might include the redwood grove, the successional growth in ponds, the uses for food and medicine by the Indians, and the uses animals find for plants. Each topic is presented the same way for children and adults by systematically combining known relationships to form a new idea.

BOTANICAL GARDEN EVALUATION

An important part of any program is evaluation, and we are evaluating our education programs as we go. Each of our tours is tape recorded so that we can evaluate the program's progress. A small tape recorder, carried over the shoulder of the guide, causes little comment from either children or adults. These tapes enable us to review each session for unanswered questions, repetitive questions, or background comments missed or overlooked by the guide during the tour. Soon, most of the bugs will be worked out of these tours and self-guiding trails put in their place. Audio tapes will be placed in permanent cabinets. Each tape or "mini-lecture" will last less than 5 minutes and be written to elicit a behavioral response from the user. From these responses, we will be able to effectively evaluate each station along the trail.

Other research on learning behavior in the Garden indicates that people read very little and their attention spans are not great. Long complicated explanations are only given a cursory glance. Scientific names have no relevance to the layman and are easily forgotten. The average time spent on any display in the Garden is 3 minutes, and during that time, the individual stops at four specific points. This means that he, or she, spends an average of three-fourth's of a minute looking at the simple explanation of a plant or group of plants.

If you are building or designing a self-guiding nature study program, you can probably expect the same results. Not more than 3 minutes will be spent at each station along the trail. Most of the information will not be read by the user. Scientific names will be forgotten, and the last part of the trail will be rapidly finished.

A NEW SET OF GUIDELINES

Out of this research I propose a new set of guidelines for designing and building self-guiding nature study programs. I propose that when you build, you use the following procedure:

(1) Start with a community relationship that everyone knows.

(2) Develop a central theme around this relationship.

(3) Associate each station of the trail with the theme and the community relationship.

(4) Tell the user at the start of the trail what he will be able to do after he uses the trail.

(5) Use no more than six stations along the trail.

(6) Make your explanations short and simple.

(7) Encourage the user to become involved by using his senses (touch, smell, taste, sight, hearing).

(8) Evaluate the trails effectiveness through the users performances.

(9) Do not let your nature trail become a museum piece.

A nature trail is for the user. Why else would you build it? ∎

The natural history of the Susquehanna Environmental Education Association.

A NATURE CORPS FOR PUBLIC ACTION

Nancy Ayers

ARE YOU aware that many conservation matters to be considered by the United States Congress come before the Committees on Interior and Insular Affairs in the Senate and the House of Representatives, chaired by Senator Henry M. Jackson and Representative Sidney L. McFarland?

Can you name the local, state, and federal representatives from your district? What are their positions on conservation issues? Do they know where you stand? Have you recognized that laws are as basic to conservation as education?

No conservationist worthy of the name can ignore these and similar questions—but how do you find the answers? The following account is a condensed history of the Susquehanna Conservation Council as it evolved into a citizens' volunteer corps to publicize ecological and environmental problems in this corner of New York and to encourage cooperative solutions in the public's best interest—and ultimately to change its name to the Susquehanna Environmental Education, as its comes of age on its fourth birthday.

It was curiosity that got the Council started. And stubbornness and sheer orneriness that kept it going, in spite of being categorized as do-gooders and rabble-rousers amid the perennial confusion about the definition and goals of conservation. SEE began its fifth year of operation in February 1970 proud to have overcome some of its growing pains and pleased over the increased awareness of the importance of conservation in our daily lives and in planning for the future.

Who are we? Originally, a small group of science teachers, college professors, youth leaders, garden clubbers, and concerned citizens who were called together by the Garden Center of the Roberson Center for the Arts and Sciences in Binghamton, New York. The initial meeting in 1964 introduced the idea of a nature center for outdoor education in Broome County and raised the question of identifying the county's conservation needs.

The first project was to find out what was—and was not—being done about conservation in the area. For the purpose of this report, "area" refers primarily to Broome County because SEE activities and membership have focused there, but it should be noted that the name "Susquehanna Conservation Council" was deliberately chosen to avoid a strictly local connotation. It was felt that the natural boundaries of a regional watershed were more appropriate to the issues confronting a conservation organization. "Council" was used to indicate the goal of bringing together local conservationists for better understanding and reinforcement of activities.

So, for a year we talked and talked and talked. We learned about the related federal, state, and local agencies, and what they said their programs and responsibilities were. We sought out legislators and got acquainted with what they were doing. We listened to preservationists, isolationists, recreationists, sportsmen, scientists, teachers, administrators, the Chamber of Commerce, and the news media—many of whom had a singular point of view. We sifted through this mountain of conflicting opinion and prejudice, and concluded that something was still missing.

Since we believed that the conservation needs in both the fields of education and legislation were neither clear nor realized locally, SEE adopted bylaws February 8, 1966, for these specific purposes. To encourage maximum participation, membership fees were set modestly at $5—Single, $10—Donor, $25 or more—Benefactor, and $1-Student.

Another year was spent in more research, discussion, and groundwork. With very few members (37) and very little income ($347), SEE concentrated on issues directly connected with local conservation problems. Our attempt to form a coalition with related groups was unsuccessful. It remains uncomfortably true that some avowed conservationists have tunnel vision in their fields of special interest, despite their technological proficiency. So we began thinking about changing our name to better identify our purpose.

Mrs. (Joseph G.) Ayers is Executive Director of the Susquehanna Environmental Education Association (SEE), and a member of the New York State Special Commission on Conservation Education.

T h e next year SEE picked up a few more members and a few more dollars (nearly all from membership dues), and went on to the complicated business of trying to stimulate community action through a public information program. Here again, we ran into trouble. How can you possibly be an unbiased pressure group with a membership of diverse interests and abilities? Even if you resolve the difficulty of consensus, how do you succeed in getting information to the voter, legislator, public official, educator?

Publicity—that was the next lesson. We went to the news people and asked for their ground r u l e s. We learned their methods, their deadlines, their interests, and their names, and did our best to cooperate with them. We didn't necessarily always agree with their advice, but generally we took it. There is a very important reason for this. Editors a n d reporters have the last word on what is presented i n the news media. Understanding and w o r k i n g with them candidly is the only practical way of getting your message across to the mass audience. It takes great patience—on all sides—to achieve success with public information, but it is an absolute imperative if a national ecological conscience is ever to be developed.

Broome County is fortunate to have two daily newspapers, four television stations, and four radio stations, because it is a mish-mash of overlapping political subdivisions including one city, two villages, 16 towns, 19 school districts, one university, o n e community college, and approximately 225,000 people at the latest tabulation. Not all of them w e r e wildly enthusiastic about conservation nor our desire to publicize the related issues.

For example, you may think what you are doing is a big deal, but who else cares about another board meeting, another lecture, another film? What they were telling us was to make some hard news and people will listen. "Hard" news is not necessarily controversial, but it is current and directly affects the community. When you tie conservation to a local issue, it gives it a clearer frame of reference, and then you have really got something going for you. Provided, of course, you make certain that a l l media are properly and regularly informed, and reminded tactfully b u t repeatedly o n each issue y o u raise. Never take anything for granted.

Utilizing this approach, SEE s e n t a legislative questionnaire to all the county supervisory candidates in 1967. They were asked if they endorsed acquisition of a fifth county park site, a county nature center, a natural resources survey, a county conservation commission, and continued roadside spraying of herbicides for weed control. A majority of the 33 candidates for the 19 supervisory positions favored the first four items and opposed the last one. Detailed results of their answers were widely p u b l i - cized prior to the election. When the new board took office in January 1968, SEE kept in touch and k e p t asking questions. The following April, the Board of Supervisors passed enabling legislation (Local Law Number 4 of 1968) establishing the Broome County Conservation Commission of nine members (believed to be the first such county commission in the State) to serve as an advisory committee to the Board o n natural resources and environmental management.

Since we like to think we may have had something

to do with that accomplishment, SEE again sent out a legislative questionnaire that fall. Because of redistricting, all Supervisors were facing the polls with 35 candidates in the race. SEE was still asking about a county conservation education center f o r outdoor studies, b u t had added several more controversial issues to the list. These included the suggestion that if Congress does not designate the Susquehanna and Chenango as scenic rivers, Broome County should do so for its own benefit. SEE also proposed county zoning for flood plains, scenic easements, open space, and park lands, and water and sewage districts; and an annual tree planting program along county roads to restore, replace, or improve existing plant material. Twenty-two candidates responded, and the answers were more thoughtful than the year b e f o r e. This was interpreted as an encouraging sign that these proposals would be carefully considered.

In its short, precarious existence SEE has also succeeded in having a number of its suggestions in the educational field accepted. Under Title III of the Elementary and Secondary Education Act of 1965, the Upper Susquehanna Regional Supplementary Educational Service Center (serving 9 N e w York S t a t e counties) added a conservation film library, a program on the wildflowers of the State with slides and script, an unique series of nature trail markers developed to arouse the students' curiosity—and most exciting of all—a Sciencemobile, a specially designed and equipped Mobile Field Laboratory for teaching conservation and natural history.

The Sciencemobile is a Volkswagen van with built-in shelves, carrier rack, and boxed units for specific study purposes. It is equipped with all necessary materials for a class of 30 students, ranging f r o m waders, collecting jars, and butterfly nets, to binoculars, microscopes, and identification g u i d e s. Through the Title III office at Roberson Center, the Sciencemobile is available to any teacher in the participating school districts. In-service classes have been offered to acquaint teachers with the equipment, and a detailed teaching guide is in preparation. One of the most successful users of the Mobile Lab h a s been the Johnson City School District under t h e i r Science Coordinator, T e r r e n c e T. McCormick (Azon Road, Johnson City, New York 13790).

In cooperation with the Title III office, SEE compiled a Selected Conservation Bibliography for Broome County which was made available to teachers, c o n - servationists, and other interested individuals. It included a county map with a list of suggested field trip sites to stimulate outdoor studies.

Another continuing advisory project is the development of the two courtyards at the Endwell Junior High School. For 3 years a student committee has been planning, working, and paying for landscaping the main courtyard. The youngsters have faced such difficulties as what to do about a dead dogwood tree which was to have been the center of attraction, and where to put 300 spring-flowering bulbs when an acute drainage problem was discovered in November. They had better luck with previous plantings of rhododendron, azalea, mahonia, and viburnum, and are using the courtyard for band concerts, art shows, and similar activities. A weather station is being considered, and it is hoped that the other courtyard can be d e - veloped as an outdoor laboratory emphasizing native plant material. Now there is talk about developing a nature trail on a nearby creek bank. This time it is the principal's idea!

It may be a cliche, but one thing does lead to another. At the Maine-Endwell Senior High School in the same district, there have been more field trips last year (ranging from the sewage treatment plant to an isolated bog); there was an experimental conservation course presented to local level students; and there were 50 student volunteers who helped nearby homeowners clean up and seed the banks of Patterson Creek. Motivated by the Teach-In and Earth Day, some 15 students have formed a Conservation Club to learn more about the problems and find out what they can do.

Also under educational activities, a committee of SEE board members and consultants prepared a broad proposal for the development of conservation education and nature study sites on a countywide basis for the consideration of the County Conservation Commission. The purpose is to seek an integrated effort by the County Legislature, the Board of Cooperative Educational Services, Broome Community College, and other educational institutions to share the responsibility for meeting these needs. The county has centrally-located land which could be designated for educational purposes. The Parks Department initiated an interpretive nature program last summer. BOCES has the Mobile Field Laboratory. Broome Tech has related facilities and staff. Nobody has a program coordinator to bring the components together.

This led to the SEE "Leadership Live-In" at the Rogers Conservation Education Center in Sherburne last year. With the joint cooperation of the New York State Conservation Department through John A. Weeks, director of the center, and Project R. A. C. E. (Regional Approach in Conservation Education, 113 W. Liberty Street, Rome, New York 13440) directed by Jerry E. Passer in the Title III Program of the Illion School District, SEE attempted to show Broome County leaders conservation education in action. A small but responsive group of 35 people visited the center, most of them for the first time. The theme of the conference was "Community Action for Conservation Education," with the first panel discussion based on "What and Why?" and the second on "Who and Where?" (The resource book used for the discussions was Community Action for Natural Beauty which is available from the Superintendent of Documents in Washington, D. C. 20402, 40 cents each.)

Preceeding this meeting, a group of Hillcrest Elementary School sixth-graders from the Chenango Valley School District took an overnight field trip to the Rogers Center. The first student group to use the dormitory facilities developed by Project R. A. C. E. at the Center, the youngsters planned the entire trip, including their meals and the itinerary. Their enthusiastic response was reported to the SEE conference by one of their teachers.

Though only one legislator of the many invited accepted, the group represented a broad cross-section of the community, and out of it developed a cadre of people and pictures to recreate the experience for key legislators and educators at follow-up meetings locally. Two such meetings were held with county legislative committees in July, followed by a presentation to the entire County Legislature in October— which is another example of evolving from one method to another, because the ends justify changing the means as often as necessary.

While the above project was going on, mostly behind the scenes, SEE was conducting a related campaign for a 17-mile linear park along the Susquehanna River throughout Broome County. Actually that was a bit of a trick because we didn't expect a public park of that dimension, but our primary objective was to generate controversy on the subject and to make conservation benefits visible to the general public. What they don't see as a direct benefit, they are not likely to understand or support. A riverbank park would come within a mile and a half of 80 percent of the county's population for hiking, fishing, boating, swimming, biking, picnicking, and just plain resting. If anything will ever catalyze interest, this should be it—and finally, there is tangible response. The County has authorized studies for both an Interpretive Nature Study Center and a Riverbank Improvement Program, and the current budget carries allocations to implement the projects.

Following its earlier opposition to the indiscriminate use of herbicides for weed control, SEE went on record in May 1969 opposing further use of DDT and related toxic chemicals until conclusive data show that there will not be harmful effects on man and his environment. Letters expressing this position were sent to the New York State Health Commissioner, the New York State Conservation Commissioner, the Broome County Legislature, and the County Conservation Commission. Subsequently, the County Executive declared a moratorium on herbicidal spraying for 1 year and instructed the county attorney to determine the County's legal ability to restrict the use of DDT. County agencies have now discontinued using both. When chlordane was suggested as an alternative pesticide, we went to press with toxicity and persistence figures.

These illustrations show the major areas of SEE activities. We experimented with various other projects, but these emerged as the most necessary and the most effective. We certainly didn't win them all, but our problems are better described as slowdowns or retrenchments rather than losses. By our definition we never had anything to lose!

Since SEE is primarily an advisory group, measurements are difficult, but in 1968 membership and income doubled (125 people and $800). Last year and this, we are holding steady. Obviously the Association is small, and its working membership is even smaller. Its success has been made possible by the generous cooperation of many expert consultants. Except for policy changes, the business of the Association is conducted by the Executive Board which includes a president, vice-president, secretary, treasurer, executive director, director for conservation education, director for public action, and chairman of the scientific advisory committee. Subcommittees are appointed only as needed for special projects. As pointed out earlier, it became increasingly apparent that our name didn't clearly define our purpose. Despite some qualms about side effects, the change has been accomplished with relative ease and general acceptance, even to the point of attracting some new members.

Doubtless there are still some who consider all conservationists as "nature fakers" and "whistle tooters," but we are sufficiently alarmed by Dr. Paul R. Ehrlich's Population Bomb and Dr. Barry Commoner's Science and Survival to believe that we must take organized action. We must recognize also that we cannot all operate on the same scale of magnitude as the Colorado Open Space Council or the Citizens Committee to Save Cayuga Lake. Any size group is valuable if it is active, flexible, and objective.

Education is one key; public information is the other with enlightened legislation as the goal—as exemplified by the national activities of the Friends of the Earth. Two of the bills supported by SEE were passed in New York last year. These were the Temporary State Commission on Youth Education in Conservation and an amendment to Article 14 of the State Constitution, known as the Conservation Bill of Rights. This year the Commission has been extended and a major new program authorized to establish a State Department of Environmental Conservation. They are good examples of the enlightened legislation SEE advocates. On the national level pending bills were also evaluated, and of the five issues SEE supported last September, four are now reinforced by law (Environmental Quality Act, Endangered Species, Water Quality Improvement, and Population Growth Commission). The fifth category which was concerned with pesticides has not fared so well and is among those now being reviewed for a current Federal Legislative Report. Copies will be available from the Association at 616 Pheasant Lane, Endwell, New York 13760.

All of these things are important in the conservation "package," and we must redouble our efforts to sell it. Just because some joker said the missing link between pithecanthropus man and civilized man is us, we don't have to let it be true. Getting started is the hardest part—but we know it can be done. How about you? ∎

The inside story of two national public opinion polls on environmental issues.

THE ENVIRONMENT: WHO CARES? WHY? SO WHAT?

Ed Chaney

IN RECENT years conservationists, environmentalists, ecologists, and others have basked in the attention of the mass media. Environmental issues moved off the sport pages and for the first time commanded more space than the bowling s c o r e s. Huntley-Brinkley aired the plight of the Everglades. Conservation was in at long last.

Everybody was for it. Politicians stumped on it. And when the band wagon came by, industry, government, and every conceivable organization jumped on it.

As the resulting barrage of newscasts, press releases, speeches, industry advertising, and television spectaculars began to flood the public with the nation's environmental crises, the longtime conservationists began to savor the delicious taste of success.

It mattered little whether the mass media's e n chantment with environmental issues was the cause or the effect of growing public concern. To many, if not the majority of conservationists, this was the fruit of their labors. Get the message to the public and in the American tradition the good of all would triumph over the greed of few. Mankind before money. Voice of the people and all that. The squeaky wheel gets the legislative grease. And the United States would be off toward developing a rational environmental ethic.

A series of sweeping conservation victories including the Land and Water Conservation Fund Act, the Water Quality Act of 1965, and a Redwoods National Park lent credence to the euphoria of a national conservation renaissance. It was a sobering scene, however, when working conservationists began to indulge in rudimentary mental gymnastics and found environmental degradation had actually accelerated while they were under the influence.

The polluters and their pollutants were more sophisticated, but more rapacious than ever. Under the watchful eyes of self interests, much beneficial state and Federal legislation turned out to be a veneer designed to take the heat off while the Juggernaut of environmental destruction picked up steam.

DDT advocates were still saying they were for people and against cabbage worms. The Federal grants-in-aid plan to assist municipalities in constructing waste treatment plants fell flat on its face. The utility industry had virtually won by default their design to give the country hot running streams despite reasonable alternatives. Every year air pollution continued to kill scores of people, jeopardize the health of millions more, and cause billions of dollars in property damage while industry b u s i l y shelled out $35 million a year to fight air pollution control and preventative restrictions.

In spite of the obvious burgeoning public concern, still far less than 1 percent of t h e Federal budget was going to programs even remotely related to environmental cleanup, and yet these were among the first to feel the bite of the economy ax.

According to the script, the unprecedented e x posure in the mass media and growing ranks of organized conservationists w e r e manifestations of burgeoning public concern. But the growing conservation crises and legislative sloth were all too familiar trademarks of public indifference.

Faced with this incongruous backdrop, the National Wildlife Federation planned two national public opinion polls to plumb the public's attitudes about the environment. The first was conducted by t h e Gallup Organization during the last ten days of January, 1969. The second during the first eight days of the following July by that other organization which shall remain anonymous pending possible litigation over use of its name.

In general, the Gallup pollsters found more than 85 percent of the public was concerned with the current state of the environment. About half (51%) of those interviewed were "deeply concerned" about the environmental effects of air pollution, w a t e r pollution, soil erosion, and wildlife destruction. Another 35 percent said they were "somewhat

---

Mr. Chaney is Director of Information, The National Wildlife Federation, Washington, D.C.

concerned, " and 12 percent were "not very con-cerned. "

When asked how much they would be willing to pay in additional taxes earmarked to improve the natural surroundings, almost three out of four indi-cated they would be willing to pay something. And this included approximately 63 percent of those with annual family incomes under $5,000. Fifty-one per-cent were willing to pay $10 or less; 18 percent $50; 4 percent $100; 9 percent none; and 18 percent "didn't know" if they would be willing to pay or not.

When shown a list and asked to identify what they thought to be the most pressing environmental prob-lem, air pollution (36%) and water pollution (32%) were ranked problems one and two with pesticides (7%), preservation of open green space (6%), wild-life preservation (5%), soil erosion (4%), and "don't knows" (10%), bringing up the rear.

Control of auto exhaust and chemical and indus-trial wastes were major remedial measures offered for air pollution. Stopping industrial pollution, en-forcing present laws, and passing new legislation were the primary opinions offered to correct water pollution.

Wildlife preservation was considered to be the most pressing environmental problem by only 5 per-cent of those interviewed. This in spite of the fact that over the years wildlife has probably been the subject of more sustained so-called conservation ed-ucation effort than other environmental issue. To wildlife managers, interesting is hardly the word to describe the public's opinion of what can be done to correct the problem: enforce game laws 40 percent; reduce hunting 25 percent; establish wildlife reserv-es, parks 20 percent; control air and water pollution 7 percent; other answers 9 percent; "don't know" 16 percent. (Total exceeds 100% due to multiple response.)

When asked if they thought it would eventually be necessary to limit human population to maintain our present standard of living, 44 percent said it would be necessary; 43 percent said it wouldn't; and, 13 percent "didn't know. "

Ironically, with approximately 70 percent of the population living on 1 percent of the land within the metropolitan environs, only 6 percent indicated they found the large city the most pleasant place to live. Rural area (30%), small city (25%), and the sub-urbs (18%) were the top three in order of preference.

A full 75 percent of those interviewed said they were in favor of setting aside more public land for conservation purposes such as national parks, wild-life refuges, bird sanctuaries, etc; 19 percent said "no" and 6 percent "didn't know. "

Poll number 2, like the Gallup survey, was de-signed to probe general environmental attitudes in addition to zeroing in on specific issues. Some near repetition was built in for comparative purposes. De-sign of the two surveys was virtually identical except that Gallup pollsters interviewed only those over 21 years of age while the subsequent survey included the 16-20 age group.

When the public was asked if programs for im-provement of the natural environment receive too little, too much, or just the right amount of attention and financial support from the government, more than half (52%) said too little; 5 percent too much; 22 percent the right amount; and a significant 21 per-cent were "not sure. "

Asked to evaluate the environmental effects of DDT and other "long-lasting" pesticides, 45 percent said they have had a bad effect; 9 percent a good effect; 23 percent not much effect; and 23 percent were "not sure. " Even though the chemical industry is working hard to foment fear of urban control over agriculture, 40 percent of the people in rural areas say DDT and other persistent chemicals have had bad effects on the environment. Only 9 percent felt they've had an over-all good effect.

Nearly one-third (29%) reported that air and wa-ter pollution have affected the personal enjoyment of their surroundings and their lives. A big 68 percent said they had not, and 3 percent were "not sure. "

Asked if they would be willing to accept a $200 per year increase in their families' total living expenses to finance environmental cleanup, only 22 percent an-swered affirmatively, while 65 percent rejected the proposition. Willingness to pay increased in propor-tion to decreasing amounts: 32 percent would pay $100; 42 percent would pay $50; and 55 percent would pay $20, 35 percent would not, and 10 percent were "not sure. " At $20, a regional comparison shows Westerners (63%) and Midwesterners (65%) more amenable than Easterners (57%) and Southerners (39%).

A second, more specific alternative was offered to test the public's willingness to pay for environmental rehabilitation. An overwhelming 77 percent said they would not be willing to pay a $2 monthly increase in their electric bill to stop air and water pollution from electric power plants. When the price dropped to $1 per month, the majority (62%) still rejected the in-crease. But if the electric companies only had to in-crease monthly bills by $.25 to stop polluting, 61 per-cent of the public would be willing to pay, 30 percent would not, and 9 percent are "not sure. "

Attitudes toward current Federal Budget priorities were measured in two ways. A portion of the people interviewed were shown a list of current budget expen-ditures expressed as a percentage of the total, i.e., National Defense 44 percent, Space Program 3 per-cent, Natural Resources 1 percent, etc. They were asked, "Considering priorities, would you like to see more or less of the Federal money go into each of these purposes?"

The remaining portion of the sample were asked the same question, but without benefit of the information as to what percentage of the current Federal Budget goes to each major category.

In general, the majority of both those with and with-out information would like to see less Federal money spent on international affairs, the space program, and national defense. A majority would like to see more money go into education, natural resources, veteran's benefits, and housing and community development. It was a draw between increasing or decreasing spending for commerce and transportation, labor and welfare, and agriculture. Specifically, supplying information on current budget allocations increased support for added natural resource expenditures from 62 percent (without information) to 68 percent. Percentage support for increased natural resource expenditures ranked second only to education (78%)

Although data on various subgroups in the two categories must be handled cautiously because the subgroups are small and in this case from only portions of the total sample, the affluent (78%), college educated (77%), and those under 30 (16-20 75% and 21-29 81%) obviously strongly favor increased natural resource spending.

Finally, each person was asked, "More specifically now, environmental cleanup could be accomplished without added taxes or costs to consumers if priorities in Federal spending were changed. In which, if any, of these areas would you be in favor of reducing Federal spending, in order to increase spending on improvement of the natural environment?"

An overwhelming 97 percent of those with information on the Federal Budget favored reducing spending in one or more areas to free money for improving the natural environment. Only one percent less (96%) of those without information supported reallocation in favor of natural resources.

Overall, national defense (51%), the space program (44%), and international affairs (42%) were the prime targets of those "with information" for budget reductions to increase environmental spending. A full 71 percent of the college educated would take money from the defense budget, and the under-30 generation leaned heavily on reducing defense and international affairs expenditures.

The pollsters of Survey number 2 observed the data are consistent in showing the affluent, educated, suburban, younger adult, and late adolescent segments of the public to be greatest proponents of environmental cleanup, which is consistent with the Gallup findings. Conversely, some combination of apathy, low expectation levels, the presence of more obvious problems, ignorance of the extent of environmental problems and how they affect the quality of life, produce an apparent low level of environmental concern among city dwellers and those within the low income and educational levels.

Obviously, data from the two polls, individually or in tandem, shouldn't be viewed as anything more than advertised: surveys of public opinion. And considering the volatile nature of the animal, not the definitive word on the public's environmental attitudes. But even though the interpretations will likely vary in direct proportion to who's behind the typewriter, it is abundantly clear the bulk of the American public is concerned about the condition of the natural environment and wants to do something about it.

Certainly that is a significant, affirmative answer to a question increasingly posed by working conservationists in the face of accelerating environmental degradation. However, this logically spawns a question equally significant for analysis and evaluation: To what may we attribute the obvious public concern for the environment?

It would be conveniently self-serving for the conservation education community to claim a modest bit of credit. Too convenient. For despite increasing academic concern for environmental issues, too few students on the whole have any exposure to ecology in their regular curricula. Too many of those few are blessed with stuffed animal displays disguised as conservation education while air pollution annually kills scores of Americans and jeopardizes the health of millions more. Too many young minds are busied with taxonomic exercises while health officials warn that 25 percent of the American public now drinks water that doesn't measure up to admittedly inadequate Public Health Service standards.

It appears far more credible that the increasing severity of environmental degradation and the unprecedented enchantment of the mass media with environmental issues is responsible for alerting the majority of the public to environmental problems and the need for remedial measures.

Ironically, a great many conservationists, environmentalists, ecologists, and others have held that herein lay the coup de grace for environmental insanity. Once the general public got religion: Zap! Pow! Out water pollution! Out air pollution! In ecological horse-sense! But it obviously hasn't worked out that way. The country is still losing the battle against environmental degradation in spite of the public's demonstrated desire to the contrary, and only a fool or a polluter would suggest this country is incapable of solving these problems if given the proper priority.

So now what? More of the same? Poll number one said 85 percent of the public was concerned about the condition of the natural environment and three out of four were willing to pay more taxes earmarked to do something about it. Poll number two said an overwhelming 97 percent of the public favors reallocating present Federal expenditures to free more money for environmental cleanup. Would it really make any difference if it were 100 percent?

In time, the mass media will inevitably lose its enchantment with environmental issues. Although ecological curricula aren't likely to attain the scholastic prominence of music appreciation, library science or ROTC, thankfully, more and more students are being exposed to some academic renditions of environmental issues.

Perhaps today's disenchanted youth will be tomorrow's disenchanted voters with a more intense, or at least more effective, environmental concern than the generation now in power. Perhaps that's the ultimate answer as it's commonly held to be. Let's hope we can wait that long.∎

Examining the ingredients of effective group pressure for environmental reform.

GUIDELINES FOR CITIZEN ACTION

Charles H. W. Foster

MY DESIGNATED subject is citizen action. This seems particularly appropriate for a forum of conservation leaders; for once national policies have been determined and science and technology geared for application, something must arise to make events happen. I contend that citizen action is the essential and often missing ingredient.

In my experience, there are three prime ingredients of citizen action: one, a receptive and substantial constituency; two, the organization of this constituency into effective mechanisms for action; and three, the application of these actions in informed and credible ways.

In terms of constituency, America is clearly riding the crest of a widespread popular movement of environmental concern. The symptoms are everywhere: increased television and radio coverage, feature articles in newspapers and magazines, even more simple—social conversation about conservation. For those of us accustomed to adversity over the years, this ground swell of popularity is heady news indeed.

For example, in a recent Gallup Poll conducted for the National Wildlife Federation, four out of every five persons interviewed were deeply concerned over the growing degradation of their environment. Three out of four expressed willingness to do something about these problems, even if it meant up to $10 more per person per year in taxes. Almost all of those interviewed were dissatisfied with the present allocations of federal dollars. A clear majority were dissatisfied with the allocations to natural resource areas. Astonishingly, of the large number of Americans who appeared willing to work personally for environmental causes few seemed to know how to go about doing it. The challenge to this audience is, I think, obvious.

Widespread though our environmental constituency appears to be, there are some obvious weak spots. For example, industries and corporations have been generally slow to jeopardize a balance sheet in favor

of a social responsibility. The conservation movement is still largely white and upper middle class in character. In a real sense, conservation needs to find ways of converting itself from an elegant luxury to an urgent necessity.

In terms of mechanisms for action, one must examine both the numbers of organizations dedicated to conservation objectives, and the quality of their efforts in this regard. Statistical information on citizen action is sketchy at best, but from the several sources at hand—namely the Conservation Yearbooks published by Erle Kaufman of the Society of American Foresters, the annual Conservation Directories of the National Wildlife Federation, and the reports of the conservation services division of The Conservation Foundation—the following estimates can be made.

At least 500 state, regional, and national nongovernmental conservation organizations are now firmly established throughout the United States. These are identifiable in various ways: by the level at which they operate, by the character of the organizations themselves, by the nature of their participants, and by the particular spheres of interest they advocate. Conservatively, at least five million Americans are card-carrying conservationists, half of whom probably live in the 11 northeastern states.

In general, most conservation organizations coalesce around a small group of individuals who are dedicated to a particular and often narrow objective. Over time, however, a certain maturation takes place. The organization tends to grow conservative and even complacent, particularly if it has already earned substantial public acclaim for its program. It can become over-institutionalized, unresponsive to current need, and thereby difficult to identify with until captured by new leadership or confronted with a new imperative for action.

Despite the limitations of some organizations, however, there are usually ample mechanisms for action in most states. In fact, proliferation of organizations,

---

Dr. Foster is a Harvard University Fellow. This paper was first presented at a special public seminar on environmental issues at Cornell University.

and subsequent duplication, overlap and even competition among programs, is a familiar headache to many in this audience. Yet, a major portion of the vitality of the conservation movement lies in its very diversity, hence my advocacy of new mechanisms to bring together organizations on problems in common without loss of individual identity.

The chronic impoverishment of most conservation organizations, however, can lead them down a particularly dangerous path, that of sheer emotional response. Regrettably, the shrill causes are still the ones most likely to bring in the resources so desperately needed. Perhaps the most perplexing problem of all in citizen action is this matter of gaining the necessary support for an organization dedicated to responsible and credible action.

This introduces my third ingredient of citizen action, credibility. Here is where conservationists are often in serious trouble, even to the point of posing a serious threat to their new and vital public constituency. For example, preservation of resources, only one part of the more substantial goal of wise resource use, tends to characterize our ranks in the public eye and, in fact, often over-dominates citizen action efforts. The "crack of doom" environmental commentators make good headlines but usually impractical allies on the actual conservation battleground. Unable (or unwilling) as we are to turn back the clock on present and future material needs, we must somehow redirect our efforts toward proper use of resources such that a high standard of living is maintained with minimal loss of environmental values. This will require both a new willingness to compromise, and the equivalent shrewd, hard-headed bargaining capabilities our adversaries now possess.

So much, then, for the philosophical side of citizen action. Let me turn next to some of the promising avenues for action at the present time in the northeast. Here are a few that have impressed me with their potential.

It seems high time to encourage the demise of our traditional provincialism. Political boundaries grow more obsolete each day in the face of mankind's mobility and economic prosperity. Innovative machinery is sorely needed, in my judgement, to preserve the good parts of our region's long heritage of self-reliance, yet enable it to address itself effectively to problems shared in common.

The New England-inspired municipal conservation commission movement strikes me as one model worth emulating, for it aims at a common failing of conservation, the tendency to pass a problem off on too high a level of government. With more than 10 years of experience under our belts, the following can now be safely said about these municipal conservation agencies.

First, commissions have been remarkably successful at harnessing a sizable and previously under-utilized civic resource for environmental action. Second, the commissions have been significantly effective both as innovative action instruments, and as environmental quality checks and balances at the local level. Finally, a strong commission movement helps insure broader conservation efforts by serving as a powerful lobby for needed actions on a statewide basis.

Unless I am mistaken. New York has given only lip service to the conservation commission idea This has been a serious error, in my judgment. I commend to your attention Dr. Andrew Scheffey's new book on the subject, just published by The Conservation Foundation, which appraises the relative merits of the movement in the seven states where commissions are now authorized.

My second suggestion relates to New York's imaginative efforts in regional and local planning. One other promising possibility appears to have been overlooked, however—better utilization of the soil and water conservation district machinery. The districts are, of course, legal political subdivisions of state government enjoying many of their powers and responsibilities. Firmly grounded in land use objectives, and with ready access to a wide variety of technical services, the districts could and should be doing much more in the broad field of environmental quality.

Not long ago, Massachusetts and Florida foresaw the possibilities inherent in a broadening of district responsibilities beyond merely soil and water. In Massachusetts, for example, re-designated conservation districts are now empowered to undertake any project in the natural resources field, thus serving as the counterpart of the municipal conservation commissions at the regional level.

The new device known as a federal-interstate agency, as exemplified by the regional economic or river basin commission, may constitute a third example of the kind of innovative machinery we need. These are joint planning and action agencies in which the federal government and the effected states enjoy co-equal decision-making powers. The collective resources of several levels of government are thus focused on a problem area without loss of individual prerogatives. If this principle works for economic development and water resources planning, why not similar approaches in such fields as recreation and open space, wood utilization and forestry, or fish, wildlife, and marine resources? Or a similar mix of state and local governments to deal with intrastate regional problems?

Assuming that suitable types of machinery are established at various levels of government and within numerous fields of specialty, the problem becomes one of harnessing all these capabilities within some sort of functional system. From this growing need for greater efficiency has evolved the concept of regional services centers to perform fact-researching and interlinking functions for nongovernmental organizations, and to serve as an effective bridge between environmental interest groups and a region's business and political leadership. Small and selectively staffed, these centers are designed to work behind the scenes and help bring about more responsible policies and programs without themselves becoming frontline action agencies.

Although relatively new, the two principal models in existence, the Potomac Basin Center and the Rocky Mountain Center on Environment, are already showing great promise. A Similar New England Natural Resources Center has matured to the point of a provisional office in Boston. In my judgment, New York would be well advised to follow these developments closely.

Now, as we all know, environmental interest groups have gained sufficient muscle in many places to virtually derail any development proposal. Under such circumstances, the burden of responsible action is heavy indeed. If confrontation and subsequent paralysis of action are not to become the environmental watchword of the 1970's. then we must evolve some alternative courses between fruitless conflict and senseless capitulation.

In this regard, I am enormously intrigued with the concept of an environmental mediation service, which could moderate disputes and steer a middle course toward constructive compromise. Judging from the labor relations experience, third party mediation is cheap, relatively painless, and remarkably successful. Such functions could be added to an existing federal, state, or municipal mediation service (all three types exist in New York State) or could be provided as a public service by some responsible non-governmental entity.

Finally, if any of these new approaches are to come into being, shouldn't the universities play a key role in their planning and execution? The answer is plainly yes, but only if substantial reforms are accomplished beforehand on the campus. From my limited experience with such institutions, few are really equipped as yet to deal with problems of a broad, environmental nature. Cramped curricula, stratified departmental structures, and jealously-guarded field of specialty offer severe handicaps to the approach that seems most needed at this time.

In this connection, I am a strong believer in the establishment of academic environmental or natural resource centers where experts from several disciplines can combine forces on a given problem. Useful extensions of this principle are represented by the cooperative wildlife research units and water resources centers which not only coordinate on-campus capabilities, but also interlink the institution with federal and state resource agencies. Every effort needs to be made to overcome the traditional isola-tion of the land-grant institution and to bridge the often painful gap between the academician and the public administrator. Scientists should be encouraged to accept appointments on public policy or regulatory agencies—in essense, to infiltrate from within rather than criticize from without. Ties of this nature can provide stronger links with the locus of real decision-making, permit better use of research and extension capabilities, and inject relevant case materials into undergraduate and graduate programs.

And so, what emerges from this random collection of observations? Simply this. There is no easy road to effective citizen action. However, we do have an urgent cause; there are tools and techniques fitted for the tasks, and willing hands are available to carry them to completion. In short, let us get on with the job no matter how imperfect it may be.

Some years ago, we attempted to spell out for our fledgling Massachusetts conservation commissions a few procedural guidelines for successful citizen action. In retrospect, they seem worth repeating today.

The first is, be prepared—have the proper facts at hand and your homework done before tackling an issue. Second, be right in the conclusions you draw. There is never any substitute for being right! Third, be practical in the course of action you advocate, mindful of the positions of others and the likelihood that your cause will be accepted. Finally, be wise in time. Knowing when to espouse an issue is often the real key to credibility and future success.

In my judgment, citizen action is what will make environmental quality a reality and not just a figure of speech. If this forum, this university, and the groups represented in this audience somehow merge their individual interests in common cause, begin to take actions in a responsible manner, and seek innovative ways of harnessing the great tide of public opinion, I can guarantee that the results will not be perfect, but the rewards will more than justify your efforts. ∎

Increasing citizen awareness through correspondence.

AN INDEPENDENT STUDY COURSE IN WATER RESOURCES

Paul F. Nowak

THE ADULT segment of our population has, for a variety of reasons, been deprived of environmental education. Many of the critical problems which now confront the environment of our society either were not considered significant or did not exist when the bulk of today's adults were involved in formal education programs. Even youth and the young adults of today, due to the lack of environmental education programs, are receiving only a haphazard smattering of educational experiences dealing with environmental issues. Most citizens have to rely upon a mixture of random formal educational experiences, self-education, and incidental information from the news media in order to understand current environmental problems. These methods have failed to fill the growing educational deficiency which exists and are compounding the apathy and frustration which, unfortunately, have been characteristic of citizen attitudes toward environmental problems. It is clearly evident that for both the present and the foreseeable future, due to the educational void which exists, adult programs will have a viable place in the spectrum of environmental education.

In response to this need for adult environmental education, Dr. William B. Stapp formed a group at the University of Michigan to develop an independent study course in environmental conservation through correspondence. A water resources course was created as an experimental segment of this total program and was developed from the innovated concepts which formed the philosophic basis of the total course. The experimental materials were used by a variety of individuals so that the innovated concepts upon which it is based could be evaluated. The individuals who were involved in the experimental procedures were identified by the same means which will be relied upon in identifying students for the total course.

The innovative techniques used are aimed primarily toward helping the students develop an awareness and an understanding of the environmental problems which exist in their local community and region and an understanding of how citizens can participate in helping to find solutions to these problems. Independent study through correspondence was chosen because it can disseminate materials to anybody who wishes to participate such as working citizens. It can cover the distances which exist in rural areas, and it can overcome the difficulties and the dangers of urban transportation. It gives the student the chance to determine his own time schedule, and it is easily administered through existing extension organizations.

Correspondence is not a new educational technique. However, it has been used very little in the fields of conservation and environmental studies, even though participants who complete correspondence studies do as well or better than classroom students.

The environmental conservation course and the water resources experimental segment of the course were designed to exploit the potential for independent study which is possible through correspondence. Course materials were designed to utilize the participant's local community as a laboratory and to let him choose the problem areas on which he would like to concentrate.

It was anticipated that by involving the participants with local, relevant, and real environmental problems, it would be possible to help citizens gain the knowledge of why they should be aware of and concerned with environmental issues. Hopefully, this would start the sequence of events which could lead to changed citizen behavior. We need citizens who are willing to be involved in influencing both public and private decisions which affect our environment because citizens ultimately are responsible either directly by their actions or indirectly through their representative governments for the quality or our environment. Education has the responsibility of providing citizens with the understandings, the skills, and the information they need in order to effectively express their environmental concerns.

EXPERIMENTAL WATER RESOURCE PROGRAM

The experimental water resource program, therefore, was developed to evaluate the innovated concepts upon which the environmental conservation course is based by measuring the changes which occurred in individuals using the experimental materi-

---

Dr. Nowak is Chairman, Department of Conservation and Outdoor Education, Southern Illinois University, Carbondale, Illinois.

als. The evaluation was also aimed at determining the characteristics of the population interested in this type of program, as well as their acceptance of the types of materials used. In order to carry out this study, both course materials and evaluation materials were created.

The course materials consisted of a text and a series of activities. The text was built upon a series of basic understandings which were defined as the minimal amount of knowledge necessary for effective citizen action. These understandings were used to reduce the substantial amount of material dealing with most environmental subjects such as water. When completed and organized, they became at once both the basis and the outline for the text. Also included as integral components of the text were a glossary and an annotated bibliography. The glossary provided a compact source for word definitions, even though all technical words or phrases were defined as they were introduced in the text. Due to the varied experiences of the students, no general background level of information was assumed and the text was written to stand on its own. The annotated bibliography was included to help the student move further into areas of particular interest. The books and pamphlets suggested were those which should be readily available in most local communities.

The series of activities for each segment of the course were of four kinds: one, the text related questions were designed to help the student give more consideration to the important aspects of the text; two, the survey activities were designed to guide the participant in looking at his local community and evaluating some of its environmental characteristics (there are one or more survey activities for each segment of the course); three, the interview activity was organized by the participant to help him collect information about a local environmental problem of his selection relative to the local area being studied; and four, a synthesis activity was used to draw together information the student had collected about the problem chosen for the interview activity, thereby giving him a chance to express proposed solutions and his concerns.

The student was required to do the first two activities for every segment of the course; however, he did the third and fourth activities for only a small number of selected segments which were of particular interest to him.

EVALUATION MATERIALS

The evaluation materials consisted of a personal data sheet, a pretest, a posttest, and an opinion questionnaire. The personal data sheet was designed to evaluate the personal characteristics of the individuals interested in this type of educational program. The pretest and posttest were basically similar instruments designed to evaluate the change in the participants' basic understanding of water resources in general and local water resources in particular. They also identified the change in the participants' knowledge of local citizen groups and governmental agencies involved with water resources and in their ability to identify locally available sources of information about water resources. An opinion questionnaire was used to evaluate the participants' feelings about the various aspects of the experimental program which related to the entire environmental conservation course.

The personal data indicated some of the important characteristics of the participants. The ages ranged from 13 to 73, with 83 percent between 21 and 50. The average age was 38.8. This was important because it indicated that busy, active individuals were interested in this type of program. There was an even split between males and females and, educationally, 82 percent had completed at least a college degree. The participants were employed in a wide range of occupations such as housewives, teachers, engineers, college instructors, planners, researchers, students, real estate brokers, secretaries, librarians, governmental officials, and others. The income level was evenly spread from $5,000 to $20,000 with 14 percent having a family income of over $20,000. Of the participants 79 percent were married, and 52 percent lived in urban residential areas, while 36 percent lived in suburban areas. Forty-three percent found out about the experimental course through the newspaper, 36 percent through club bulletins or club newsletters, and 17 percent by word of mouth. The course was taken by 72 percent because of a personal interest in conservation, while 27 percent took it, in part, for occupational reasons.

Using the test instrument created for evaluating the experimental materials, the participants showed a 44.6 percent increase in their general knowledge of water resources and a 35 percent increase in their knowledge of local community water resources. The participants increased 60 percent in their ability to identify sources of information about water resources; 78 percent in their ability to identify public agencies concerned with water resources; and 187 percent in their ability to identify private organizations concerned with water resources.

The opinion questionnaire provided some very helpful data about length, completeness, style, and difficulty, which was extremely helpful in revising the text and in providing guidelines for the development of other units. It also showed that 56 percent of the participants found the text interesting and 35 percent found it very interesting; 57 percent liked the activities quite well and 38 percent liked them very well. The participants, for the most part, found the experimental water resource course increased their interest, concern, general knowledge, and specific local knowledge of water resources. The program was considered to be good by 31 percent while 61 percent felt it was very good.

It seems evident from this study that environmental education programs for adults are needed and wanted. It also shows that correspondence is an acceptable means for disseminating adult educational materials, even to busy and influential citizens, and that independent study can, in reality, make environmental conservation more relevant and meaningful. There are, of course, any number of ways of improving the techniques and the materials used. Many improvements have already been incorporated. If the materials are to remain viable, this must become a continuous process. Perhaps the most exciting prospect for this entire project is that it will act as a model upon which a whole series of independent study courses in environmental education, as well as a wide range of other subject matter areas, can be based. ∎

"Welding diverse organizations and viewpoints into an effective force for a quality environment."

CONSERVATION SYNERGISM:

NEW DYNAMICS FOR EFFECTIVE ACTION

Roger P. Hansen

HOW DOES one overcome the enormous odds in favor of the polluters, the despoilers, the uglifiers of our land? How does one make his neighbors concerned, his legislature listen? How can conservation-minded citizens be an effective force in the real social revolution that is occurring in America today—a revolution that centers on a quality of life versus a quantity of existence? How can conservation organizations take advantage of a conservation climate more favorable than at any time in our history?

A major reason for the failures of conservationists—in terms of influencing social decision-making—has been their historical inability to weld themselves into an effective force, ready for battle on the great environmental issues of the day. Instead there are dozens of diverse groups, each hawking its particular brand of conservation elixir. Meanwhile, back at the state or national capitol, a united and disciplined army of resource commodity groups, commerical interests, and power-hungry bureaucracies grinds mercilessly forward, ignoring ecological principles that may determine our survival as a species.

HISTORY OF COSC

Until a few years ago Colorado conservationists were no different from their "soul" brothers elsewhere. Bird-watchers screamed at hunters; backpackers battled car-campers. Arguments raged over whether a trail should be wide enough for man, horse, or jeep—or whether there should be any trail at all.

But in September, 1964, some 200 Colorado fishermen, back-packers, botany experts, park promoters, outdoor educators, and pollution abaters met

and decided to form a united conservation movement— the Colorado Open Space Coordinating Council, now known as "COSC."

It wasn't easy. There were fears of takeover, worry about organization autonomy, disagreement over who could speak for whom. Finally, in April, 1965, by-laws were adopted and articles of incorporation filed. COSC organizers were all too aware that they were a minority group of "outsiders" in a cattle-baron climate, aligned before the bastions of mining, grazing, timbering, oil, gas, and water development interests. The initial participating organizations in COSC numbered only six; influence potential seemed about equal to a tumbleweed blowing in the wind.

Today, COSC serves as a coordinating "umbrella" for 26 organizations representing some 30,000 citizens in Colorado and the Rocky Mountain area concerned about the quality of their environment. Nearly all the major conservation groups in Colorado are members of the Council and are represented on the Board of Directors. The whole spectrum of conservation, outdoor recreation, and environmental concern runs through COSC activities. It is particularly significant that a birth control agency, Planned Parenthood of Colorado, is represented on the Board, for no resource problem is more fundamental than the human population crisis.

COMPOSITION AND PURPOSE

The purpose of COSC is "to provide an effective and continuing coordinating structure in working for the conservation (preservation and wise use) and appreciation of scenic, historic, open space, wildlife, wilderness, and outdoor recreational resources as related to the total environment, through a program

Mr. Hansen, a lawyer and recreation planner, is Executive Director of the Colorado Open Space Foundation and the new Rocky Mountain Center on Environment, Denver. This article is excerpted from a speech and a longer paper, "How Coloradoans Win Conservation Battles," which appeared in Catalyst, Vol. II, No. 4.

of coordinated action, for the cultural, education, physical, health, spiritual, and economic benefit of our citizens and our visitors."

METHOD OF OPERATION

Conservationists from other areas are often skeptical about the ability of COSC to weld greatly diverse organizations and viewpoints into an effective force for a quality environment. They ask these questions: How is coordination accomplished? What happens when organizations fail to agree? How do small groups keep from being swallowed up? How is Council action communicated so as to influence the decision-making process?

Here are the key COSC guidelines:

1. Organizations coordinate interests and efforts on particular conservation issues by pooling time, talents, and energies on COSC committees, sometimes called "workshops."

Members of COSC committees may come from 5, 10, or 20 different organizations. Currently, there are 11 such committees or workshops. They are devoted to: clean air, water quality, water resources, political education, legislative action, outdoor education, public land law review, roads and highways, wilderness, and wildlife. These committees do not supplant or duplicate committees of organizations within COSC; rather, they serve as a coordinating device.

2. Each COSC organization, workshop or committee serves as a specialist in some area of environmental expertise: the Wilderness Workshop in wilderness; the Colorado Mountain Club on the National Trails System; the Sierra Club on national parks and monuments; the Colorado Wildlife Federation on wildlife management problems. In turn the committees, drawing from a "talent pool" of 26 organizations, are able to provide expert leadership on almost all issues.

3. COSC may be used as a coordinating device for any number of organizations which want to act in concert on a given issue. Neither a "majority rule" nor a "unanimous opinion" is necessary.

There is one key to COSC success—flexibility of action. COSC can speak for any number of organizations on any given issue. The privilege of associating with COSC is not used as a device for whipping organizations into adopting some "straight conservation line." Obviously all 26 organizations are not going to take a single position on every issue, even though this might be desirable. To date there has not been a "minority report" within COSC, although this is theoretically possible and anticipated in the by-laws. The COSC system of coordinated action has worked on nearly 200 issues.

Further, and most important, no action taken by COSC as a council of organizations precludes any or all of the same organizations from taking independent action on the same issue. In fact, Colorado conservationists are constantly urged to act at three levels: (1) as individuals; (2) through their organizations; (3) through COSC. Thus COSC is not a

substitute for action by either individuals or their organizations; instead, it gives both a greater dimension for effectiveness.

4. COSC relies on informality and total citizen involvement to get a job done.

COSC policy provides opportunity for every conservationist to become as deeply involved as he desires. This does not exclude those who may be among the so-called "opposition." For example, highway officials attend meetings of the COSC Roads Committee, which resoundingly defeated a proposal to route Interstate 70 through Colorado's Gore Range-Eagle Nest Primitive Area. Industry representatives are not barred from water quality meetings. Anbody who wants to work can.

5. COSC makes a continuing effort to keep channels of communication open with major agencies and interest groups.

In October, 1966, COSC-CACI Intercom was organized to establish regular dialogue with the Colorado Association of Commerce and Industry. That such "natural enemies" as conservationists and business leaders would actually sit down with each other and talk was almost unheard of. It was assumed that the chasm of misunderstanding would remain bottomless. COSC was accused by some of a "sellout" to big business.

Other inter-communications committees have since been established with the mining industry, the timber industry, the U. S. Forest Service, the National Park Service, the Army Corps of Engineers, the Bureau of Land Management, and several state resource agencies. Representatives of state and federal resource agencies sit on the COSC Board of Directors in a non-voting capacity.

THE COSC PHILOSOPHY

The term "conservation" seems adaptable to almost any resource philosophy. To a powerful Western Congressman, "conservation means wise use, and wise use means conservation." To most Western resource user groups—timber, grazing, mining—conservation means "multiple use" of land resources and "the greatest good for the greatest number." Conservation has been so victimized by clever sloganeering that a whole new terminology embracing environmental quality concepts must be invented.

In many ways, Colorado conservationists have redefined conservation—if not by word, by deed. Perhaps this redefinition process can best be expressed by relating certain touchstones of the COSC philosophy of conservation effectiveness:

A) A belief that responsible conservationists should be concerned and involved with the total environment.

Most conservation groups seem organized to "save" a particular bird, tree, park, or swamp. While such specialized organizations make a great contribution, it is very easy, in concentrating on a single problem, to lose sight of the broad ecological picture and fail to realize that all issues are part of a total environmental ethic. The intricate relationships between seemingly isolated problems such as bird habitat, pesticides, water quality, urban design, and wilderness preservation can easily escape us. Conservationists are not always aware that the total environment is a complicated tapestry; that when a single thread is pulled the whole business starts to unravel.

Only as the environmentally aware become truly ecological in their thinking will they be able to work effectively on one part of the total problem without sacrificing the whole. By the same token, ecological thinking melts away the jealousies and petty competitions that arise between conservation organizations.

B) A conviction that conservationists will become influential in the great social decision-making processes that count only if they are informed and responsible.

Conservationists are often attacked for being ill-informed, failing to do their homework, or acting for emotional reasons. Unfortunately, these charges are sometimes true.

It often seems that the only argument needed to drain a swamp, flood a river valley, slash a freeway through parklands, or strip the earth bare for wood products is that such steps are "necessary for economic development." This is usually accepted as a truth so self-evident that no further investigation is needed. So, for now, conservationists must bear the greater burden of proof if they would challenge the conventional wisdom. Their viewpoints, their arguments, even their philosophy must be researched, documented, and organized with near-faultless logic. They must enlist economists, sociologists, architects, engineers, ecologists, and business leaders on research teams. A responsible, interdisciplinary approach is essential.

C) A belief that intensive communications with major segments of society are indispensable if the conservation philosophy is to prevail.

The many COSC communications committees with industry, government agencies, and interest groups have been mentioned. To further advance this dialogue, Colorado Conservationists have, for the past two summers, cosponsored with the Thorne Ecological Foundation at Aspen, Colorado, a national Seminar on Environmental Arts and Sciences. The main purpose: "To offer an intensive exploration of ecological principles for leaders in business, industry, government, politics, education, religion, the professions, the arts, and the communication field."

D) A belief that conservationists have a responsibility to offer positive programs; particularly, to discover alternative ways of doing things.

It is frequently noted by conservation opponents that they are "against" rather than "for." While this is often an exercise in semantics, it results frequently from the failure of conservationists to offer valid alternatives to environmental destruction. Take the extraction of minerals, for example. In Colorado, conservationists don't oppose mining per se; they work with the mining industry to seek alternatives to mining methods that desecrate the landscape, destroy wildlife habitat, and pollute streams.

There are, of course, points of principle past which COSC will not retreat and on which they can never compromise. The integrity of the national park system—constantly threatened with dams, reservoirs and highways—is a prime example.

There is not space available to record the hundreds of activities in which COSC has become engaged in order to maintain and enhance a quality environment. Its efforts have been recognized by many organizations, including the National Wildlife Federation, the Sears Roebuck Foundation, the City and County of Denver, Holiday Magazine, Field and Stream, and the American Association for Conservation Information. Perhaps its greatest honor is that citizen conservationists in numerous states are following the COSC lead in building effective coordinating structures. The Wyoming Outdoor Coordinating Council, Nevada Open Spaces Council, Utah Open Space Council, Idaho Environmental Council, California Planning and Conservation League, Washington Environmental Council, and Virginia Conservation Council are a few of the new statewide councils which are patterned, at least in part, after COSC.

Now a unique regional environmental effort is also starting in Colorado. The Rocky Mountain Center on Environment was established in August, 1968, with assistance from the Conservation Foundation and the Ford Foundation to provide education, coordination, publications, information, research, and field services for efforts to improve the environment in eight Rocky Mountain States—New Mexico, Arizona, Nevada, Utah, Idaho, Montana, Wyoming, and Colorado. Alan H. Morgan, Executive Director of the Massachusetts Audubon Society, heads a similar organization in Boston—the New England Conservation Service Center.

A Los Angeles business executive recently said: "Conservationists are the wave of the future. They are going to win! I don't see how anybody can avoid getting on their bandwagon." Conservationists will win a quality environment only if all the wheels on the bandwagon are well-oiled and rolling in the same direction.

"The future depends on the shaping of attitudes, beliefs, and values through education."

ENVIRONMENT AND THE SHAPING OF CIVILIZATION

Lynton K. Caldwell

CAN WE really elect to have a high-quality environment? Does the structure of American society — pluralistic, democratic, historically biased in favor of an "everyman's laissez-faire" — permit the shaping of its environment in any way other than by combat and compromise? The question is not whether conflict of interests in the environment can be eliminated. There is no prospect, in a finite world, that they will be. A second practical question is how to raise the levels of information and social concern at which the process of bargaining and accommodation occurs. To improve the human environment, both man and politics must be improved. Men make politics; political institutions influence human behavior; and behavior is heavily influenced by attitudes, beliefs, and values. Purposeful shaping of the environment involves the purposeful shaping of outlooks on life. The quality of the future environment depends, therefore, upon the shaping of attitudes, beliefs, and values through present education.

Some aspects of human conduct are expressions of psychophysical nature. As a civilizing animal it is natural for man to substitute reason and culture for subrational drives, but rational behavior may serve irrational motives. It is, therefore, important to our welfare to understand the nature and effect of physiologically conditioned behavior. If man is a territorial animal, and if he displaces onto the environment aggression generated in his social relationships, knowledge concerning these circumstances could greatly assist development of feasible strategies for effective environmental policy. Yet not all men nor all societies project destructive impulses against the environment. The improvement of man can proceed through education, in the broad sense, while efforts are made also to improve the psychophysical endowment of the human species.

What are the implications for an educational process that will help build better environmental relationships in the future? The structuring of the entire process of formal education around man-environment relationships is not necessarily indicated. Many of the attitudes, beliefs, and values that would improve prospects for better environments in the future are equally suitable to help society to set goals and establish priorities for the future. Education limited to information is of little help. The question becomes one of what attitudes, beliefs, and values the system inculcates. In the broadest sense, the issue is what kind of civilization the process of education will produce.

Within this broader context of educational policy an increased and, in some measure, new focus on environmental relationships and policies will be necessary. This basically ecological aspect of research and teaching has long been neglected to our detriment and to our increasing peril. Recent moves to establish centers or institutes for environmental studies in numbers of colleges and universities indicate intention to remedy the neglect. Through the organization of new courses of study and the reorganization of old ones, higher education is better equipping today's youths to perceive and to assess the meaning of environmental change. Only a beginning has been made and much more needs to be done. It is especially important that basic environmental concepts be built into secondary education where they have heretofore generally been lacking. Education is more than schooling, but it is through formal systematic mass education that the greatest single impact on attitudes, beliefs, and values can be made.

In a techno-scientific age there is no end to the need for learning. Planned, systematic education now continues through adult life and is increasingly civic as well as vocational in character. With the displacement of traditional culture by techno-science, we are confronted with the necessity of working to obtain our civilization. We can no longer merely inherit it. To preserve the culture of the past, whether in art, ethics, historic sites, landscapes, or social institutions, requires unremitting effort. It also requires reappraisal; for not all we inherit is necessarily good.

In the new world struggling to be born it is we who must struggle. The disintegration of traditional culture is a grim and tragic process. We see its consequences in starkest relief in catastrophes that have befallen the ancient civilization of China. Fortunately for us of the Western World, the concepts of self-actualization and of the evolution of man and society are embodied in our culture. Yet, although these internalized concepts may have helped to spare us the misfortunes of China, they have not helped us to be self-actualizing in all respects. Why have they not been more effective in guiding public effort toward better environmental decisions? The explanation

Dr. Caldwell is Professor of Government at Indiana University, Bloomington. This paper is excerpted from his "Epilogue" to Congress and the Environment, edited by Richard A. Cooley and Geoffrey Wandesforde-Smith, University of Washington Press, 1970.

lies perhaps in the complexity of our culture and in the particular ways in which these concepts are expressed in our society. More certainly, our educational system has not equipped people to make well-considered environmental choices.

We are not yet able to explain why some societies adopt ecologically valid goals and practices and others do not. Simplified explanations are likely to be wrong, but it is possible to draw certain general conclusions from the courses that contrasting cultures have taken, without fully understanding the causal factors. For example, although no simple explanation seems adequate to account for the decline of Chinese civilization, the inadvertent overstressing of the environment by sheer numbers of people seems to have been a critical factor. The ethos of China, less complex and more dogmatic than the ideologies of the West, was more congenial to harmony with nature. Yet neither philosophy, bureaucracy, nor science enabled China to avoid the environmental impoverishment that followed a slowly increasing but unremitting pressure of man on the land. In the West, science and technology enabled society to achieve a more productive and better balanced relationship to the natural world even though, paradoxically, the dominant attitudes toward nature tended as much toward hostility as toward harmony. Industrialization and the colonization of the Americas relieved in Europe the inordinate stress of man on his environment that accompanied the decline of Chinese civilization. But we have no assurance that the combination of culture and technology that, with obvious exceptions, has worked well for the West will continue to do so in the techno-scientific society of the future.

Two obvious aspects of the historical threshold over which all society is now passing are exponential increases of people and of power. The danger in destructive or misguided attitudes toward nature has become greater today because of the greater means to translate attitudes into action. Guided ignorance in the form of dogma appears to have been a factor in the decline of old China; unguided knowledge in the form of technocratic optimism appears to have been the characteristic danger to the West. Today, the establishment of guidelines for knowledge in the application of science and technology to the human environment is a task of urgent importance everywhere. The task is urgent because until it is accomplished there will be no adequate basis in theory or principle upon which to base public and international policies for the custody, care, and development of the human environment.

In America, we have no corpus of ecological doctrine in our public life comparable to that which now influences or governs our economic decisions. Our public life is shaped by particular interpretations, or misinterpretations, of self-actualization and freedom to change that tend to contradict the concepts that they are presumed to exemplify. These misinterpretations although deeply rooted in American society are neither uniquely nor necessarily American. They may be changed, and they must be changed, if the shaping of American civilization is to enlarge the public happiness and welfare. Among the attitudes that misinterpret the meaning of human freedom the following are especially familiar and especially harmful to the quality of civilization and its environment;

first, an uncritical bias for growth; second, techno-economic determinism; third, cultural relativism; and, fourth, self-centered individualism—the "everyman's laissez-faire."

These attitudes share certain negative characteristics significant for the environment-shaping process. None of them imply or require self-restraint or control, none suggest individual or collective accountability, none concede the existence of criteria for evaluating the use of the environment that are independent of individual interest or preference. All of these attitudes suggest resistance to any general pattern of environmental development in society or to any meaningful standards of environmental quality, per se. They do not preclude the imposition of social control where a clear and present danger to individual well-being can be proved. But they severely retard the establishment of general principles of ecological policy upon which more specific standards can be based. More critical attention to their effects is therefore needed.

The "growthmanship" attitude is deeply embedded in American culture. Whether our national obsession with quantitative growth can be transformed into qualitative growth, or growth within a self-renewing or an internally dynamic homeostatic system is conjectural. The most problematic growth of all is that of numbers of people. In America there are grounds for cautious optimism that the national enthusiasm for numbers may someday be displaced by a concern for the quality of human life generally.

Techno-economic determinism, or the "you can't stop progress" attitude, is still firmly ascendant in American life—despite critical attack from both science and aesthetics. Supersonic transport and airports unlimited are only current examples of a national tendency. It is curious that people vigilantly jealous of their rights in relation to government will permit their privacy, convenience, and even health to be jeopardized by costly and unnecessary technological innovation that yields little, if any, social benefit. More strange is the tendency of science-oriented, rational people to accept the metaphysical dogma of technological inevitability. It is, as we have emphasized, a contradiction to the tacit belief of Americans in the self-actualization of the human personality. It is an example of compartmentalized thinking against which education has not yet provided sufficient protection.

Cultural relativism has permeated the social sciences and has strongly influenced ethical and religious thought. The value of a demonstrably valid set of ecological principles by which public policy could be guided would be very great. It could provide a common ground for greater consensus. But it would encounter objections from those who hold that science has nothing to do with values, and that one man's values are as good as another's. Our slowness in exploring the biosocial interface in science has kept us from providing an adequate and convincing answer to arguments over relativity or priority among values in the environment. Political accommodation among conflicting interests therefore tends to occur at too low a conceptual level to give adequate weight to scientific knowledge or ecological wisdom.

The laissez-faire attitude toward the rights of individuals in relation to the environment has suffered some attrition through public action on behalf of public health and safety. Land-use planning and zoning, and emerging pollution control legislation, further constrain individual behavior in relation to the environment. We are beginning to lay a foundation for a legal doctrine of public rights in the environment, as distinguished from the specific and discrete prohibitions that have hitherto characterized our environmental policy. Yet at the local level of government and throughout large areas of the country where pressure on the environment has not been felt acutely, the right to exploit the environment for personal advantage is still very broadly construed. Here again culture shapes environmental attitudes. The psychology of the frontiersman is still vigorous and when reinforced by techno-scientific capability can be a very potent force, usually in ways harmful to environmental quality.

A characteristic common to all of these foregoing attitudes is that each of them is highly dysfunctional to the effective public control of applied science or technology. They derive from viewpoints formed mostly in the prescientific world, although cultural relativism reflects to some degree an inclination to be scientific. Relativistic thinking that dismisses weight of evidence and insists upon incontrovertible proof of the validity of one environmental attitude as against another has abandoned science for a philosophical fetish. In actuality these attitudes do not appear as clear-cut or consistent categories of belief or behavior. They are interwoven in the fabric of our social, political, and economic life, and this is why it becomes so difficult to change them. It is why environment shaping becomes culture shaping, and why attack upon the environmental abuses of our industrial society readily becomes an attack upon certain aspects of the structure of the society itself.

These remarks began with an allusion to the concept of two worlds—the familiar but no longer viable past and the future which, more than a transition from the past, appears to bring a change of state in the human condition. Related to this concept is that of two cultures, popularized by C. P. Snow. Each of these concepts is expressive of the change that science has brought into the world. Both imply discontinuities in culture: chronological, intellectual, and emotional.

The truth of these interpretations of present history is perhaps more poetic than rigorously factual, more qualitative than quantitatively demonstrable. A truth may be substantial without being universal. And it seems true that the means to shape the environment of civilized societies belong largely to science; whereas the purposes of men, the standards of beauty, order, aesthetic satisfaction, welfare, and even of some aspects of health belong to the humanities. This separation between the custodians of means and ends in our society creates weakness and discontinuity at the point of social decision. It is in the process of public policy making that the respective contributions of the "two cultures" are needed to form a mutually comprehensible and coherent unity.

The size and complexity of modern society require specialization. In the absence of integrative forces, occupational differences tend to fractionalize society.

Communication across occupational lines becomes difficult, and no common set of assumptions or values provides a meeting ground for differing interests. The openness of modern society is deceptive. Freed from barriers of class and caste, it is more subtly fragmented by techno-scientific specialization and by the progressive isolation of the traditional culture from techno-science.

Here perhaps lies the answer to the question of why contemporary Western techno-scientific society has not dealt more effectively with its environmental problems. Means and ends are separated. The wholeness of man and of society requires a synthesis or integration in orientation toward the world and life that conventional education has not provided. Thus, as we earlier observed, contradictory tendencies of modern American society are built into its social system. And it is this schizoid tendency that most of all makes it difficult for the United States of America to develop a guiding set of environmental policies or to employ more than a fraction of the potential power of science and technology on behalf of human welfare.

Science has placed in the hands of man knowledge and power that makes him responsible for his future; it has not given him the moral compulsion to act responsibly. The substantive values that science and technology serve are articulated in the humanities, but are seldom amenable to scientific verification. It is at this interface between science and the humanities that environmental policy, if made, is made. And it is at this interface also that higher education can contribute to resolving what some observers have called our environmental crisis.

How this task can be accomplished in the colleges and universities is yet to be discovered, and it must also be acknowledged that education alone will not solve our problems. There is no master blueprint equally applicable to all institutions or to all aspects of the educational task. But these elements in that task are universal: first, it is primarily one of synthesis—its basic data will be derived largely from the established disciplines that individually are unable to bring together knowledge relevant to environmental policy in a comprehensive or coherent system; second, its concern is not merely with the appearance of things, but with the purpose, quality, and worth of man-environment relationships; third, it reinforces rather than dilutes efforts in the separate sciences and humanities because it establishes or clarifies their relevance to life; fourth and finally, it emphasizes a truth that is too often forgotten—that through education the civilization of the future is shaped.

Past generations of Americans, and men generally, have understood education as preparation for life. It is that, but that is its smaller dimension. Its larger dimension and equally important task is to shape life as well as to help prepare for it. In some degree education has always done this, but often without conscious effort or intention. If man is to be the master of his own ingenuity, and not its victim, he will have to find better ways to relate means to ends, and to evaluate the ends that science makes available to him. In summation, the major task of education and politics is to shape a world in which preparation for life is worthwhile. ∎

Is public environmental awareness a passing fad or a permanent fixture?

AFTER THE TEACH-INS------WHAT?

The Editor

WHEN THE very first settlers came to the region around the tip of Lake Michigan in the early 1800's, they found much of the land covered with "oak openings," or savanna—a striking combination of scattered, mature trees amid prairie patches, the whole array appearing, in the eyes of one early observer, "like so many old orchards" (22).

The trees were principally bur oaks, their characteristic thick bark protecting them uniquely from the fires that raged over the prairies each year. When the fires were stopped by the settlers, a rapid change took place in the oak openings: they became filled with dense stands of oak saplings. But surprisingly, the new oaks were not burs; they were largely blacks. Frequently a pure stand of black oak would spring up amid widely spaced bur oaks even though there might not be any mature blacks for miles around. Some early observers attributed this black oak irruption to a mass seeding of the openings by flocks of passenger pigeons. Each bird was presumed to have carried a single black oak acorn across the prairies to the bur oak grove and dropped it, in concert with his fellows. We now understand that no such charming an explanation is necessary. The black oaks had been there all the time, growing as brush or grubs among the prairie grasses, suppressed by annual fires. When the fires stopped, the black oak developed swiftly into tall, mature trees, gradually shading out many of the open-grown bur oak veterans (11). Today a prairie grove with an intact ground layer is the rarest plant community in the Midwest, yet there are more oak forests than there were in 1800.

I cite this bit of ecological history because it may help us to understand, I believe, what is happening, and what may happen, in the area of what has been called conservation information and education (I &E).

Since the 1900's the American conservation landscape has resembled a savanna. Here and there on a broad prairie of indifference you could identify scattered bur oak individuals, organizations, and agen-

cies, their tough hides protecting them from annual fires of covert carelessness and overt retribution. Now, with breathtaking scope and velocity, the scene has changed. The oak openings of conservation today are thick with saplings. And these saplings are a different species, springing from submerged roots, displaying a distinctive foliage. This much we can see. What lies ahead is problematic. Will the black oak environmentalists grow straight and tall to form a dominant forest, shading out the bur oak veterans? It may indeed be that the militant ecology movement is leading squarely to a broad rearrangement of basic social and economic institutions, as Pekkanen writes (33). Clark, on the other hand, says environmentalism offers nothing really new, and that we had better get back to fundamentals (10). So, will the new cohorts succumb to renewed fires of convention, leaving only the old, gnarled sentinels of concern? Or could we see emerge a unique community of symbiotic relationships between old and new, exhibiting heterosis—hybrid vigor.

If those of us in environmental communications and education are to continue to contribute effectively to the emergence of a broad ecological conscience, it will be helpful if we speculate sensibly about possible answers to such questions as I have posed. But before we can do so, we must ask several more. What characterizes the "new conservation"? Who is the "new conservationist"? What was responsible for his irruption? And then, finally, where are we all going?

THE NEW CONSERVATION

In another paper (42) I have gone to some lengths to delineate the differences between the old "conservation" and the new "environmentalism." While some differences may be more apparent than real, others are quite distinctive. They may be summarized as follows:

In terms of its scope, the new environmentalism attempts to be all-encompassing. Whereas yesterday

---

Professor Schoenfeld's article is based on addresses to the Wisconsin Governor's Conference on Environmental Education, Wausau, Wisconsin, February 25, 1970, and to the 35th North American Wildlife and Natural Resources Conference, Chicago, Illinois, March 25, 1970.

we tended to treat soil conservation, water conservation, forest conservation, wildlife conservation, and so on, as separate units, today we try to understand and explain the ecological unity of all man-land relationships. In terms of its focus, then, the new environmentalism is man-centered. That is, our primary concern has shifted from the survival of remnant redwoods and raptors to the survival of nothing less than the human species itself. At the same time we are not so much concerned about quantities of natural resources as we are about the quality of human experience. "Conservation used to be merely a hobby practiced above the 10,000-foot level by a few eccentrics," Bylin has said. "Today it has become a universal synonym for human survival" (6).

In terms of its locus, while the old conservation conjured up images of open country, the new environmentalism incorporates the pressing problems of the city. In terms of its emotional underpinnings, the new environmentalism is based more on fear for man's tomorrow than on a love for nature's yesterday. Thus today's "preservationist" is not a lover of wilderness; he is one who fears the four horsemen of "conquest, slaughter, famine, and death." In terms of its political alliances, the old conservation was linked to such orthodox causes as depression pump-priming, national defense, and outdoor recreation; the new environmentalism, on the other hand, encompasses the hitherto unmentionable demands of the neo-Malthusians for population control.

It is in its basic cultural orientation, however, that the new environmentalism differs most strikingly from its antecedent, conservation. The latter, in the words of one patron saint, stood clearly for economic development for the infinite goodness of American "progress" (36). But environmentalism reflects a growing suspicion that bigger is not necessarily better, slower can be faster, and less can be more. As Pett has written recently, "more and more people actively seek to conserve a tree, a lake, a view. More people question the Biblical injunction to be fruitful and multiply. More people question the old American faith in growth and expansion, and suggest that maybe what we don't need is another factory in town. More middle-aged people have begun to sense the validity in the young who scorn the plastic life" (34). Upon viewing a new smokestack, millions of Americans used to see a sign of progress; now they see a sign of pollution. The mammoth motor car used to be a symbol of affluence; now it is a symbol of effluence.

If anything surely marks this revolutionary nature of both the rise and rationale of the new environmentalism, it would be the recent words of a Republican President of the United States, telling us that "wealth and happiness are not the same thing," that now is the time to "make our peace with nature," and that we must "measure success or failure by new criteria" (32). Not even F.D.R. would have said that!

If it all sounds suspiciously like echoes of Thoreau and Leopold, it only suggests that the black oaks were indeed here all the time, waiting only for a favorable concatenation of events to vault the philosophies of a Walden or Sand County muse into a State of the Union address.

THE NEW CONSERVATIONIST

Now, who is the "new conservationist"? He

comes, of course, in pellage of many colors, and it will take years of sociological research before we can arrange him by phylum and genus. But on the basis of subjective analysis it seems to me that we can take note of at least three types.

First, there is the old conservationist who has acquired an awareness of the global nature of what once seemed a parochial problem, an understanding of some new points of entre toward constructive action, and a vastly heightened sense of urgency. He is the erstwhile County Conservation League member who has shifted his emphasis from prairie chickens to air pollution. He is the Sierra Clubber who has added "human survival" to his agenda. He is the Park Service specialist who is trying to take his parks to the people instead of vice versa. Witness the words of the National Wildlife Federation: "Conservation is no longer just the story of vanishing wildlife and vanishing wilderness areas. There is a new urgency in the word today. Suddenly, as we stop and look at our total environment, it has taken on the meaning of human survival" (47). Yet by no means have all old conservationists boarded wholeheartedly the ecological express. After all, like bur oaks, they have survived by resisting the fires of their surroundings, and they see the present situation as but another momentary diversion. We can expect to see them dotting the landscape indefinitely, lending perspective if not punch.

The second distinct type of new conservationist is a "she." But she is not the proverbial "little old lady in tennis shoes" who has graced the ranks of the bird watchers. She is the sharp young housewife whose automated kitchen has rendered her under-employed, and who, in looking around for new worlds to conquer, has discovered the environment and its problems. Through such local fire brigades as Capital Community Citizens and such national organizations as the League of Women Voters she is lying down in front of bulldozers, accosting legislators in their lairs, baiting conservation bureaus, plumping for bond issues, and in general raising polite hell in the best traditions of American Populism.

Perhaps the truest type of new conservationist is the committed college student who is making his presence felt through such activities as a national campus environmental teach-in. He is indeed a new breed in several respects. As a matter of fact, he is several breeds. At the far left is the true radical who sees environmental degradation as the Achilles heel of capitalism, and hence is riding conservation as his current hobby-horse toward revolution. For this "Maonow" clique, the mouthy revolutionaries who profess to see some social Nirvana beckoning at the end of a trail of brutal confrontation, real conservation is the least of their concerns (29). At the opposite end of the spectrum is the professional student in one of the resource management fields who is doing what comes naturally to him, in orthodox ways yet with early verve and elan. They are saying to their elders, in effect: "It is you and your system that have brought about the environmental mess which is making much of the world unlivable. Now, before it is too late, let us have a say about the profession and the planet that we are to inherit" (7). It is the students occupying the great middle ground of the movement who are unique. They represent everything from art to zoology. They come from Boswash and Grover's Corners. They have long and short hair, full pocketbooks and lean. Their folk heroes may be George Wallace or Bertrand Russell. They may know everything or nothing about the hydrologic cycle. Yet they have certain attributes in common: a neo-Transcendental feeling for the man-land community, a revulsion for the excesses of a technological society, a suspicion of the Establishment, a sense of so little time, and a consuming desire to act, now, and the devil take anybody who doesn't. As a Washington observer reports: "No g r o u p is more concerned, or more disgusted, about the growing destruction of the American environment than the young. First, they haven't been around long enough to become accomplices in the pollution violence, assuming they might want to. Second, the young a r e more concerned about saving the environment because they will be the worst casualties if it is not saved. Although many student environmental activists are using little more than the scream method, others are digging in for a long seige by finding out about the economics, the technology, and the politics of environmental problems" (28). The young e c o-activist, in sum, is the same disenchanted American who came over in steerage, who pushed into the West. He is the same American who took off with a song for Bull Run, Belleau Woods, and Buna. Now the environment is his only frontier left, and the eco-war the only one he wants to fight. He insists on doing his own thing. He is willing to cooperate with the old-line conservation organizations, but he lives in fear of being coopted by them—that and the fear that a fatal public paralysis will render his cause impotent. He may call his mission impossible, but he still has an innate faith in the future, if only we act in time.

In essence, the practitioners of the old conservation have been exponents of the art of the possible. The new recruits see environmentalism as the science of the impossible.

THE NEW ENVIRONMENT

Now, what has triggered today's mass irruption of the new conservationist? Historians, with the perspective of 50 years, have never been able to agree on the factors responsible for the so-called "first wave" of conservation at the turn of the c e n t u r y. Hays (19) says conservation had its origin in a concern for scientific management and efficiency among a relatively small group of planners and technicians. Bates (3), on the other hand, argues that the movement was a grass-roots upswelling of many passionate people versus the special interests of the d a y. From current experience, perhaps we can see that both of these explanations have their points.

Unquestionably today's environmentalism has its roots in the labors of a handful of leaders: particularly ecologists turned writers like Leopold, Carson, Darling, Commoner, Allen, Dasmann, and Ehrlich; and politicians turned ecologists like Udall, Nelson, Muskie, and Jackson. Unquestionably, too, the movement is taking on all the dimensions of a somewhat spontaneous general revolution in thinking, if not in action. In this transmutation of environmentalism from a learned cult to everybody's cause, many factors have surely been significant.

Gaus (16) once pinpointed the critical elements in the ecology of any institution o r movement a s "people, place, physical technology, social technology, wishes and ideas, catastrophe, and personality."

A brief examination of these factors at work in the America of the latter 1960's may illuminate the origins and development of our new ecological conscience.

The American people in 1970 are simply ready for the conservation message in a way they have never been before (40). They have been on a decade-long emotional binge that has left them both frustrated and pent up: multiple assassinations, civil rights confrontations, campus unrest, Vietnam, cost of living, crime in the streets—as F. Scott Fitzgerald once described a somewhat similar era, "all gods are dead, all wars fought, all faiths in man shaken." L i t t l e wonder that Americans are turning to their original font of solace, inspiration, and challenge—to nature, its ways and wise use. Countless individual leanings toward environmental concerns have been reinforced by the sense of community growing o u t of a timely Gallup poll, which indicated that conservation now is everybody's "thing" (8). Another key social force is that ever-growing army of the young: "Modern technological society postpones the age of work and responsibility. Many of the young must be trained through high school, university, graduate school, and apprenticeship. In the meantime, the student can afford the luxury of a strictly ethical view of the world—uncluttered by those compromises and deals that are the glue of any society" (24). And in this long meantime, the student moralist is having a profound impact on politics—and on pollution abatement.

Yesterday's environmental degradation was usually over the hill and far away—in somebody else's dust bowl, somebody else's Echo Canyon, somebody else's boundary water canoe area, somebody else's forest. But the place of today's environmental degradation is where we live—in the foul air, rancid water, and clogged arteries of our cities. Millions can see, smell, taste, and hear the problem now: "The environment may well be the gut issue that can unify a polarized nation in the 1970's. It may also divide people who are appalled by the mess from those who have adapted to it. No one knows how many Americans have lost all feeling for nature and the quality of life. Even so, the issue now attracts young a n d old, farmers, city dwellers, and suburban housewives, scientists, industrialists, and blue-collar workers. They know pollution well. It is as close as the water tap, the car-clogged streets a n d junk-filled landscape—their country's visible decay" (45:56).

Continuing along the Gaus outline, t h e physical technology of the 60's has been responsible for o u r current state of mind in a striking way. It has vaulted us to the moon, and thus has given us renewed faith in our capacity to conquer, but from our new vantage point in the cosmos we have also been struck as never before by the fragile, finite character of Spaceship Earth. By invading one frontier we have rediscovered another, the state of harmony between man a n d land. So we are appalled that the combined governmental expenditure at all levels on natural resources, including agriculture, amounted to less than $7 billion last year, while we spent $9.7 billion for tobacco, $15.5 billion for liquor, and $5 billion for c o s-metics (18). We are particularly appalled because the technological eye of the decade—the TV camera—has brought environmental degradation right into our living rooms with stark realism. Along with scenes from Selma and Saigon, we have squirmed at scenes from Santa Barbara and Sanguine.

Developments in the social technology of the 60's have likewise played a part in the rise of eco-awareness and eco-action. The voice of the mass media has become increasingly dominated by a coterie of magazine editors and TV commentators, so when these gatekeepers of communications have seized on pollution as the big story, the snowball effect has been dramatic. Not in our wildest dreams as conservation I & E people have we thought that Time, Life, Newsweek, Look, Fortune, and Sports Illustrated would ever devote simultaneous issues to ecology, yet that is exactly what happened earlier this year, accompanied by electronic voices like those of Walter Cronkite, Eric Sevareid, John Chancellor, David Brinkley, and Ed Newman, not to mention Arthur Godfrey, Eddie Albert, Johnny Carson, and Pete Seeger.

(What got the media onto the population-pollution story so compellingly? It is probably not without significance that the big media messages in this country originate from our two most populated and polluted places—New York and Los Angeles.)

The media calls to reveille might still have met with no response were there not throughout the land a spirit of rank-and-file activism, particularly on the part of the young. Whether you call this spirit a new "participatory democracy" or a throw-back to the Boston Tea Party, the result is the same— a confidence in the tactics of confrontation. Americans have witnessed the subtle yet sure effects of civil rights marches and peace moratoria, they have seen the results of brass-knuckles conservation as practiced by the Environmental Defense Fund, they have watched a David like Ralph Nader take on the Goliath auto industry; and now they are ready to practice the same guerrilla warfare on a broad scale for a cause that is easily identified with all the better angels.

In their wishes and ideas, all the great ecological philosophers have always expressed frankly the belief that true conservation would require a profound change in American values. But nobody really listened. We went right on basing our practices on economics at the expense of the esthetic and the ethical. Now, however, the youth of America are beginning to get the real message that was there all the time. It fits right in with their basic anti-materialism, anyway. Probably nothing so accounts for the current popularity of conservation on our campuses as this marriage of orthodox ecological doctrine with the innate iconoclasm of the young. In environmentalism there is no generation gap: "It is possible that ecologists can eventually stir enough people to an emotion as old as man—exaltation. Ecology, the subversive science, enriches man's perceptions, his vision, his concept of reality. In nature, many may find the model they need to cherish" (45:63).

Social scientists are saying that only once before in recent American history has there been so profound and rapid a change in American public opinion as the rise of eco-understanding. That was the flip-flop from isolationism to interventionism occasioned by Pearl Harbor. So it is all the more striking that the emergence of ecology as everybody's "bag" has not been triggered by a single catastrophe. We have had, in recent months, our Everglades, our Storm Kings, and our Alaskas, but these have not been continental disasters. Yet this is just the point. Today's catastrophe is not a single clap of thunder; it is a pervasive drizzle, and thus all the more far-reaching. There is literally no dry spot. Millions can sense that swelling population, rampant technology, and fragile biosphere are on a collision course, threatening the quality of the human experience if not the very survival of man.

No single personality dominates the ecology of environmentalism as T. R. and F. D. R. dominated the first two waves of conservation. President Nixon has tried to preempt the movement, but it is doubtful that he will be able to make his image stick. Nor will any one scientist or interpreter likely run away with the show. Rather, the new conservation is characterized by the diversity of its exponents and troopers. It is, in itself, a complex ecosystem, and this speaks well for its stability and longevity. "Few of the (conservationist) troops know who their generals are, or even their sergeants" (26). Perhaps one day a Bill Mauldin will capture in cartoons the personality of this new-style World War III, and it will not be a Patton, but the peace-time equivalent of G. I. Joe.

Out of the changing people, places, technology, aspirations, conflicts, and personages of America at the turn of the decade has come a new spirit and a new agenda. The spirit is an embryo ecological conscience. The agenda is clean air, clean water, open space, zero population increase—an illusive yet essential entente between modern man and the only home he has. In short, we sense that "we have mortgaged the old homestead and nature is liable to foreclose" (39). Or we may sense that "the real specter that pollution casts over man's future is not, perhaps, the extinction of Homo sapiens but his mutation into some human equivalent of the carp now lurking in Lake Erie's fetid depths, living off poison" (31). Dubos speculates that man can indeed adapt to most anything, even the dirt, pollution, and noise of the city And that, he says, would be the real tragedy, worse than extinction—a progressive degradation of the quality of the human animal (12).

TURMOIL AND TRENDS

Will we make it? What will our prairie grove look like 30 years from now? Will the black oaks of the new environmentalism be the dominant species, the old burs rotting and fracturing in the shade? It could happen. After all, the veteran resource management agencies and organizations are not particularly ecological in their orientations. On the contrary, they tend to espouse unilateral programs and cultivate special-interest clientele. For example, the Soil Conservation Service supports the drainage of the same wetlands the Bureau of Sport Fisheries and Wildlife seeks to preserve, the Corps of Engineers would innundate a national park without batting an eye, the Forest Service has never been much of a custodian of wilderness, the Bureau of Outdoor Recreation already represents yesterday's patrician focus, and "the farm-subsidy program encourages the misuse of toxic chemicals, one-crop farming that destroys ecological diversity, and mechanization that drives jobless rural laborers into packed cities" (45:63). If these agencies and their publics are so inflexible as to resist coordination, they may well wither. Indeed, the white light of publicity we have all caused to fall on conservation can hasten the demise of the organization that temporizes in adjusting to changing times, changing priorities, and changing audiences. As Pitzer says, "We can make no greater mistake than to shrug off the ideas of the young as foolish and impractical. It will be at our peril that we encourage them to point the way to a better world, only to tell them later that nothing can be done about it. Conversely, youthful idealism and energy represent a potent force for good if only we can give it productive and creative outlets. We must be willing to change" (37).

On the other hand, our prairie grove of the year 2000 may be punctuated only by the old bur oaks. It could happen. The new environmentalism could turn out to be only a passing fad, like hula-hoops. Americans are given to switching issues in mid-stream. Whatever happened to United Nations Day? Some are already saying that while "the conservation and proper use of natural resources may be a fundamental problem, that should not divert the nation's attention from the problems of social justice and racial equality" (45:8). Writes Beyers, "I particularly note a growing resentment among blacks that environmental interests may represent a white 'cop out' from pressing issues of race and poverty" (5).

Or perhaps the sonorous voices of gloom and doom will render us absolutely insensitive to any possibilities for progress. The fallout scare of the 50's produced precious few underground shelters. You already hear the complaint: "We have read the statistics of degradation, and heard them, and flinched at them, and even wearied of them; statistics that boggle the mind, and that are repeated like clockwork every year, inching higher and higher. It takes something really different—like a river so filthy it actually catches fire—to engage our jaded attention" (1). The Jeremiahs of the movement could indeed have such a narcotic effect on public opinion that masses of Americans will "tune out." Taffler has already written of the danger of "future shock" which forces us to crawl into our shells in utter despair (46).

The new recruits may also just plain run out of gas "when the bandwagon stops coasting and has to be dragged up the hills" (9). Or they may climb off "when the limits of present ecological expertise become apparent" (21).

There is another danger: If the eco-activists on college campuses become dominated by neo-Fascist hooligans, irreparable damage will be done to the new environmentalism. Riots will repel, not attract, support. The single thing more dangerous to man than environmental pollution could be the growing clamor over the issue, according to Theobald. Intense efforts to change the established social order could produce a reactionary backlash that would pit man against man in a most unecological fashion (44).

Hopefully there can be a third broad possibility a welding of old and new. In many cases today, what was once a natural prairie grove is dominated neither by bur oaks or blacks but by thrifty white oaks. These white oaks exhibit some resistance to fire as well as a tolerance of shade. Perhaps we will likewise see emerge a lay ecologist with all the lore and savvy of the old-line conservationist and all the heightened idealism and sense of mission of the new environmentalist. We need both, as Margolis has pointed out. If the traditional conservation organizations had just

spent all their time worrying about ecology, fewer woods and waters would have been saved in recent years. If the new conservation is to succeed, it will be through the mainstream of going groups, he says, yet groups that grasp the technical and radical rules of the new ballgame (26). We must seek a conservation movement old enough to have traditions and young enough to transcend them.

In this regard it is particularly intriguing to see the hesitant yet healthy emergence of an eco-industry. We are beginning to hear of "ecological stocks" pacing the New York exchange. If Americans can learn to make as much money out of environmental husbandry as we have out of environmental exploitation, the problem will be solved with some dispatch. It will be particularly important that the private sector lend a massive hand, because environmental reclamation is not a nice, neat governmental package like a Manhattan project or a lunar landing. It is more like the Depression or World War II in its breadth and diversity. True, "attacking environmental ailments has a special appeal for Americans; in large part they are technical and mechanistic problems that involve processes, flows, things, and the American genius seems to run that way" (45:7). So a typical American response to a series of crises in a given field has been to smother it with money and expect solutions to appear promptly. "But environmental-quality problems do not lend themselves to this kind of approach. There is no single goal toward which technology, economics, and management can marshal their forces. Environmental pollution and degradation appear in many forms and many places, and successful programs of prevention and amelioration will be difficult and many-sided. The complex scientific-engineering-economic-political-management-educational programs for cleaning up the air, the water, and the landscape will have to be tailored to meet different situations in various regions of the country, in various industries, and in various social conditions" (13). Furthermore, "practical ways to resolve the obvious conflict of economy and environment are far from clear for a free society. There is real danger that the current emphasis on the importance of ecological balance will obscure the importance of economic balance." Certainly we cannot go back to some Medieval womb. We must start with what we have and work forward.

One way to make the economic system accountable for the damage it does to the environment is to work the costs of avoiding environmental damage right into the pricing system. As higher prices then begin to show up for goods whose manufacture damages the environment, the mass re-examination of values necessary to the beginnings of broad environmentalism may begin to take hold (2). In a real sense the revolution in the way we view things may already be happening. That is, we may already be seeing a mutation of our bur and black oaks, so to speak. For a particularly perceptive analysis of this new "counter-culture," I quote from Edward Kern in a recent issue of Life:

Gradually but imperceptibly, the ties that held people to the old ways of thinking are loosening and new ties are being formed to a new outlook. It is often said that we are in the midst of a social revolution. The truth, probably, is both something less and something considerably more. There is a social revolution, which seems only

to have begun; but there is also something
more profound—a revolution of consciousness. Conceivably it could alter the whole
aspect of America and produce a new species of American. If it does, this would
not necessarily doom the existing structure
of institutions or the present forms of political life. The impersonal pressures of
advancing technology are certain to have a
great effect on these, and trends point to
larger and more complex organizations in
the future rather than to the simplicities of
the counter-cultural commune. But organizations, from one standpoint, are social
vessels which are designed to contain humanity. What matters most is the quality
of human consciousness that is poured into
them, and time may prove that it is possible,
after all, to pour new wine into old bottles (23).

THE BIG TEST

In summary, what is really on trial in the tension
zone of the '70's is not a movement. It is the processes of American education, American democracy,
and American culture.

Can education go beyond a mere imparting of ecological facts to inculcate a will and a way for the
individual and collective solution of environmental
problems?

One difficulty in changing attitudes toward environmental exploitation is that attitudes toward the
environment are tied to overriding values which are
highly resistant to change. There are many basic
values in Western culture that support environmental destruction—the Abrahamic concept of land, for
example. But there are also basic values which
support environmental conservation—the survival instinct, for instance (38). We need not be discouraged. When threatened, man is capable of almost
anything. Today, nothing less than our survival is
at stake. The problem is getting enough people to
realize this blunt truth while there is still time to
act (25). Yet fear will not be enough as a long-term
motivating factor. We need love: "The one thing
needed to recover and preserve the American environment is a reverence for earth—paying fair homage
to the soil, the winds, the waters, and honoring the
very spirit of their places" (27). Whatever the
theme, the practitioners of conservation information
and education have one easy test of their solvency
today: If they are not drawing fire from the flanks,
what they are putting out is not getting to the heart
of the problem. There is simply no easy compromise between the old economics and the new ecology
(41). All this suggests to us purveyors of ecological information and education that if we are indeed
to be "in tune with the dynamics of the age," which
J. A. R. Pimlott once described as the essence of
public relations (35), then we had better desist from
merely husbanding our particular organizations and
agencies. We must "get with" producing an enlightened citizenry that will, in the words of the author
of the Environmental Quality Education Act, understand "man's unquestioned interdependence with
nature," appreciate that "scientific advance is not
always synonymous with progress," and "use an

ecologic filter when making important policy decisions" (30).

Can industry and government move beyond mere
tokenism in their response to environmental degradation, with imaginative programs that demonstrate
the relevancy of capitalism and democracy to gut issues?

The political and economic conflicts growing out
of militant ecology will be enormous, Gerlach pre-
dicts: "The question is whether or not those responsible for damaging the environment will be wise enough
and adaptable enough to see what is being demanded
of them and accommodate to it. The key to holding
us together is how business and political leadership
responds. Confrontation is unavoidable because the
environmental problem does not lend itself to tokenism—too many people are aware; too much is seen;
the crisis is too great. The strongest argument for
optimism is that the leaders of the movement are the
educated people who know where the levers of power
are and who are willing to use them short of taking
to the streets" (17).

Can our society create a new consumerism that
demands less goods and gadgets, and more capacity
to preserve, protest, and defend our natural heritage?

The answers to most population-pollution problems can only be found in trade-offs. If something
undesirable is to go, something desirable may have
to go as well. You can't air-condition your home,
for example, unless somebody is burning fossil or
nuclear fuel to produce electricity. It is the making
of sophisticated choices, then, the rendering of subtle
value judgments, that is the essence of conservation
today. Our first task is a good old American goal—
to restore more freedom of choice. The consumer
who wants to conserve must be given the chance to
conserve—in the marketplace, in his home, at the
ballot-box. And then we in positions of leadership
will be increasingly put to the test of outlining the
options in an unemotional, objective, self-disciplined
manner. "If expertise comes wrapped in pretentious-
ness, over-emotion, and intellectual dishonesty, we
only add moral insult to environmental injury" (43).

The United States simply must start inventing genuine "political, economic, and intellectual processes
that will give us, as a society and as individuals, more
real choice about how we live" (4). These are not
the words of a Berkeley fanatic; they are the words
of Fortune magazine. We must, in short, begin to
engage, once and for all, in ecological thinking. As
someone has said, we cannot ever do only one thing.
When we try to pick out anything by itself, we find it
inexorably connected to something else. And we cannot do everything all at once. We must rid ourselves of the mentality of the 30-second commercial and
the 30-minute comedy. Environmental housekeeping
is a never-ending serial.

Put another way, what is really at stake in the
'70's is US. We must demand of ourselves the same
high quality we demand of the environment.

What is necessary is an unflagging respect for the
world, and for man. For dissent and diversity. For
those natural amenities that husband the prosperity
of the human spirit. For those human institutions
that protect freedom of choice. If we simply regret

what we have done, we must regret that we are men. It is only by accepting ourselves for what we are, the worst of us and the best of us, that we can hold any hope for the future (20).

To paraphrase John Gardner:

We will not find our way out of our present troubles until a large number of Americans acknowledge their own special contribution. The path to recovery will call for courage and stamina. Our salvation will not be handed to us. If we are lucky we will have a chance to earn it. Many things are wrong. Many things must be done. There is no middle state for the spirit. It rises to high levels of discipline and decency and purpose—or it sags and rots. We must call for the best or live with the worst (15).

REFERENCES

1. Allen, James E., Jr., "Education for Survival," U.S. Office of Education, Washington, D.C., January 13, 1970, mimeograph, p. 3.

2. Anderson, David C., "Policy Riddle: Ecology Versus the Economy," Wall Street Journal, February 2, 1970, p. 8.

3. Bates, J. Leonard, "Fulfilling American Democracy," Mississippi Valley Historical Review, 44:29-57.

4. Bowne, William, "Our New Awareness of the Great Web," Fortune, February 1970, p. 199.

5. Byers, Bob, Stanford University New Service, personal correspondence from author's files, February 24, 1970.

6. Bylin, James E., "Conservation Gains Political Weight," Wall Street Journal, November 26, 1969, p. 8.

7. Cahn, Robert, "Youth Takes Over at National Environmental Conference," Christian Science Monitor, December 4, 1969, p. 10.

8. Chaney, Ed. "The Environment: Who Cares? Why? So What?" Environmental Education, Spring 1970, pp. 80-82.

9. Chaney, Ed, "Oh, Those Precious Bodily Fluids," Conservation News, February 1, 1970, p. 3.

10. Clark, Wilson B., "The Environmental Education Banner," Environmental Education, Fall 1969, p. 7.

11. Curtis, John T., The Vegetation of Wisconsin, The University of Wisconsin Press, Madison, 1959, pp. 334-337.

12. Dubos, Rene, "We Can't Buy Our Way Out," Psychology Today, March 1970, p. 20.

13. Fisher, Joseph L., "Looking Ahead to the 1970's," Annual Report, Resources for the Future, Inc., Washington, D.C., 1969, p. 4.

14. Fortune (special issue on "The Environment: A National Mission for the Seventies"), February 1970, editorial, p. 93.

15. Gardner, John, quoted in Saul Pett, "Something's Rotten in the U.S.," Wisconsin State Journal, Madison, February 15, 1970, p. 4.

16. Gaus, John, Reflections in Public Administration, University of Alabama Press, University, Alabama, 1947, p. 6.

17. Gerlach, Luther, quoted by John Pekkanen in "When People Begin Making Sacrifices, You'll See More Militancy," Life, January 30, 1970, p. 30.

18. Hartzog, George B., National Park Service, Washington, D.C., December 1969, mimeograph, p. 6.

19. Hays, Samuel P., Conservation and the Gospel of Efficiency, Harvard University Press, Cambridge, Massachusetts, 1959.

20. Hochbaum, Albert, quoted in Susan Flader, "Deer Management: Ecology and Politics," unpublished PhD thesis, Stanford University, January 1970.

21. Housman, William, The Environment Monthly, February 1970, p. 1.

22. Hoyt, J.W., "Natural Resources of Wisconsin," Transactions of the Wisconsin State Agricultural Society, 6:46-49, 1960.

23. Kern, Edward, "Can It Happen Here?" Life, October 17, 1969, pp. 67-78.

24. Knebel, Fletcher, "Why We Need New Politicians," Look, January 13, 1970, p. 74.

25. Look, November 4, 1969, editorial: "Agenda for Survival," (special issue on "America the Beautiful?").

26. Margolis, John, "Our Country 'Tis of Thee, Land of Ecology," Esquire, March 1970, p. 124.

27. McCarthy, Colman, "Needed: A Reverence for the Earth," Capital Times, Madison, Wisconsin, February 23, 1970, p. 34.

28. McCarthy, Colman, "Students Digging in for Ecology Fight," Washington Post, January 26, 1970, p. 16.

29. Milwaukee Journal, editorial, Milwaukee, Wisconsin, October 6, 1969, p. 16.

30. Nelson, Gaylord, "The New Conservation," Congressional Record, January 21, 1970, p. S283.

31. Newsweek, editorial: "Needed: A Rebirth of Community," January 26, 1970, p. 47, (special issue on "The Ravaged Environment").

32. Nixon, Richard, quoted in Time, February 2, 1970, p. 7.

33. Pekkanen, John P., "A Cause Becomes a Mass Movement," Life, January 30, 1970, p. 30, (special issue: "Ecology Becomes Everybody's Issue").

34. Pett, Saul, "Something's Rotten in the U. S. ," Wisconsin State Journal, Madison, (Associated Press), February 15, 1970, p. 4.

35. Pimlott, J. A. R., quoted in Clarence A. Schoenfeld, Publicity Media and Methods, Macmillan, New York, 1963, p. 325.

36. Pinchot, Gifford, The Fight for Conservation, Harcourt Brace, Garden City, New York, 1910, p. 42.

37. Pitzer, Kenneth S. , "Closing the Generation Gap," Stanford University News Service, Stanford, California, January 26, 1970, p. 1.

38. Pyron, Bernard, "Toward an Increase in Ecological Awareness," Center for Environmental Communications and Education Studies," The University of Wisconsin, Madison, mimeograph, February 20, 1970, p. 10.

39. Ritchie-Calder, Lord, "Mortgaging the Old Home-stead," Sports Illustrated, February 2, 1970, p. 51, (special issue: "The Last Chance−Now").

40. Schoenfeld, Clay, "Educating the Public in Natural Resources," Journal of Soil and Water Conservation, November-December 1968, p. 124.

41. Schoenfeld, Clay, "Toward A National Strategy for Environmental Education," The Journal of Educational Research, 64:3, September 1970.

42. Schoenfeld, Clay, "What's New About Environmental Education?" Environmental Education, Fall 1969, p. 7.

43. Scientific Research, editorial: "A Matter of Restraint," September 1, 1969, p. 4.

44. Theobald, Robert, "Clamor Perils Pollution War," Milwaukee Journal, Milwaukee, Wisconsin, February 11, 1970, p. 3.

45. Time, February 2, 1970, pp. 7, 8, 56, 63, (special issue: "The Emerging Science of Survival").

46. Toffler, Alvin, "Future Shock," Playboy, February 1970, p. 94.

47. Zinn, Donald J. , At War With Waste, National Wildlife Federation, Washington, D. C. , p. 1. ∎

INVENTORY 74

SUMMER 77